PROBABILITY

AND

INDUCTION

PROBABILITY
AND
INDUCTION

BY

WILLIAM KNEALE

FELLOW OF EXETER COLLEGE
LECTURER IN PHILOSOPHY IN THE
UNIVERSITY OF OXFORD

OXFORD
AT THE CLARENDON PRESS
1949

Oxford University Press, Amen House, London E.C.4

GLASGOW NEW YORK TORONTO MELBOURNE WELLINGTON
BOMBAY CALCUTTA MADRAS CAPE TOWN

Geoffrey Cumberlege, Publisher to the University

PRINTED IN GREAT BRITAIN

PREFACE

THIS book is based on lectures I have given to students of philosophy, and it is intended for readers who are interested in the philosophical problems suggested by the title. I do not pretend that it is either a treatise on the mathematical theory of probability or a practical guide to scientific method. For I have not the ability to produce the former, and I do not think it is the business of a philosopher (or perhaps of anyone) to try to provide the latter. So far as mathematics and natural science are concerned, I shall be content if I have avoided howlers.

The philosophical problems discussed are elementary in the sense that they have to do with first principles, and I have tried to make my treatment of them elementary also in the other sense of the word, that is to say, intelligible without much previous reading about the subject. But some of the statements to which I have committed myself are very controversial, and it may be useful to make clear that I do not attach equal importance to them all. In Part I, for example, I have written of knowledge as though it were indefinable, but this is merely because I have seen no satisfactory analysis of knowledge and do not think it necessary for my present purpose to try to find one. In spite of what I have said, I should welcome a new attempt to analyse this notion. At the other extreme, the general account of induction given in Part IV seems to me substantially correct, and I wish to stand by it. The theory of natural necessity in Part II and the range theory of probability in Part III come between these contentions in order of importance. I am acutely conscious of the difficulties of my views and the insufficiency of my arguments, and yet I cannot at present see any other way of describing matters which seems at all plausible. If I am mistaken in what I have said about these topics, I hope that I have at least written clearly enough to be found out quickly.

In accordance with the conventions of the Clarendon Press, logical and mathematical symbols have been printed without quotation marks even where they are themselves the subjects of discourse. I hope no reader will be seriously distressed by this usage, which is almost universal in mathematical texts. In certain contexts it can lead to dangerous confusion, and my own preference is for a rigorous distinction between use and mention at all times;

but no real ambiguity results here from the omission of inverted commas, and I have therefore not felt justified in pressing for their restoration at the expense of much valuable labour.

My debt to Lord Keynes's *Treatise on Probability* is obvious even where I criticize his doctrines. On the history of induction, or rather of philosophical views about induction, I have learnt much from *Les Théories de l'induction et de l'expérimentation* by M. André Lalande. To my friends Professor Gilbert Ryle, Dr. Friederich Waismann, and Dr. Karl Popper I owe a great deal that I cannot now disentangle from my own thought; but I am afraid they may be surprised and shocked by my conclusions. The fact that I have not made full use of some important recent contributions to the subject, in particular those of Professor R. Carnap and Professor G. H. von Wright, is due to the circumstances in which I have written this book. The first draft was begun in the summer of 1939, laid aside during the war while I was engaged on other work, and finished in the short period of comparative ease before the universities became crowded with men returning from military service. Since the autumn of 1946 I have had no time to do more than remove some of the faults which became evident when the whole was in typescript.

I wish to thank Professor Henry Price very warmly for the great care with which he read my work and advised me about the revision of it. His kindness has saved me (and the reader) from some silly passages and many that were obscure.

Finally, I wish to dedicate this book to my wife, who has helped me with advice and encouragement throughout the making of it.

July 1948   W. K.

CONTENTS

PART I

INTRODUCTORY: KNOWLEDGE AND BELIEF

PART II

THE TRADITIONAL PROBLEM OF INDUCTION

PART III

THE THEORY OF CHANCES

CONTENTS

PART IV

THE PROBABILITY OF INDUCTIVE SCIENCE

PART I

INTRODUCTORY: KNOWLEDGE AND BELIEF

§ 1. THE SCOPE OF THE INQUIRY

THE extent of our knowledge is less than we could wish. It may perhaps be wider than some philosophers have supposed, but it is clearly not wide enough to enable us to answer with certainty all the questions that arise in the practical affairs of everyday life and the still more numerous questions that puzzle us when we study history or science. Probability may be described as the substitute with which we try to make good the shortcomings of our knowledge. It does not fill the gap entirely, for there are many questions about which we cannot even form opinions; but it often enables us to act rationally when without it we should be reduced to helplessness, and it gives at least some satisfaction to our intellectual curiosity. This was perhaps the meaning of Bishop Butler's famous remark, 'To us, probability is the very guide of life.'[1] He was contrasting our state with that of an infinite intelligence which could discern 'each possible object of knowledge, whether past present or future, . . . absolutely as it is in itself'; and he wished to argue that, as in the common pursuits of life we rely on a kind of reasoning which can provide only probable conclusions, so too in theology we should be prepared to make tentative arguments from experience. I do not know whether his method is in favour now among theologians, but there can be no doubt of the importance which empirical scientists attach to it.

The variety of the situations in which we use the notion of probability is illustrated by the following sentences, each of which contains the word 'probable' or one of its derivatives:

(a) It is probable that there will be rain before the day is over.

(b) It is very improbable that a man with testimonials as good as these will fall into dishonesty.

(c) Stonehenge was probably built for use as a temple.

(d) If Hannibal had marched on Rome, he would probably have taken it.

(e) We know now that the stories which Marco Polo told on his return to Venice were true, however improbable they may have been for his contemporaries.

---

[1] *Analogy of Religion*, Introduction, § 4.

B

(*f*) The probability of throwing a number greater than four with a true die is 1:3.

(*g*) Statistics indicate that if a wounded man is treated immediately with penicillin the probability of his escaping sepsis is more than 9:10.

(*h*) We cannot assign high probabilities to the generalizations made in sociology, because the number of cases in which we are able to confirm them is not very large.

(*i*) The probability of the atomic theory of matter has been greatly increased by the evidence which physicists and chemists have collected during the past century.

In ordinary life we often have occasion to make remarks like (*a*) and (*b*), and we often meet statements such as (*c*), (*d*), and (*e*) when we read works on history. Example (*e*) is worth special notice, because it shows that what is improbable may nevertheless be true. Although as plain men we do not often try to make precise numerical estimates of probability, we all recognize that statements like (*f*) and (*g*) are needed in various branches of science and in certain specialisms such as actuarial work. Examples (*h*) and (*i*) are interesting as specimens of the way in which we pass judgement on scientific generalizations and explanatory hypotheses.

Our dependence on the notion of probability is not confined, however, to those cases in which we employ the word 'probable' or one of its derivatives to state our views, for there are other ways of expressing the same thought. Sometimes we speak of the balance of chances. At other times such words as 'likely', 'reliable', 'trustworthy' seem more appropriate. And we must admit on reflection that in many cases in which we do not ordinarily use the word 'probable' or any equivalent expression it would be wiser to do so if there were any danger of misunderstanding. I may, for example, assert without qualification that Julius Caesar landed on the south coast of England and even count this as an item of my knowledge, but if I am pressed to say whether I know it for certain, I can only reply that I have it on good authority and consider it extremely probable or almost certain. It is clear, therefore, that the realm of probability is very large indeed and covers even much of what we loosely call our knowledge.

In this book I wish to consider the philosophical theory of probability. The subject has also been investigated by mathematicians, and I shall have to say something about their work, but only in so far as it is relevant to the discussion of the philosophical problems. How the philosophical problems arise and how we should try to solve them will become clear, I hope, in the course of the book. I do not propose, therefore, to say anything here in general terms about the aim and method of philosophical inquiries; but it will be obvious already that the philosophical theory of probability is part of epistemology, that is to say, of the philosophical discipline in which we study the different kinds of knowledge and related topics such as the nature of belief.

§ 2. SUBJECTIVIST THEORIES OF PROBABILITY: MEANINGS OF 'BELIEF'

If, as seems natural, we start by contrasting probability statements with statements in which we express knowledge, the question immediately arises: 'What then do we express by probability statements?'

One of the commonest ways of introducing the notion of probability into discourse is by means of an adverb. We may say, for example, 'It is probably raining in the Hebrides.' In late antiquity any statement which included an adverb of this kind or any similar expression (e.g. 'it is probable that . . .' or 'it is possible that . . .') was classified as *modal*, and it is now the custom for logicians to use the name 'modality' for that division of their study in which they treat of necessity, possibility, and probability. This terminology is not illuminating, and may even be misleading. In what sense does the adverb 'probably' signify a mode or manner? Clearly it is not used in the same way as ordinary adverbs, which qualify verbs much as adjectives qualify nouns. When I say that it is raining heavily, I mean that it is raining in a special way, but when I say that it is probably raining, I certainly do not want to suggest that there is a special mode or manner of raining which I call 'probably raining'. Such an interpretation is so obviously absurd that it has never been seriously defended. On the contrary most persons who give any thought to the matter are inclined to jump immediately to the opposite extreme and say that probability must be subjective.

One subjectivist theory which has found its way into many of the older text-books of logic is presented as a doctrine about different modes or manners of assertion. It is argued that a man who utters the sentence 'It is probably raining' is asserting the proposition that it is raining but doing so in a special fashion or with a special qualification, much as a man who says 'Unfortunately it is raining' may be held to assert the proposition that it is raining but with an additional comment about his own state of mind in making the assertion. It is difficult to attach any precise meaning to the phrase 'mode or manner of assertion' as it is used in this theory; but we need not trouble ourselves about the matter, for the doctrine seems to be founded on the mistaken assumption that any sentence which contains one of the modal adverbs must be taken as an assertion of the proposition which would ordinarily be asserted by the use of the sentence without the adverb. This assumption is only plausible when we are dealing with modal statements which contain the adverb 'necessarily'.[1] If I say 'It is necessarily raining', I am indeed committed to the assertion that it is raining. But if I say 'It is probably raining', I am not asserting in any way that it is raining, and the discovery that no rain was falling would not refute my statement, although it might render it useless. The mistake seems to be due to overmuch concentration on the adverbial expression of modality. In order to escape from it we need only remember that 'It is probably raining' is equivalent to 'It is probable that it is raining'. In the second formulation we have no excuse for assuming an assertion that it is raining, since the words 'it is raining' occur here only as they do in 'It is false that it is raining', i.e. as a subordinate clause. In short, the view that probability is a mode of assertion is derived from the same source as the view that probability is a mode of being, namely, from a failure to see that modal adverbs function in a quite peculiar way.

The most common subjectivist theory of probability is based on the very different assumption that a probability statement is really an assertion about the speaker's own state of mind. According to this doctrine probability is neither a mode of being nor a mode of assertion. It belongs to propositions (i.e. thinkables or assertable contents), but not as an intrinsic property, for it is simply the degree of belief which we attach to them. James Bernoulli, who made great contributions to the mathematical theory of probability, appears to have held some such view, and he has been followed by a number of other distinguished persons. We must therefore examine the suggestion carefully.

Having started with an antithesis between probability and knowledge, it is natural that we should go on to connect proba-

---

[1] Or 'actually', if that is allowed to be modal.

bility with belief, since the word 'belief' is commonly supposed to stand for a mental attitude by which we supplement our meagre knowledge. We must be cautious, however, for the word appears to have two very different senses. These can be distinguished most easily by means of examples.

If I say of a man in a lunatic asylum 'The poor fellow believes he is Napoleon', I mean that the man is wholly convinced he is Napoleon and would when questioned say he knew he was Napoleon. This kind of belief may be said to ape knowledge, since it is expressed in precisely the same way as knowledge and is for the believer indistinguishable at the moment from knowledge. It is most striking in lunatics, who maintain their beliefs against all evidence, but it occurs in normal men whenever they fall into error. Anyone who unthinkingly mistakes a stranger for a friend or makes a false step in a calculation is in this condition, although, unlike the lunatic, he can be brought without much difficulty to change his mind. It is not even essential to this use of the word 'belief' that what is believed should be false. Most of us when doing simple calculations in arithmetic speak without apprehending the truth of what we say. No doubt a man who says 'Seven and five make twelve' can, if he chooses, either see the necessity of his statement or at least reflect that he has been well trained and is probably giving the right answer like a well-made calculating machine. But in practice we rarely do either the one or the other; and it is fortunate that we do not, because life is too short for us to be rational all the time. The state of mind which I have described has been variously called 'being under an impression', 'thinking without question', and 'taking for granted'.[1] I shall use the last of these names because such belief is a kind of behaviour rather than a kind of thought in the strictest sense of that word. It consists in behaving as though one knew something which one does not in fact know. Here 'behaviour' must be understood to include not only overt bodily movements, but also the use of symbols for making assertions to oneself.

If, on the other hand, I say of myself 'I do not know whether it is raining in the Hebrides, but I believe it is', the situation which I describe is very different. No one would say of himself that at the time of speaking he was behaving in all respects as though he knew something which he did not in fact know. Furthermore,

---

[1] J. Cook Wilson, *Statement and Inference*, p. 109, and H. H. Price, 'Some Considerations about Belief', in the *Proceedings of the Aristotelian Society*, 1934–5.

when I contrast my present believing with knowledge, I am prepared to admit, in principle at least, that what I believe may not be the case. Sometimes this situation is distinguished from taking for granted by an antithesis between partial and complete belief; but this terminology is unsatisfactory for technical use in philosophy, because it suggests that we have to do only with a difference of degree whereas in fact there is a difference of kind. It seems desirable, therefore, to drop the use of the word 'belief' in this connexion, whenever there is any possible danger of misunderstanding, and to speak instead of opinion, which can scarcely be confused with taking for granted. What I suggest involves admittedly a small modification of ordinary usage, since we do not commonly apply the word 'opinion' in cases where we claim very high probability for our views. It may also be objected that the verb 'opine' is an unpleasant archaism. These disadvantages are, however, a comparatively small price to pay for clarity about a fundamental distinction.

Corresponding to the difference between taking for granted and opinion there is a difference to be noticed between two senses in which we may speak of the degree of a belief. A man who takes something for granted may be said to believe it more or less firmly, according to the difficulty which there would be in bringing him to change his mind. Normally a man who takes something for granted can easily be brought to realize his situation; but it is well known that emotional prejudice may render a man blind to evidence. In the extreme case of lunacy irrational convictions may become unshakable. What the upholders of the subjectivist theory of probability mean when they speak of degree of belief is clearly not this, but rather the strength of opinion in the mind of a man who admits that what he opines may not be the case. Some philosophers and psychologists speak in this connexion of the degree of confidence which a man feels while opining, and I think this phrase would be acceptable to the supporters of the subjectivist theory as a description of that by reference to which they try to define probability.

According to this interpretation, the subjectivist theory of probability is open to the same objections as have often been urged against subjectivist theories in moral philosophy. If the probability of a proposition for any man were simply the degree of confidence which he felt in it, every man would be the best judge of the probability of a proposition for himself, and there could be no useful argument about probabilities, since every probability statement would be a report of the speaker's feelings and nothing more. There would be no incompatibility between a statement by one man that it was probably raining and a statement by another that rain was unlikely at that time. We do not in practice admit this. On the contrary, we think it possible to argue about probabilities and maintain that some men's judgements are better than those of others. If an expert says that a picture is probably the work of Rembrandt, we pay more attention to his view than we should to a similar pronouncement from an ignorant man. When a man sees a black cat on his way to a casino and says 'I shall probably win to-day: give me your money to place on your behalf', we decline the invitation if we are prudent, even although we believe the man to be honest.

These considerations have led some philosophers to put forward a revised version of the subjectivist theory according to which the probability of a proposition A is the strength of a rational opinion that A. This new version is much more plausible than the old and has many supporters, but it cannot be regarded as satisfactory without some explanation of the meaning of the word 'rational' in this context.

If the act of opining A is to be called rational the proposition A which is opined must be self-consistent. This much is obvious, but there is also another sense, not so obvious, in which consistency or coherence is required for rationality in opinions. This can be explained most easily by consideration of betting, in which men are said to express the strength of their opinions. Let us suppose that a bookmaker offers odds of two to one against each of four exhaustive and mutually exclusive alternatives. If a client lays bets on each of the alternatives at these odds, he is behaving irrationally. Any one of the four opinions to which he gives expression by his bets may be rational, but they cannot all be rational. Since the alternatives are related in the way described, the strengths of rational opinions concerning them cannot be independent. We have, so to say, a limited fund of confidence to distribute between the four alternatives, and if we give more than a quarter to one we must give less to some of the others. The man in the example is over-generous somewhere in his distribution and ends with an overdraft on his confidence account. This shows itself in the fact that he is bound to lose by his bets, whatever happens. Indeed, the whole art of the bookmaker consists in so adjusting the odds which he offers that the body of his clients considered as a whole must lose, whatever happens; and this is not difficult, because the opinions expressed by the clients are for the most part not co-ordinated one with another.

These considerations are important (we shall see later that they form the basis of the whole mathematical theory of probability), but they do not provide an explanation of the sense in which the supporters of the revised subjectivist theory speak of rational opinions. For we have shown only that rational opinions must be coherent in so far as they are concerned with related propositions, and we cannot say that coherence is enough to guarantee the rationality of any opinions which cohere. There must, then, it seems, be some sense in which a single opinion can be rational without reference to other opinions. Now the persons who introduce the revised subjectivist theory apparently consider that an act of opining is rational if, and only if, the person who opines has the degree of confidence which he ought to have in what he opines. How are we to interpret the word 'ought' in this context? There is no question of moral obligation here, nor yet of aesthetic fitness, and the only possible explanation seems to be that a man has the degree of confidence which he ought to have in a certain proposition when he has that degree which is logically justified. But in what sense can a certain degree of confidence be logically justified?

It may perhaps be suggested that a certain degree of confidence is justified by the intrinsic character of the proposition opined, and that rational opinion is simply the appropriate attitude to that proposition; but I do not think that anyone would wish seriously to defend such a view. No proposition (unless it is either a truism or an absurdity) contains in itself anything to indicate that we ought to have a certain degree of confidence in it. On the contrary, if we are to do justice to common usage, we must allow that the same proposition may have different probabilities at different times, and this is plainly inconsistent with any attempt to make the probability of a proposition depend on its intrinsic character. There is only one possible account of the matter which makes the revised subjectivist theory at all plausible, and that is to say that the degree of confidence which a man ought to have in what he opines is the degree justified by the evidence at his disposal. When, however, this account is properly developed, it shows that the subjectivist project of defining probability by reference to our feelings of confidence is useless and misguided.

§ 3. THE RELATION OF PROBABILITY TO EVIDENCE

The principle that probability is relative to evidence was first enunciated by Kahle in his *Elementa Logicae Probabilium* of 1735.[1] Unfortunately, it has not always been stated explicitly by writers on probability after that date. Indeed Lord Keynes, who published his *Treatise on Probability* in 1921, is perhaps the first writer to insist on the point throughout his exposition, although many others, as might be expected, have assumed it implicitly in parts of their work.

In order to make clear what is involved in the principle, let us consider an example. Suppose that we are inquiring whether a certain man will live to be sixty years of age. If we know facts *A* and *B* about him, for example, that he is fifty years of age and that his father lived to be ninety, we may ascribe a high probability to the proposition that he will survive. If, however, we learn in addition the new fact *C*, that he is already a sufferer from delirium tremens, we may immediately lower our estimate. Sometimes in such a case we speak as though there were a single probability of the man's surviving to be sixty, something independent of all evidence, and our second estimate were better in the sense of being nearer to this single probability than our first. But this view is surely wrong. If we were omniscient, we should be able to forecast with certainty whether or not the man would live to be sixty; but the word 'probability' would not then be devoid of meaning for us, as some writers, including Bishop Butler, have apparently thought. Probability is relative to evidence; and even what is known to be false may be described quite reasonably as probable in relation to a certain selection of evidence. We admit this in writing history. If a general, having made his dispositions in the light of the evidence at his disposal, was then defeated, we do not necessarily say that he was a bad general, i.e. that he had a poor judgement about probabilities in military affairs. We may say that he did what was most sensible in the circumstances, because in relation to the evidence which he could and did obtain it was probable that he would win with those dispositions. Similarly what is known to have happened may be extremely improbable in relation to every-

---

[1] I take this remark from Lord Keynes's *Treatise on Probability*, p. 90, having been unable to find a copy of Kahle's work.

thing we know except that fact. 'Improbable but true' is not a contradiction in terms. On the contrary, we assert just this whenever we say of a fact that it is strange or surprising.

The reason why we may easily overlook the relation of probability to evidence is that in ordinary life we commonly state probabilities in relation to all the knowledge we have at the time and therefore feel no need to specify the evidence. In other words, our probability statements are commonly elliptical. And sometimes when the relevant evidence is specified, it is wrapped up in an adjective or a relative clause, so that it is not immediately recognizable. To take a not very difficult example, when we ask 'What is the probability that this card, which has been drawn at random from a complete pack, is a court card?', the evidence to be considered is that the card has come from a pack constituted according to the rules, but we may be tempted to think that we are concerned with one proposition only. Phraseology of this kind occurs frequently in the examples discussed by the older writers on the mathematical theory of probability, and may account for their failure to state explicitly that probability is relative to evidence. But even in ordinary life we sometimes ask questions of the form 'What would be the probability of B in relation to A?' where A includes something not known at the moment. When, for example, an historian or a detective looks to see whether a certain proposition is true, because he knows that if it were it would be strong evidence for some hypothesis in which he is interested, he must already have asked and answered such a question. Similarly any one who tries to forecast the behaviour of another person must from time to time ask himself 'What would be the probability of B in relation to A?' where A is the information available to the other person and excludes some facts known to the questioner.

The situation which I have been trying to describe can be made more intelligible by a comparison between the way in which we talk of probability and the way in which we talk of necessity. If I know a fact A and also know that A is *conclusive* evidence for B, I may say 'Because A, therefore necessarily B'. But if there is no special reason to mention the evidence for my conclusion, I may content myself with the remark 'Necessarily B'. This shows that I put B forward as the conclusion of an inference, but does not specify the evidence for it. If I do not know A, or am not concerned for the moment at least to claim knowledge of it, but wish to point out that A would be conclusive evidence for B, I use the hypothetical form and say 'If A then necessarily B'. For the case in which A is *inconclusive* evidence for B all these phrases can be adapted by the substitution of 'probably' for 'necessarily'; and as in the first case we can say that A necessitates (or would necessitate) B, so in the second case we can say that A probabilifies (or would probabilify) B. There is, however, an important difference. Whereas, if A necessitates B, any conjunction of propositions which includes A must also necessitate B, it is possible for A to probabilify B to some degree although some conjunctions containing A would not probabilify B to the same degree or even at all. This is illustrated by our example about the probability of a man's surviving to be sixty. When we discover that he is already a sufferer from delirium tremens, we say that his survival is not so probable in relation to the evidence now available as it was in relation to the less complete evidence we had before. If we are to avoid mistakes in the discussion of probability, it is therefore essential that we should give special attention to the precise formulation of the evidence in relation to which we estimate the probability of any proposition.

Acceptance of the argument outlined above enables us to escape completely from the subjectivism which confused the work of most of the early writers about probability. If we ought to have a certain degree of confidence in B on evidence A, that is, if A *justifies* a certain degree of confidence in B, this can only be because A probabilifies B to a certain degree, whatever degree of confidence we may or may not have. We think as we ought to think when we think of things as they are in reality; and there is no other sense in which it can be said that we ought to think so and so.

Admittedly the notion of probabilification requires further elucidation. But perplexities about the analysis of the relation should not prevent us from admitting that it is in some sense objective. The essential point is that the thinking which leads to the formation of rational opinion does not *make* any proposition probable. Like any other thinking worth the name, it *discovers* something independent of thought; and what it discovers is apparently a relation between a proposition and something else called the evidence.

After insisting on the objectivity of the probability relation Lord Keynes writes:

'A *definition* of probability is not possible, unless it contents us to define degrees of the probability-relation by reference to degrees of rational belief. We cannot analyse the probability-relation in terms of simpler ideas. As soon as we have passed from the logic of implication and the categories of truth and falsehood to the logic of probability and the categories of knowledge, ignorance, and rational belief, we are paying attention to a new logical relation in which, although it is logical, we were not previously interested, and which cannot be explained or defined in terms of our previous notions.'[1]

That probability cannot be defined by reference to the notions used in the logic of implication (by which I understand Lord Keynes to mean the logistic calculus as it is found in such works as the *Principia Mathematica* of Russell and Whitehead) we can readily admit; but this is not to say that the notion of probabilification is unanalysable. It would, indeed, be very strange if we had to admit such a relation as ultimate and indefinable.

In the first place, the relation holds, as Lord Keynes rightly says, between propositions, but it is now generally recognized that propositions are not to be accepted as ultimate entities. We are, of course, entitled to say that two men are entertaining the same proposition, or that the same proposition is propounded by two different sentences. This is merely common usage which it would be foolish to reject. But after a period of wandering in Meinong's jungle of subsistence[2] (during which Lord Keynes produced his book) philosophers are now agreed that propositions cannot be regarded as ultimate entities, independent alike of facts, sentences, and acts of thinking. From this it follows that relations between propositions must be capable of analysis. To refuse to draw the conclusion would be as foolish as to maintain that international relations are simple and unanalysable although nations are logical constructions out of individual human beings.

Secondly, probabilification admits of degrees, and if we are to explain, as we surely must, why one piece of evidence gives higher probability to a proposition than some other piece of evidence, we must find a definition of probabilification which allows for this difference. Lord Keynes's treatment of this point is unsatisfactory. He admits that probability always has some degree, but he says that, whereas in some cases the degree is measurable by a fraction between 0 and 1, in other cases it is not measurable even in principle.[3] He may be right in making such a distinction, but if he is,

---

[1] *Treatise on Probability*, p. 8.
[2] The jungle is described in Meinong's book, *Über Annahmen*. Cf. J. N. Findlay, *Meinong's Theory of Objects*.   [3] *Treatise on Probability*, pp. 20 ff.

he must surely be wrong in talking of one indefinable notion of probability. The difference between being measurable and being incapable of measurement even in principle is so great that it cannot be maintained without a distinction of two species of probability; and if we are to distinguish species of probability, we must at least analyse the two species far enough to show in what the distinction between them consists.

To explain the nature of probabilification and how it admits of degrees will be the principal task of this book, but before we proceed to investigate these problems in detail there are some preliminary points to be considered.

§ 4. THE NATURE OF OPINION

So far we have spoken of opinion as though it were a mental activity distinct from knowledge and involving or accompanied by a feeling of greater or less confidence. This treatment is suggested by the ordinary linguistic usage according to which opining A is contrasted with knowing A. If, however, the arguments put forward in the two previous sections are correct, it is possible to simplify our account and to explain more clearly how opinion is related to knowledge.

A man who opines A cannot, it seems, be said to have a rational opinion unless the degree of his confidence in A is justified by the evidence before his mind. But it is not sufficient for rationality that the evidence should in fact justify the degree of confidence which he has. The man must also know that it does so. Otherwise his condition is like that of a schoolboy who gives the right answer to a mathematical question without knowing why it is right. Even machines may sometimes give right answers to questions, but we do not call them rational, because they do not know the reasons for the answers which they give. Now a man who knows that the evidence at his disposal justifies a certain degree of confidence in proposition A must know that the evidence probabilifies A to a certain degree; for it is only so that the evidence can justify any degree of confidence. But if a man who has a rational opinion knows all this (even although he may not have the terminology in which to state it explicitly), why need we say in addition that he has a certain degree of confidence in A which somehow corresponds with the degree to which the evidence probabilifies A ? Can we not content ourselves with the assertion that rational opinion is the knowledge that the available evidence probabilifies a proposition to a certain degree?

One possible objection to this simple account of the matter is that, since we began by contrasting opinion with knowledge, we must not end by defining opinion as a kind of knowledge. There is, however, a confusion of thought in this argument. A man who opines A is certainly not knowing A. Indeed, in order to opine A he must know that he does not know A; for we form opinions on questions only when we have realized that we cannot answer those questions with knowledge. But, according to the definition which I have suggested, a man who rationally opines A is knowing not A but a relation between A and some facts which we call the available evidence. It is convenient to state the whole situation by saying that the man opines A, but we must not therefore assume that opining is a simple attitude towards a proposition and excludes knowledge of any kind. We have already seen that, if it is to be rational, opinion must involve knowledge that the available evidence probabilifies a proposition to a certain degree, and there should therefore be no objection on this score to saying that rational opinion is just such knowledge. We may, of course, continue to contrast opinion with knowledge in the ordinary way; for when we do so, we mean by 'opinion' what is opined and we distinguish this from what is known.

A more formidable objection to the proposed definition of rational opinion is based on an appeal to introspection. It is said that, if we examine our state of mind when we are rationally opining, we can discover a certain feeling of confidence in addition to the knowledge which has been mentioned as essential for rational opinion. For my own part, I can discover no such feeling, although I admit that, like other people, I often use such phrases as 'I am confident that . . .'. It is unprofitable, however, in such a matter as this to set one report of introspection against another. If the issue were to be decided in this way, we might conceivably have to conclude that some people have the feeling and others do not, just as some people can hear shrill noises when others can hear nothing. We none of us believe that this is a satisfactory end to the dispute, and I shall therefore try to show that those who maintain there is a specific feeling of confidence must be misreporting their observations.

The degree of confidence felt by a man while he is in the state of rational opinion is supposed to correspond with the degree to which the evidence at his disposal probabilifies the proposition he is entertaining. I have spoken in an earlier section of the distribution of a fund of confidence between various alternatives, and there may be some persons who are disposed to take such metaphors seriously, but on reflection we must surely recognize that there cannot be any feeling of which these things can be said with literal significance.

In the first place, degrees of probability are sometimes measured by fractions between 0 and 1. Are we to maintain that for every conceivable fraction there is some appropriate degree of confidence? Feelings have only intensive magnitude. They may be graded as more or less intense, and we may, if we choose, assign proper fractions to them, so that more intense feelings are co-ordinated with larger fractions. But it is absurd to say of one feeling that it is just twice as intense as another of the same kind, because feelings of great intensity do not have parts which are themselves feelings of less intensity. There can therefore be no measurement of feelings in any strict sense of the word 'measurement', and feelings of confidence cannot correspond in any *necessary* way with probabilities which are measured by fractions. It seems fantastic, indeed, to maintain that there are infinitely many distinguishable degrees of confidence from zero to some maximum intensity, but, even if there were, we could only say that between any two degrees it was possible to find a third, and this would not suffice to connect each necessarily with a particular fraction.

Secondly, even if those who believe in feelings of confidence are content to say that the feelings do not correspond exactly and necessarily with different degrees of probability, they have to face a serious difficulty about the existence of a maximum intensity of confidence. Their account of the matter seems to require that there should be such an upper limit to which feelings of confidence approach asymptotically with increasing probability. I say 'approach asymptotically' because all probability falls short of the certainty which we have in knowledge and it is obvious that knowledge itself is not accompanied by confidence. When we realize that $2+2 = 4$, we do not sweat with any feeling of supreme intensity. But there is something absurd in the suggestion that any kind of feeling should have an upper limit of the sort required by this theory. There may in fact be a maximum intensity for feelings such as joy and sorrow, but we do not suppose that the limit is imposed in these cases by logical necessity, or that it is a limit in the sense of something to which actual feelings approach asymptotically. If, however, there are feelings of confidence, they must all, it seems, lie within a range of which the unattainable upper limit is perfect or complete confidence, and this implies that lesser feelings of confidence must be in some way imperfect or incomplete, which is impossible if they are simple feelings such as the upholders of the theory seem to postulate.

When we speak, as we admittedly do, of feeling confident, we are referring, I think, to the absence of serious doubt or questioning from our minds, much as when we speak of feeling tranquil we are referring to the absence of uneasiness. I do not mean to suggest by this that doubt is a simple feeling which can correspond exactly in degree with the interval by which the probability of a proposition falls short of certainty, for such a suggestion would lead us back into difficulties of the same kind as those which beset the doctrine about confidence we have been examining. Doubt appears rather to be a complex state involving (a) a wish to find the answer to some question, (b) a realization that one cannot answer the question with knowledge, and (c) a feeling of frustration and restlessness. Whether pleasure or displeasure predominates in the experience seems to depend on such factors as the relevance of the question at issue to the emotional interests of the doubter, the nature of his mood at the time, and the duration of the doubt; but in general the tone is unpleasant. Anyone who opines feels some doubt about what he opines, but it is undesirable to include a reference to doubt in our definition of opinion, because the emotional element in doubt (i.e. the feeling of frustration and restlessness) is not part of what we have in mind when we use the word 'opinion'. Our attention is directed then to the estimation of probabilities, and doubt is connected with this only in a causal fashion. For it is doubt which provides our motive for seeking fresh evidence and trying to reach rational opinions.

When an opinion has been formed, a disposition to doubt may, and indeed should, persist, since the question at issue has not been answered with certainty; but a wise man tries to prevent the emotional element from disturbing him unduly at this time. If we know that we cannot get more evidence, and that in relation to what we have the probability of a proposition is very high, we may even decide to dismiss all further doubt about the proposition as unprofitable. Such a decision is not a voluntary transition to a state of taking for granted, for we cannot will ourselves into a blind acceptance of anything. It is rather a resolution to treat the question as though it were settled and to take no more steps, whether practical or intellectual, to cope with the contingency of the proposition's being false. We say to ourselves that we have more important things to occupy our minds. No historian, for instance, thinks it worth while to try to work out an historical hypothesis based on the supposition that Julius Caesar did not land in Britain or to look for more evidence in favour of the commonly accepted view. Sometimes, as in the example just cited, no effort is required to reach a state of equanimity, but at other times, when strong emotional interests are concerned and there is a natural disposition to optimism or pessimism, it may be very difficult indeed to dismiss unprofitable doubt. A man who knows that there is only one chance in a thousand of his surviving a serious injury may continue to think of that possibility when he would be better employed in preparing to die; and a man who knows that there is only one chance in a thousand of his being killed in an air-raid may continue to worry about that contingency when he would be better employed in composing himself for sleep by reading a novel.

If anyone maintains in spite of all these arguments that he can still detect by introspection a positive feeling of confidence, with various degrees on various occasions, he must, I think, be confusing confidence with a somewhat vague memory impression of the number of past cases on which his estimate of probability is based. Such memory impressions play a very important part in some of our thought about probabilities, and it will be necessary to consider their use in a later section.

If rational opinion is to be defined as the knowledge that some proposition is probabilified to a certain degree by the available evidence, irrational opinion may be defined as taking the probability of a proposition for granted. There are, however, two ways in which opinion may fall short of rationality. Some proposition which is treated as evidence (in the sense in which evidence must be known) may be merely taken for granted, or the probability relation itself may be taken for granted. These two possible defects are analogous to, although not identical with, defects which may occur in a deductive argument. A man who argues that because A therefore B may be taking A for granted or may be taking for granted that if A then B. The fault of treating something as evidence which is not known calls for no special comment

C

in a discussion of probability, but some of the ways in which we may depart from rationality when thinking about the probability relation itself will have to be considered in due course. It is perhaps worth repeating here that taking for granted need not necessarily involve error, and that no man can be wholly rational in every minute of his life.

The result of our analysis is a very simple account of the relations between knowledge and belief. In the past some philosophers have grouped these together as kinds of judgement, and then sought vainly for differentiae by which to distinguish them. Others, protesting against this confusion, have assumed that there are two or more faculties (loosely called cognitive) whose exercise may lead to the affirmation of a proposition. According to the view presented here, knowledge is *sui generis* and the two varieties of belief are to be defined by reference to it. The belief we call taking for granted is behaving as though one knew when one does not in fact know, and the belief we identify with opinion is either knowing or taking for granted probability relations. Each of the terms 'knowledge', 'taking for granted', and 'opinion' can, of course, be used either in an actual or in a dispositional sense, but the dispositional sense must always be defined by reference to the actual sense. Actual knowledge, that is to say, noticing or realizing, is therefore the fundamental notion in the study called theory of knowledge.[1]

§ 5. OPINION AS A BASIS FOR ACTION

Although some analysis of the intellectual processes involved in our thought about probabilities is necessary in order that we may avoid confusion, we must not allow our interest in these topics to blind us to the fact that knowledge of probability relations is important chiefly for its bearing on action. In practical life we frequently have to take decisions without knowledge of all the relevant facts. When I set out for a walk, I cannot be certain that the weather will remain fine until I return. If I knew that there would be no rain, I should leave my raincoat at home. If I knew that rain would fall I should take my raincoat with me. But I cannot obtain such knowledge, and I must base my decision on

---

[1] The dispositional use of 'know' is much commoner than the actual in ordinary speech, but it is not, as some philosophers have maintained, the only permissible usage. Consider, for example, the sentence 'When a bomb fell in the next street, he knew that it was time to take shelter'. Here 'knew' is equivalent to 'realized'.

opinion, that is to say, on knowledge of the degree to which the evidence at my disposal probabilifies the proposition that rain will fall before I return. If the probability is high, I take my raincoat, and it will be generally agreed that I act rationally, even though the weather in fact remains fine. If the probability is low I may decide to risk getting wet, because this danger is outweighed by the discomfort of carrying a coat. Whether or not I decide to run the risk depends, however, not only on the degree of probability of the proposition that it will rain, but also on the value I attach to my clothes. If they are the only decent garments I possess and I have to appear in them later at an important meeting, I may consider it wise to carry a raincoat, although the coming of rain is fairly improbable.

Even in history and pure science the importance of probability considerations is due partly to their bearing on action. When a geologist says that certain marks on a mountain-side were probably caused by a glacier during the Ice Age, it may seem that the question at issue has no relevance at all, or only the most remote, to any practical decision, but it should be remembered that intellectual inquiry is itself a kind of practice which requires decisions from time to time. If the marks were probably caused by a glacier, it is reasonable to proceed with the construction of a theory according to which the whole region was once much colder than it is now, and a decision to work this hypothesis out in detail is practical in the sense that it commits the geologist to a great deal of activity. At the least he will have to direct his attention to other consequences of the hypothesis, but there may be need also for physical actions, such as travelling to places where he can make new observations or consult the books of other scientists. Whenever we choose to pursue one line rather than another in our theorizing, we make a practical decision; and it often happens that such decisions can be justified only by considerations of probability.

A satisfactory account of probability, then, must allow us to maintain that it is rational to act on opinion in the manner just explained. This does not mean that we have to define probability in such a way that anyone who acts on a knowledge of probability will invariably be successful in attaining his ends. To ask this is to demand the impossible, for whenever we act on mere opinion we inevitably run some risk of failure. On the other hand, it is not sufficient to say that action based on a knowledge of probabilities is rational because such action, whether successful or unsuccessful, is included by definition within the meaning of the word 'rational'. It is, indeed, a truism that such action is rational, but only because a reference to rational action is conveyed by the terminology in which we talk of probability. When in ordinary speech we say that an opinion (in the sense of something opined) is probable, we imply already that it is approvable. This was the original meaning of the word 'probable', for our English adjective is derived from the Latin *probabilis*, which has just this sense. There is the same suggestion also in such words as 'likely', *vraisemblable*, and *wahrscheinlich*. If we say that a proposition which we cannot assert without reservation is nevertheless like a truth, we cannot mean that we have compared it with the truth about the question at issue, since *ex hypothesi* we do not know that truth. Our meaning must be that it resembles truths in general as being acceptable or approvable. Although the etymology of the various words I have mentioned may not be present to our minds when we use them in ordinary speech, the suggestion of merit still attaches to them. Now 'approvable' clearly means in the context the same as 'fit to be approved' or, more precisely, 'such as a rational man would approve as a basis for practical decisions'; for there is no other relevant sense in which a *proposition* can be supposed to be approvable. And so the statement that it is rational to act on considerations of probability means only that it is rational to act on considerations such as a rational man would approve for the purpose. But this explanation of common usage does not provide a full understanding of the situation. The approvability of a proposition as a basis for action by an agent who possesses only certain limited evidence must be distinguished from the objective relation which holds between the proposition and that evidence. For convenience we may speak of the second as the probability relation, but, if we do so, we must remember that we are now using the word 'probability' in a technical sense which is supposed to exclude all reference to human interests.

Our requirement may therefore be put as follows: no analysis of the probability relation can be accepted as adequate, i.e. as explaining the ordinary usage of the word 'probability', unless it enables us to understand why it is rational to take as a basis for action a proposition which stands in that relation to the evidence at our disposal. We shall find, in fact, that much of the debate about rival definitions of probability has turned on this question and that our requirement can scarcely be ignored by anyone who tries to make his choice between the alternatives. But it is desirable to establish the point at the outset of the discussion, because recognition of it will make the course of the argument more intelligible. An admission that the ordinary usage of 'probability' contains a reference to human interests may also serve to set at rest the minds of those who feel that there must be some germ of truth in the subjectivist doctrine.

§ 6. PROBABILITY AND INDUCTION: THE PLAN OF THIS BOOK

So far we have been concerned with certain general remarks about probability which seem to hold good for all possible applications of the notion. In order that the plan to be followed in this book may be intelligible it is necessary to add something here about the use of the notion in connexion with induction.

At the end of the list of examples of probability statements cited in the first section of this part are two concerned with the judgements we pass on scientific generalizations and explanatory theories in empirical science. It is now a commonplace of epistemology that the results achieved in such sciences as physics, chemistry, biology, and sociology are fundamentally different in character from the conclusions of pure mathematics. At one time this difference was not generally recognized either by philosophers or by scientists, as it is now. But it was set beyond all doubt by the British empiricists, Bacon, Locke, Berkeley, and Hume, and, like some other achievements of philosophical analysis, has become so firmly established in our intellectual tradition that we can scarcely understand how intelligent men ever failed to appreciate it. The sciences I have mentioned are called inductive, and their conclusions, unlike those of pure mathematics, are said to have only high probability, since they are not self-evident and cannot be demonstrated by conclusive reasoning. Some of the results of induction, for instance the generalizations of elementary chemistry, are, indeed, so well established that it would be pedantic to use the word 'probably' whenever we mention them, but we can always conceive the possibility of experiences which would compel us to revise them. The importance of the inductive sciences is so great, not only for practice but also in the formation of an intellectual view of the world, that consideration of their method must inevitably form a very large part of any discussion of probability.

There is, however, another reason why we must devote special attention to induction. Very many of our most useful probability statements are themselves established by inductive argument. When, for example, I say that it is very improbable that Jones will fall into dishonesty since he has a record of twenty years' faithful service, I use a rule to the effect that it is very improbable any man with such a record will fall into dishonesty. This rule, which is general in form, has been derived by induction from my own experience and what others have told me. A few men with such records have in the past fallen into dishonesty, but they form a very small proportion of all the cases observed. The probability rule which I bring forward as the justification for my judgement about a particular man bears the same relation to these facts of experience as a law of universal connexion would to an observed uniformity. Our account of induction must therefore be wide enough to cover the argumentation by which probability rules are derived from experience.

This demand reveals serious problems. If the results of induction as practised in the inductive sciences are only probable, the announcement of a probability rule which has been established by induction should, if strictly expressed, take the form of a second-order probability statement, that is, of a probability statement about a probability. This is a very difficult conception, and I shall try to show that in order to remove the difficulties we must distinguish two senses of 'probability', one applicable in matters of chance and the other applicable to the results of induction. Something of the kind is suggested by a distinction of Lord Keynes's to which I have already referred, namely, that between probabilities which can be measured at least approximately and others which cannot be measured even in principle. The same thought is to be found also in other recent writings on probability, but little has been done so far to clarify that notion of probability which is supposed to be applicable to the results of induction or to explain why it seems appropriate to use the word 'probability' in this connexion as well as in reference to matters of chance.

In order to find our way through this maze of problems it seems wise to begin by considering what has been said or can be said about induction without detailed reference to probability. Historically the discussion of induction by philosophers has preceded the investigation of probability, and it will be convenient to concentrate attention first on the old problems, because then we shall be in a position to understand why it is said that the results of induction can be only probable. This procedure also has the advantage of enabling us to prepare the way for the introduction of certain notions which seem to be essential in the theory of chances. We shall find in particular that some disputes about the nature of scientific laws which have occurred in philosophic discussions of induction have their parallels in recent debates about the interpretation of probability rules in matters of chance.

The theory of probability in matters of chance, to which we shall turn after our consideration of the traditional problem of induction, was developed first by mathematicians. This book is concerned primarily with the philosophical analysis or clarification of the notions of probability and induction, but it is impossible to understand the questions at issue without some account of the mathematical calculus of chances. I shall therefore devote some space to an elementary explanation of the scope of the calculus. The mathematical knowledge required for an understanding of the main theorems is comparatively simple, but there are few subjects which have given rise to so much confusion and sophistry as the calculus of chances, and for this situation mathematicians bear as much responsibility as philosophers. Until recently there has been little or no attempt to state the theorems precisely, although by the use of some special logical symbolism most of the sources of misunderstanding can be removed. In this way I hope to show that to expect from the calculus results which it cannot possibly provide and to attack it as though it necessarily involved the fallacies committed by some of its exponents are equally foolish attitudes.

In particular, I shall try to show at the end of this part of the book that the theory and calculus of chances cannot provide a solution to the problem of induction. Consideration of this problem has led philosophers to the conclusion that the results of induction can be no more than probable, and many of them have supposed that inductive arguments must therefore be justified within the theory of probability which has been elaborated for dealing with matters of chance. I have already suggested that this is a mistake, and I shall try to explain in the proper place what are the fallacies in the two main attempts to provide such justification.

Finally, in the fourth part of this book I shall try to explain the sense in which inductive conclusions are probable. This undertaking will involve a reconsideration of the programme of the inductive sciences and in particular of the logical character of the propositions which scientists seek to establish.

PART II

THE TRADITIONAL PROBLEM OF INDUCTION

§ 7. ARISTOTLE'S DEFINITION OF INDUCTION

THE word 'induction' is now part of the common vocabulary of educated men. But it was originally invented as a translation for Aristotle's technical term ἐπαγωγή, and for a proper understanding of the discussions which have taken place among philosophers about the nature and method of the inductive science it is useful to begin with Aristotle's usage. We shall find that he had no theory of that kind of induction which is connected with probability, but an examination of his views about the kinds of induction which he did recognize will show what is peculiar in the variety which interests us.

Throughout Aristotle's writings ἐπαγωγή means the establishment of universal propositions, i.e. propositions expressible in the form 'All α things are β', by consideration of particular cases which fall under them. Originally the Greek word had the sense of 'leading to', and it was probably used by Aristotle to suggest the role of examples in the activity to which he was referring, but the precise point of the derivation is not clear. Some say that when he first used the word in logical discussions he was thinking of the leading of a pupil from the singular to the universal, others that he had in mind the citing of witnesses in a law-court or the bringing in of examples adduced as evidence for a general conclusion. But the question is of no great importance. In Aristotle's usage ἐπαγωγή is already a technical term. He sometimes uses the verb ἐπάγειν without an object, as though it meant 'to make an induction',[1] and he even uses it once with τὸ καθόλου ('the universal') for its object, as though it meant 'to establish by induction'.[2]

According to Aristotle induction is not the only method of establishing universal propositions. Sometimes we can use syllogistic argument for this purpose. A syllogism is an argument of some such form as 'All animals are mortal; and all men are animals; therefore all men are mortal'. Here the predicate is proved to hold of the subject of the conclusion by means of a middle term, and the conclusion is said to be mediated by, or

---

[1] *Posterior Analytics*, 91ᵇ35.　　　　　　[2] *Topics*, 108ᵇ11.

grounded in, its premisses. In his *Prior Analytics* Aristotle works out the possible varieties of syllogism according to figure and mood and shows that any valid syllogism which has a universal conclusion must have two universal propositions for its premisses. Now a proposition which is a premiss of one syllogism may be the conclusion of another, but it is clear that we cannot proceed with this regress *ad infinitum*, and so we may say that syllogistic reasoning is not an independent way of establishing universal propositions. It must in the last resort use premisses which are established by induction.

This much is clear in Aristotle's doctrine, but when we try to go farther we find that he has two different accounts of the nature of induction. These appear in different places, and they are not connected by any systematic discussion. It is therefore not clear what Aristotle supposed to be the relation between them. I shall try to show that he had in mind two quite different methods of establishing universal propositions.

§ 8. SUMMATIVE INDUCTION BY COMPLETE ENUMERATION

In his *Prior Analytics*[1] Aristotle tells us that induction proceeds by enumeration of all the particular cases falling under a generalization and gives as an example the following argument: 'Man, the horse, and the mule are long-lived; but man, the horse, and the mule are all the bileless animals; therefore all the bileless animals are long-lived.' This example is curious. It does not matter whether the propositions which Aristotle cites are true. The trouble is that they do not appear to illustrate his general thesis. For, whereas he says that we proceed by enumeration of all the particular cases, what he here enumerates are species. 'Man is long-lived' is already a universal statement about all the individuals of a biological species, although the subject term is grammatically singular. It is not clear how he thinks such a proposition is to be established. Nor is it clear how we are supposed to know that man, the horse, and the mule are all the bileless animals. Sometimes we can know that certain species are the only possible species of a genus according to some principle of division, for example, that equilateral, isosceles, and scalene are the only possible species of triangle in a division according to equality or inequality of sides; and when we have such knowledge we may assert universally of the members of the genus what we have asserted universally of

[1] 68b8–37.

the members of each of its species. But we certainly cannot do this in biology.

It is not difficult, however, to construct an example in which a universal conclusion is established by complete enumeration of the particulars which it covers. We may say, for instance, 'Brown is wearing shoes, and Jones is wearing shoes, and Smith is wearing shoes; but Brown, Jones, and Smith are all the men in the room; therefore all the men in the room are wearing shoes.' Let us, then, ignore the peculiar difficulties raised by Aristotle's example and consider what is involved in an argument such as that just mentioned.

Although Aristotle commonly draws a distinction between syllogism and induction, the reasoning which he here presents as inductive looks very like a kind of syllogism. We can make the point clear by slightly rewording our own example. Let us say 'All the members of the Brown–Jones–Smith set are wearing shoes; but all the men in the room are members of the Brown–Jones–Smith set; therefore all the men in the room are wearing shoes.' Aristotle himself goes so far as to call his argument a syllogism on occasions, but he tries to distinguish it from syllogism proper by saying that it does not establish its conclusion by means of a middle term. His meaning is that in a syllogism proper the middle term must be intermediate between the subject and the predicate of the conclusion in the sense of being the ground for the inherence of the predicate in the subject. Now we cannot say that membership of the Brown–Jones–Smith set is the ground for the possession of shoes by all the men in the room. The inductive argument considered here gives only a *ratio cognoscendi*, not a *ratio essendi*. Since Aristotle is the originator of the theory of the syllogism, he is clearly entitled to say what is to be accounted a syllogism; but whether or not we follow him in using the word 'syllogism' in the strict sense just explained, we may say that the kind of induction we are now examining is a variety of deduction, that is to say, a variety of argument in which the conclusion is seen to be entailed or necessarily implied by the premisses. It is the custom among modern logicians to oppose all induction to deduction, but this opposition is a mistake if 'induction' is used to include induction by complete enumeration.

The question about the use of the words 'syllogism' and 'deduction' is merely verbal, but there is a more serious difficulty in Aristotle's remarks about the role of induction in science. He tells us that induction is the ultimate source from which we derive knowledge of universal truths, but he also insists, quite rightly, that induction by complete enumeration itself requires a universal premiss. If we knew only that Brown, Jones, and Smith were wearing shoes and that they were men in the room, we should have to content ourselves with the conclusion that some men in the room were wearing shoes. It is the premiss that Brown, Jones, and Smith are *all* the men in the room which justifies us in asserting that *all* the men in the room are wearing shoes, and this premiss is universal, for it can be expressed in the form 'All the men in the room are members of the Brown–Jones–Smith set'. How then is it established? In trying to answer this question we shall find that only a certain sort of universal propositions can be established by complete enumeration.

If I wish to prove by this method that all α things are β, I must first establish a conjunctive premiss by examining each α thing separately. But it is impossible to examine each thing in a set unless the set is finite. The reason is not that men grow tired and die after a certain time spent in enumeration, but rather that there is an internal contradiction in the programme of enumerating all the members of an infinite set. It is clear, then, that the first term of the statement to be established must be a description which applies only to a finite set of things. This, however, is not enough by itself. When I have examined the members of the set, I must be able to know that there are no more. It would be absurd to try to establish this premiss by examining everything else in the universe to see whether it was α. If I am ever able to say that there are no α things except a, b, and c, it must be because I know that there can be no others. My first term must therefore be a description which from the nature of the case cannot be satisfied by more than a finite number of things, and it must be such that I can at least in principle work out a procedure for exhausting the set. Let us call a term of the required kind a *restricted description* and a universal statement in which it occurs as first term a *restricted universal statement*. We can then say that the only statements which induction by complete enumeration is able to establish are restricted universal statements, but we have still to ask what makes a description restricted.

There is one almost trivial case in which we can say that a description is restricted, namely, when it embodies an enumeration of the things to which it applies. Thus, for example, the description 'member of the Brown–Jones–Smith set' is obviously restricted because it contains in itself a list of the items in the class it specifies. We can, if we like, say with complete assurance, 'Brown, Jones, and Smith are all the members of the Brown–Jones–Smith set', because this statement is a tautology, but we rarely have occasion to make such remarks. A more common case is that of a description which is defined by means of an enumeration of the things to which it applies although it does not itself contain such an enumeration. 'Members of the Cabal' is such a description, since it is merely an abbreviation for 'Clifford, Arlington, Buckingham, Ashley, and Lauderdale'. The expression 'numbers between 23 and 29' is also a description of this kind, although it has not the same artificiality as 'members of the Cabal'. For by '29' I mean the number next after 28 in the number series, and by '28' the number next after 27, and so on, from which it follows that the description 'numbers between 23 and 29' is equivalent to the enumerative expression '24, 25, 26, 27, and 28'. And again it is a tautology that 24, 25, 26, 27, and 28 are all the numbers between 23 and 29. It does sometimes happen that we use induction by complete enumeration to establish universal statements with first terms of this kind. I might, for example, undertake to prove by such induction that none of the numbers between 23 and 29 is prime.

Apart from these rather curious cases, the only way in which a description can be restricted is by the inclusion in it of a limitation to some finite region of space and time. In our original example the first term of the conclusion is a description restricted in this way. The set of men in the room at a particular time must be finite because the space of the room is finite, and the set can be enumerated completely because the room can be surveyed completely. It will be found on examination that many descriptions are implicitly restricted in this way although at first sight they do not seem to include any reference to a region of space and time. Thus when I speak of Napoleon's marshals I know that there can be only a finite number of them, because the time-span of Napoleon's life was finite and therefore did not allow for the creation of more than a finite number of marshals, and I can conceive of a procedure by which they might be completely enumerated. I do not say that I can now be sure that I have a full list of them, for Napoleon may possibly have created a marshal without leaving a record of his act; but the obstacle is only the familiar one which prevents us from answering any historical questions with complete certainty, and nothing peculiar to the programme of enumeration.

With a term which is restricted in this way it is possible to formulate a restricted universal proposition which is not merely a compendious restatement of the evidence adduced in favour of it, but rather an abstract of that evidence. The statement 'All the men in the room are wearing shoes' is not equivalent to the statement 'Brown, Jones, and Smith are wearing shoes, and there are no other men in the room', for I can quite well understand the first without having seen or heard of the individuals mentioned in the second. Enumeration is here part of the method by which the conclusion is established, not a feature of the conclusion itself.

Further consideration of the way in which we establish such propositions as that Brown, Jones, and Smith are all the men in the room brings to light an interesting fact about our use of the word 'all'. In order to convince ourselves of the truth of the universal premiss just mentioned it is not sufficient that we should inspect Brown, Jones, and Smith. And it will not help to look at any number of things outside the room. We must look all over the room to make sure that it is all occupied in a way inconsistent with the presence of men other than Brown, Jones, and Smith. The fact that we proceed in this way shows that our premiss can be regarded as a statement about the room as a whole. And the same must be true of the conclusion which we derive from the premiss. That is to say, the statement 'All the men in the room are wearing shoes' must be equivalent to the statement 'The room is all free from shoeless men'. If we regard the conclusion in this way we see that it could have been established directly in the same way as its universal premiss, i.e. by a survey of the room. When instead we formulate two premisses and deduce the conclusion from them, we do so only in order to economize effort. It may be that when we first ask the question 'Are all the men in the room wearing shoes?' we are already satisfied that Brown, Jones, and Smith are the only men in the room. In that case we naturally content ourselves with examining them in order to convince ourselves of the truth of the conjunctive premiss which together with our assumption entails the required conclusion. If, however, we are not already satisfied about the number of men in the room, we proceed directly to look all over the room for men without shoes. In short, any universal statement which is restricted by the inclusion in its first term of a limitation to some finite region of space and time is equivalent to a *totality* proposition about that region.

It must be admitted, of course, that if the region is large we may find it impossible to take in the whole at once. We then work out a scheme for dividing the whole into an exhaustive set of parts each of which can be inspected in turn. But in the last resort our procedure depends on the power of apprehending certain wholes as units. If in order to establish a proposition about a continuous whole it were always necessary to enumerate the several parts contained within it, our procedure would be useless. For even a finite continuous whole must contain parts within parts *ad infinitum*. But we do in fact apprehend certain finite continuous wholes as units, and so the imagined difficulty vanishes. The use of the word 'all' in restricted universal statements of the type we have been considering can therefore be explained by reference to its use in the singular in such totality statements as 'The building is all stone' or 'Africa is all hot', but the use of the word in what I call totality statements is primitive and does not admit or require explanation by reference to any other use. We are only inclined to suppose that it does because logicians have concentrated their attention on the use of the word in the plural in universal sentences.

Aristotle's induction by complete enumeration has sometimes been called perfect induction, as though to distinguish it from some other form of induction which is imperfect because it does not employ complete enumeration. The name is unfortunate, since the other varieties of induction which we shall have to consider are not merely imperfect approximations to induction by complete enumeration but proceed by entirely different principles. I shall therefore drop the traditional name and speak instead of *summative* induction whenever there is need for a short description of the argument by complete enumeration.

§ 9. INTUITIVE INDUCTION: FACTS AND PRINCIPLES

When we turn to Aristotle's *Posterior Analytics* we find a different account of induction. He is there concerned especially with demonstration, by which he means syllogistic reasoning from necessary premises, but he recognizes that there must be some other source of knowledge of universal truths. 'Our own doctrine', he writes, 'is that not all knowledge is demonstrative. On the contrary, knowledge of the immediate premises is independent of demonstration. The necessity of this is obvious, for, since we must know the prior premises from which the demonstration is drawn and since the regress must end in immediate truths, these truths must be indemonstrable.'[1] And later he adds: 'Since there cannot be discursive knowledge of the primary premises, it must be intellectual intuition (νοῦς) which grasps them.'[2] This intellectual intuition is not, like Plato's reminiscence or Descartes's intuition, the uncovering of something innate in the mind, but a kind of induction which 'exhibits the universal as implicit in the clearly known particular' (διὰ τοῦ δῆλον εἶναι τὸ καθ' ἕκαστον).[3] It would be impossible without experience.[4]

In order to understand this doctrine we must remember that Aristotle is thinking here of the establishment of necessary universal truths, e.g. such truths as that whatever is coloured must be extended. He says in effect that, if in any single instance I can know that α-ness necessitates β-ness, then I can know that whatever is α must be β. If his doctrine is correct, he has explained how some unrestricted universal propositions can be established. When I say that all coloured things are extended, I speak of anything whatsoever which may at any time or place be coloured. My first term is a description which may be satisfied by infinitely many things. This does not mean that there is or may be an infinite number of things satisfying the description (for the expression 'infinite number' is dangerously misleading), but rather that we have no good reason to suppose there is any answer to the question 'How many coloured things are there in all?' In short, the class determined by the description is open. Clearly an unrestricted universal proposition about the members of such a class could never be established by summative induction; but it can be established by Aristotle's *intuitive* induction if, as he suggests, it is possible to apprehend a necessary and therefore universal connexion as implicit in a particular case. Since a correct appreciation of the question at issue is important for the understanding of what follows, I shall try to say something in explanation of the doctrine which I here attribute to Aristotle.

It is customary to formulate a distinction between necessity and contingency by reference to the notion of alternative possibilities. A truth such as that $2+2 = 4$ is said to be necessary because there is no conceivable alternative to it. On the other hand, the sentence 'My pen is red' is said to state a contingent truth because

[1] 72^{b}18.   [2] 100^{b}12.   [3] 71^{a}8.   [4] 81^{b}5.

it so happens (*contingit*) that my pen is red, although this is only one among a number of possible alternatives. We can, as it were, think the fact away and suppose that the pen were of some other colour. I do not want to suggest that this account of the matter is mistaken, but I think it requires further elucidation to meet the difficulties which have been raised by philosophers of the most opposed schools. In the past philosophers of the rationalist tradition have argued that contingency is merely an illusion of low-level thinking. According to them our ability to conceive alternatives to the facts discovered in experience results from an imperfection of our understandings. Perhaps they have been guilty of a confusion between that which is necessary in itself, and that which is necessary only in relation to something else, but their arguments show at least the need for a more precise formulation of the notions of contingency and necessity. In more recent times philosophers of the positivist persuasion have tried to prove that all necessity is the result of linguistic convention. I do not think they fully realize the strange implications of their own assertion, but again their arguments show the need for a reconsideration of the distinction between contingency and necessity. And, apart from our need to meet the difficulties of the extremists on either side, we may well feel dissatisfied with a formulation of the distinction which involves talking of unfulfilled possibilities. With the horrors of Meinong's jungle fresh in our minds, we cannot accept such language until we are convinced that it is harmless. We do not wish to admit entities which are somehow like facts but without their full-blooded existence.

In order to escape from these perplexities we must distinguish truths of two different orders, which I shall call *matters of fact* and *principles of modality* or, for short, facts and principles. The sense of the distinction can be understood easily from examples. It is a fact that my pen is red, but it is a principle that a cylindrical thing can be green or again that a thing which is red cannot also be green at the same time. Facts are identical with the contingent truths of which we have spoken above, but principles are not to be confused with the truths commonly called necessary. Principles are concerned with possibility or impossibility, necessity or non-necessity, and they are in a sense more fundamental than facts, since they determine what facts there can be. The truths commonly called necessary, e.g., that nothing which is red is also green, are, however, not themselves principles of necessity but merely consequences of these. They might perhaps be called truisms. Principles may be what some philosophers have called truths of reason, relations of ideas, or *a priori* truths, but I think it important to avoid epistemological phrases in formulating the distinction to which I wish to draw attention. Anyone who talks, as we all do from time to time, about unfulfilled possibilities is claiming implicitly to have knowledge of principles. When, for example, I ask whether a certain pen is green, I conceive the possibility of its being green or, to use the language of some modern logicians, I entertain the proposition that it is green, but to do so I must know that it is possible for a pen to be green. If, having inspected the pen, I report that it is not green, I reject as false the proposition which I have entertained, but I cannot do this by finding a simple fact which verifies directly the statement that it is not green. There are no simple negative facts to be discovered in experience. I must first learn that the pen is of some other colour, say, red, and then employ my knowledge that it is impossible for a red thing to be green at the same time. Anyone who reflects on the matter afresh will surely recognize that he knows a host of principles, although he very rarely bothers to state them explicitly because he can safely assume that anyone to whom he can communicate anything knows them too. The connexion between our knowledge of principles and our ability to use language is indeed extremely close and deserves special attention.

Principles are truths about the suitability or unsuitability of certain elements or features (e.g. redness and squareness) to go together as partners in facts of certain structures, and are therefore, as I have already said, in a certain sense more fundamental than facts. But the ability to state principles presupposes the ability to state some facts. We could not be familiar with any elements of the world, if we knew no facts; and we should have no means of symbolizing possible structures for facts, if we had not already stated some facts. Precisely because principles are truths about the possibility or impossibility of there being such-and-such facts, the symbolism for the statement of principles must include the symbolism for the statement of facts. Clearly no one could say anything of the form 'It is possible that an α thing should be β' unless he could already say something of the form 'An α thing is β', because the complex sentence pattern presupposes the simpler sentence pattern, although the truth that an α thing is β presupposes the truth that it is possible for an α thing to be β.

It is a misunderstanding of this situation which has led some positivists to say that all statements which purport to record principles are statements about language put in a misleading form, for example, that the statement 'It is impossible for anything to be both red and green' is merely a record of an arbitrary convention that no expression of the form 'x is red and x is green' is to be admitted as a sentence.[1] We may readily admit that the truth of the printed statement 'It is impossible for anything to be both red and green' is guaranteed by our rules for the use of the shapes 'red' and 'green', and we may admit also that we could, if we wished, use these shapes differently. But we must insist that there is nothing in all this inconsistent with the account of principles given above. It is, no doubt, arbitrary that we should forbid ourselves to use the shapes 'red' and 'green' together in a certain way, but only because it is arbitrary that we should use these shapes to mean red and green respectively. It is not arbitrary that we should forbid ourselves to use together in that way those shapes, whatever they may be, which are to mean red and green. If we decided to use the shape 'green' in such a way that 'x is red and x is green' was a permissible sentence form, then the shape 'green' would not mean what it does now in English but something else, e.g. crimson or coloured or square, according to the rules of the new language. If, however, we are to be able to refer to those characters which we now signify by the shapes 'red' and 'green', we must have in our language two shapes which obey a rule similar to that now holding in English for the shapes 'red' and 'green'. The rule is not something which has been introduced by an unmotived convention and without regard to the use of the shapes in the statement of empirical facts, but rather a necessary condition of their signifying what they do signify. If there is any doubt about this, it should be set at rest by consideration of the way in which words like those mentioned in our example acquire meaning.

If a sound or a shape is to be a word with meaning, rules must be established for its use. The establishment of these rules and the assignment of a meaning are indeed one and the same convention. From consideration of the way in which we have learnt foreign languages, i.e. by translation, we may be inclined to suppose that the fundamental linguistic rules are of the form 'Whenever such-and-such is the case, say so-and-so'. But this is a mistake. Obser-

---

[1] Cf. Carnap's *Logical Syntax of Language*, pp. 302 ff.

vance of such rules by all the members of a society would lead only
to continuous babbling from which no one could get any information about the attitude of another, because there would be nothing
to indicate whether the utterances of a speaker were made in
observance of the rules or from mere exuberance. For communication between speaker and hearer the rules must be of the form
'Do not say so-and-so, unless such-and-such is the case', e.g.
'Do not say "Wolf!" unless you know there is a wolf in the
neighbourhood', 'Do not say "Is it raining?" unless you wonder
whether it is raining.' The rules which a child has to master
when he learns his mother tongue are obviously of this kind.
There is no need to incite him to make noises. He learns rather by
accepting restrictions on his natural propensity to chatter in an
imitative way, and he is said to know his mother tongue when he
can make the various sounds commonly heard in his society, but
makes them only in certain circumstances according to the rules
for the several sounds and their combinations. In order, then, to
understand the meaning of a word such as 'red' I must be able to
recognize occasions on which the restrictive condition for its use
in a statement is *not* fulfilled, and this is as much as to say that I
must know some principles of incompatibility.

Our knowledge of principles is ordinarily a knowing-how rather
than a knowing-that. If ever we say to ourselves that it is impossible for a thing to be both red and green at once, we have
already learnt to use the words 'red' and 'green' correctly, and
it is precisely in this ability to use words according to the rules of
language that our knowledge of principles ordinarily shows itself.
It is even possible to conceive a language which would be adequate
for the ordinary purpose of stating facts but such that principles
could never be expressed in it. Let us suppose, for example, that
the only way of stating that a thing was of a certain colour was to
utter the name of the thing in a certain pitch of voice chosen
according to a rule by which colours and pitches were set in
one-one correspondence, and that the only way of making a conjunctive statement was to produce the conjoined statements simul-
taneously. In a language with such rules we could say that a thing
was red, and we might be able to say that a thing was both red
and square, but we certainly could not say that it was impossible
for anything to be both red and green at once, because we could
not construct any expression of a form analogous to 'x is red and
x is green'. The impossibility of anything's being both red and

green would, however, be represented in the language by the impossibility of saying that anything was both red and green; and it may be argued that this would be the perfection of symbolism. For my own part I consider that loss of the power of talking sense about principles is too big a price to pay for immunity from the not very serious danger of talking nonsense about facts, and I bring forward this curious example only for the light which it throws on the connexion of linguistic rules with principles.

Because principles are truths about the compatibility or incompatibility of recurring features such as redness and greenness, they are always general in form. They may be said to have essential universality in contrast with the accidental universality of truths such as that all the men in the room are wearing shoes. We can, of course, construct true sentences which combine use of modal phraseology with reference to particulars, but these can be adequately explained without assuming that they record separate principles about particulars. Indeed, they must be so explained, for no meaning can be attached to the suggestion that there are truths of possibility and impossibility about particulars as such. Normally, when we make statements of this kind, e.g. 'The pen in the next room may be green' or 'My pen cannot be green', we wish to convey something about the extent of our factual knowledge. We say in effect that some character is or is not compatible with the characters that we know some particular object to have. When, however, philosophers talk of alternative possibilities and claim that they are not merely referring to the extent of their own knowledge, they are, I think, merely noting that certain sentences do not violate the rules of language. Similarly, what is called entertaining a factual proposition (i.e. not necessarily a true proposition but one which if true would be a fact) may be explained as the having before the mind with understanding some sentence which would ordinarily be said to express the proposition. This understanding is not the contemplating of a special sort of object signified by the sentence, but the ability to deal with the sentence according to the rules of the language to which its constituent symbols belong, for example, to affirm or deny it in suitable circumstances and to recognize its relations of entailment to other sentences. If the rules of language were entirely arbitrary, such an explanation would, of course, be insufficient, but once it is admitted that these rules incorporate our knowledge of principles the linguistic solution of the problem seems unobjectionable, indeed inevitable.

We must now reconsider Aristotle's account of intuitive induction in the light of the distinction between facts and principles. The truths which such induction establishes are apparently principles of compatibility and incompatibility. If we assert on the strength of intuitive induction that whatever is coloured must be extended, this is only another way of saying that being coloured and being unextended are incompatible. Furthermore, apprehension of these principles presupposes the occurrence of certain experiences. So much is clear and satisfactory, but it is not easy to see in what Aristotle thought the induction consisted. His expositors sometimes write as though we first apprehended a truth about a particular and then generalized this. Now we can create the appearance of an argument with premiss and conclusion by saying 'This coloured thing must be extended; therefore all coloured things must be extended', but closer examination shows that this is an illusion. We do not begin by noticing a truth about a particular and then proceed to a universal conclusion for which it is evidence. There is indeed no argumentation at all here, since recognition of the necessity and recognition of the universality of what we assert are not distinguishable acts; and it is a mistake to suppose that the contribution of experience to this kind of knowledge is in providing *premisses*. Its contribution consists rather in providing instances. The source of the misunderstandings seems to be the use of the word 'induction', which in other contexts stands for a method of argumentation. If we are to retain the phrase 'intuitive induction', we must therefore make clear to ourselves that we mean no more by 'induction' in this context than a method of establishing universal truths otherwise than by subsumption under universal truths of greater generality.

§ 10. RECURSIVE OR MATHEMATICAL INDUCTION

In comparatively recent times the name 'induction' has been applied to a special procedure by which truths of essential and unrestricted universality are established in mathematics. Like summative and intuitive induction, this form of argument must be distinguished from the reasoning used in the inductive sciences. It is mentioned here only in order that the contrast may be made clear.

The procedure was first formulated explicitly in the seventeenth century by the French mathematician Fermat, who used it in his work on what is now called the theory of numbers. He argued that if a certain property can be shown to belong to the number 1 and also to the immediate successor of any natural number which has the property, then the property must belong to all natural numbers. Let us take as an example the proof of the theorem that the sum of the cubes of the first n natural numbers is equal to

$$\left[\frac{n(n+1)}{2}\right]^2,$$

whatever n may be. We can easily see by trial that

$$1^3 = \left[\frac{1(1+1)}{2}\right]^2.$$

Let us assume that for some number c

$$1^3+2^3+...+c^3 = \left[\frac{c(c+1)}{2}\right]^2$$

and add the $(c+1)$th term, i.e., $(c+1)^3$, to each side. Then

$$1^3+2^3+...+(c+1)^3 = \left[\frac{c(c+1)}{2}\right]^2+(c+1)^3$$

$$= (c+1)^2\left(\frac{c^2}{4}+c+1\right)$$

$$= \frac{(c+1)^2(c^2+4c+4)}{4}$$

$$= \left[\frac{(c+1)(c+2)}{2}\right]^2.$$

But this result is of the same form as the equation we assumed to hold for c terms. The only difference is that '$c+1$' takes the place of 'c'. In other words, if the equation is true when we take a certain number of terms, whatever the number may be, it is true also when we increase the number by 1. Now the equation is true for $n = 1$, and must therefore be true for $n = 2$, $n = 3$, and so on up to any value of n we may choose.[1] This is our justification for asserting the universal theorem.

The procedure is not unreasonably called induction, since it is a method of establishing universal propositions by consideration of cases which fall under them. But it differs from summative induction in that it does not depend on a complete enumeration of

[1] The argument may also be conceived as a *descent* to 1 from any selected value of n. Hence the name 'recursive'.

cases, and it differs from intuitive induction in that it does depend on the ordering of its cases in a series. It is precisely because the cases are ordered in a series according to a rule that we are able to talk about them all, although they are infinitely many and therefore incapable of being enumerated.

Recursive induction of this kind was once believed peculiar to the theory of numbers. It was thought that universal propositions could be established in other branches of mathematics by more direct methods. But examination of the foundations of mathematics has shown that that all mathematical proofs of universal statements about numbers depend in the last resort on Fermat's procedure. All theorems which involve higher types of numbers (i.e. signed integers, rational numbers, real numbers, and complex numbers) are to be regarded as abbreviations for complicated statements about natural numbers. This is the truth in Kronecker's epigram 'God made the natural numbers; all the rest is the work of man'. And there is no way of proving universal statements about natural numbers without the use of the recursive procedure. When we think we are giving more direct proofs, we are relying on what we call the basic principles of algebra, for example, on the associative law for addition:

$$x+(y+z) = (x+y)+z.$$

These principles seem very simple, but they are themselves universal statements about all natural numbers and it is necessary to ask how they are established. There is no method available except recursive induction. It may perhaps be objected that recursive induction cannot be the fundamental method of establishing universal truths about numbers since it too requires a universal premiss to the effect that if a certain property belongs to a number c it belongs also to $c+1$. The answer is that recursive induction must start from recursive definitions of the mathematical operations. I shall try to explain this by giving the proof of the associative law for the addition of natural numbers.

What do we understand by the word 'addition' in mathematics? It is easy to see that by 'the addition of 1' we mean an operation which leads us from a given number to its successor in the number series. It corresponds to the phrase 'And there's another!' as we use it in counting. But we wish to have a general definition of addition which will cover such expressions as '$x+59$' and '$x+273$' as well as '$x+1$'. Now to add 2 to a number is the same as to make two successive additions of 1 and to add 3 is the same as to make three successive additions of 1, and so on. If we try to represent this in a table we get the following scheme:

$$x+2 = (x+1)+1$$
$$x+3 = [(x+1)+1]+1 = (x+2)+1$$
$$x+4 = \{[(x+1)+1]+1\}+1 = (x+3)+1$$

. . . .

In short, whatever c may be, '$x+$the successor of c' means the same as 'the successor of $(x+c)$'. With this identity we have all that we require to complete our recursive definition of addition. For if we understand what we mean when we speak of the addition of a certain number, we understand also what we mean when we speak of the addition of the successor of that number; and, since we understand what we mean by 'the addition of 1', we can work out what we are to understand by 'the addition of n', whatever number n may be. Our second identity is, as it were, a general direction according to which we can formulate as many special definitions as we may need. Writing 'x'' for 'the successor of x' we can express our recursive definition of addition as follows:

(i) $x+1 = x'$;   and   (ii) $x+c' = (x+c)'$.

Now it is required to prove that according to this definition of addition

$$x+(y+z) = (x+y)+z.$$

By (ii) we are allowed to say that, whatever x and y may be,

$$x+y' = (x+y)',$$

and if we transform both sides of this equation according to (i) we get:

$$x+(y+1) = (x+y)+1,$$

which verifies the associative law of addition for the case of $z = 1$. Let us next suppose that the law holds for $z = c$, that is,

$$x+(y+c) = (x+y)+c.$$

Since, whatever x and y may be, the expressions on the two sides of the identity sign must stand for the same number and a number can have only one immediate successor, we are entitled to write:

$$[x+(y+c)]' = [(x+y)+c]'.$$

By transforming both sides of this equation according to (ii) we get:

$$x+(y+c)' = (x+y)+c',$$

and another transformation of the left side according to (ii) gives:

$$x+(y+c') = (x+y)+c'.$$

That is to say, if the associative law holds for $z = c$, it holds also for $z = c'$. And since it holds for $z = 1$, it must therefore hold for all values of z, whatever x and y may be.

From the recursive definition of addition and similar definitions of the other mathematical operations such as multiplication and exponentiation we can in this way derive all the principles of algebra. Now every schoolboy knows that algebra is a study in which we use letters such as 'x' and 'y' instead of the numerals '1', '2', '3', &c., of elementary arithmetic. And every intelligent schoolboy knows that we use these letters as variables, that is, for the purpose of making statements about all numbers. It seems clear, then, that we have in the notion of recursion the foundation of our general study of numbers. Let us examine the situation more closely in order to reach a proper understanding of the nature of recursive induction.

When we speak of establishing truths about all numbers by induction of any sort, we seem to be treating the several numbers, 1, 2, 3, &c., as particular instances of a universal, numberhood, much as we treat this and that red patch as particular instances of redness. And yet this is scarcely a view which we can maintain on reflection. If we try to take seriously the suggestion that the various numbers are particular things, we soon become bewildered by questions about the manner of their existence. And our bewilderment is increased when we consider that anyone who understands the meaning of the word 'number' can say straight away 'The numbers are 1, 2, 3, &c.', although it is not ordinarily supposed that from the mere thought of a universal one can determine what instances it has. There must, then, be a philosophical mistake somewhere in this way of regarding numbers, and the source of the trouble is not far to seek. We have adopted in our study of mathematics a habit of using the signs '1', '2', '3', &c., as though they were nouns, whereas in ordinary speech they occur rather as adjectives.

The numerals are, however, rather curious adjectives. If we say

'There are three men in the room' our adjective 'three' appears to qualify our noun 'men'. In some languages the numerical adjective agrees with its noun in gender, case, and number. But it is certainly not true that each of the men of whom we speak has the character of being three. If, therefore, we wish to insist that we are ascribing a character to something when we say 'There are three men in the room', we must maintain that this thing is the group of men in the room. In order to make this clear we can, if we wish, coin some new numerical adjectives which apply explicitly to groups and say 'The group of men in the room is threesome'. In following up this line of thought we are led to the notion of onesomeness, twosomeness, threesomeness, &c., as specific varieties of a generic character, numerosity, which belongs to all groups but to nothing else. We may then treat all mathematical assertions as condensed statements about groups. We may say, for example, that '$2+2 = 4$' is an abbreviation for 'Any group which is composed of a twosome sub-group and another twosome sub-group is itself a foursome group'. In this way we can remove some of the puzzles which formerly bewildered us, but it would be better if we could eliminate all references to groups. For it is clear that groups are not basic entities, and they seem to be introduced in this doctrine only in order that we may be able to say that numerical adjectives stand for characters of things of some sort. The suggestion that numbers are properties of groups is indeed only a half-way house on the road to the true view, much as the suggestion that existence is a property of propositional functions is a half-way house on the road to a true view of existential propositions. We must try to go a step farther.

Let us suppose that we decide to use the expression 'There are aa men in the room' as an abbreviation for 'There is a man in the room, and there is another man in the room', and the expression 'There are aaa men in the room' as an abbreviation for 'There is a man in the room, and there is another man in the room, and there is another man in the room', and so on. By our convention we have established a new system of signs 'aa', 'aaa', &c. What do these signs signify? Not things, nor yet the characters of things, but rather certain features of structure in the facts they are used to state, namely, recurrences. In the unabbreviated sentences these recurrences are shown by recurrences of whole phrases, in our new symbolism by recurrences of the letter 'a'. Let us call them recurrence signs, including under this name for the sake of convenience the letter 'a' when it is written by itself. We can now define the notion of a recurrence sign as follows:

(i) 'a' is a recurrence sign; and

(ii) any expression which consists of a recurrence sign followed by the letter 'a' is itself a recurrence sign.

Although we have introduced our new signs for the sake of abbreviation, it must be admitted that they soon become cumbrous. Let us, then, agree to write 'a' in place of 'a', 'b' in place of 'aa', and so on up to 'i' in place of 'aaaaaaaaa', and for the next recurrence signs after that let us put '$a*$', 'aa', 'ab', &c. Surely it is obvious by this time that our recurrence signs are numerals with which we can perform all the usual calculations? To say, then, that 2 is a number is simply to say that '2' functions in language like our recurrence signs. If we wish to give a general definition of number, we may write:

(i) 1 is a number; and

(ii) $c+1$ is a number, if c is a number.

But this definition presupposes that we know how '1' and '$+1$' are used in ordinary speech.

The argument called mathematical induction now loses its appearance of mystery. Since the definition of number is itself recursive, it is not surprising that arguments to prove universal propositions about numbers must take the recursive form. The sentence form 'All numbers have the property P' is merely an abbreviation for the more complicated sentence form '1 has the property P, and if c has that property so too has $c+1$'. The theorems of mathematics are propositions of essential universality, but they differ from the universal truths established by intuitive induction in that the whole nature of the objects with which they are concerned, i.e. numbers, is to lie in a sequence generated by addition.

§ 11. AMPLIATIVE INDUCTION AND THE SEARCH FOR CAUSES

We have now considered three kinds of induction—or, to speak more strictly, three applications of the word 'induction'. They are not species of a genus, since, although they are all methods of establishing universal propositions otherwise than by subsumption, they differ as being concerned with different kinds of universal propositions. Summative induction is the method by which we establish propositions of restricted universality in studies such as history. Intuitive induction is the method by which we establish propositions of unrestricted universality in phenomenology and metaphysics. Recursive induction is the method by which we establish propositions of unrestricted universality about numbers in mathematics. But we have still to find the method by which universal propositions are established in natural science, i.e. such propositions as that salt dissolves in water, that copper conducts electricity, that a kettle of water will boil on a hot fire, that pigs cannot fly. These propositions cannot be established by summative induction, because they are apparently unrestricted. When I say that copper conducts electricity, I seem to be talking not about pieces of copper to be found in some limited region during a certain period but about anything which satisfies the definition of copper anywhere at any time. Again, they cannot be established by intuitive induction, because the connexions with which they are concerned are not evidently necessary. It is true we often call them laws of necessary connexion, but we cannot in any such case see the necessity of the connexion asserted. Finally, the universal propositions of natural science cannot be established by recursive induction, because they are not mathematical propositions about numbers. We sometimes say that natural science has become more and more mathematical during its development, but this only means that natural scientists have made greater use of mathematical terminology in their attempts to formulate laws and in their deductions from laws. It does not mean that natural science has become assimilated to mathematics; and anyone who thinks clearly will see that the suggestion that it should be so assimilated is absurd.

One of the most striking characteristics of the induction used in natural science is that it goes in some sense beyond its premises, which are the singular facts of experience; I propose, therefore, to call it *ampliative* induction when there is need to distinguish it from the types of induction which we have already considered.[1] Since, however, in what follows we shall be concerned almost exclusively with the procedure of natural science, I shall frequently omit the qualification 'ampliative' when there is no danger of confusion. The fact that induction in natural science goes beyond its premises is at once the reason for its great importance and the source of the problem with which we have to deal.

---

[1] My use of 'ampliative' is derived from that of C. S. Peirce in volume ii of his *Collected Papers*, but the word is not one of his inventions. It was used in a somewhat similar way by earlier writers on logic.

One of the principal aims of natural scientists when they practise induction is to make possible rational inference from observed
to unobserved matters of fact, and, in particular, prediction, or
inference to the future. This interest of the scientists is easily
intelligible, for we must guide our behaviour by such inferences,
and we cannot make them without relying on laws or rules of some
sort. Attempts have, indeed, been made to show that we need not
rely on laws, but without success. J. S. Mill, for example, argues
in one place that we can make inferences directly from particulars
to particulars.[1] He imagines one mother saying to another: 'You
had better give your Johnny such-and-such a medicine. My Lucy
had a cough like that and she got better after taking the medicine.'
This is an example of the kind of argument called analogy. In
such reasoning it is surely assumed, although not perhaps explicitly stated, that something is to be found in *all* cases of a certain
sort. If Mill means only that we often take laws for granted
without stating them and that it may be desirable we should so
in many of the practical affairs of life, what he says is obviously
true; but he is wrong if he thinks that there can be any inference
from the observed to the unobserved without at least tacit reliance
on laws. Even astrologers, crystal-gazers, British Israelites, Buch-
manites, and people who claim second sight take laws for granted
when they make their predictions. Thus people who claim second
sight assume some such law as that all involuntary images occurring to a seventh child of a seventh child of Highland ancestry are
followed by similar percepts. If there were direct perception of
future events, this would, indeed, require no law as a premiss, but
only because clairvoyance in this sense (if there is such a sense)
would be a kind of observation, not a method of making inferences
beyond the limits of observation, and so would not be covered by
this discussion.

Just because they are required for use as premisses in inferences
to the unobserved, the laws on which we rely to supplement our
observations cannot be established by summative, intuitive, or
recursive induction. A universal proposition established by summative induction may sometimes be used as a premiss of inference
by one who has forgotten the evidence on which it was based or
has taken it on trust from another, but the matter of fact inferred
with its help must be something which was formerly observed by the
person who made the induction. Similarly, a universal proposition

[1] *System of Logic*, II. iii. 3.

established by intuitive induction may cover instances other than those by consideration of which it was established, but it is useless for inference from the observed to the unobserved because it is concerned with a necessary connexion between attributes which can be observed together in each instance. I never need to argue that something I have found to be coloured must therefore be extended. And recursive induction is clearly not concerned with connexions between distinguishable matters of fact. In short, any universal proposition which is to be useful in inference from observed to unobserved matters of fact must go beyond the evidence on which it is based. If, for example, I see dark clouds in the sky and predict that there will shortly be a thunderstorm, my prediction is made in reliance on a law of meteorology which I assume, namely, that, whenever there are clouds in the sky such as I now see, a thunderstorm follows. Such a law must, from the nature of the case, have been established by consideration of instances in which thunderstorms were observed to follow the appearance of dark clouds, but it is used to forecast the occurrence of thunderstorms which are still unobserved. Our account of ampliative induction must show how, if at all, this procedure can be justified. There is, of course, no problem for those who take their laws for granted without even trying to state them explicitly. Unreflective reliance on laws is not very different from the behaviour of animals, who also form habits of expectation, although none so wild as some formed by human beings. This is not to say that it is useless. On the contrary, it is indispensable for survival. But there can be no science until the importance of natural laws has been recognized explicitly, and then the demand for a justification of induction must presently follow.

Since in each of the so-called varieties of induction which we have examined the method of establishing universal propositions is appropriate to the kind of propositions to be established, it is natural to begin our inquiry about ampliative induction by trying to define more exactly the logical character of natural laws. Now it has long been a common assumption among philosophers that the laws which natural scientists formulate are all laws of causal connexion, and that the problem of ampliative induction is to give a method for the discovery of causes. According to the modern supporters of this view it is one of the chief tasks of philosophy in our time to vindicate the principle of universal causation against the wicked attacks of Hume and his followers. There are some who think that Kant has given a sufficient answer to the arch-enemy and that it is only necessary to present the Kantian philosophy in a modern dress, but there are others who feel that new arguments must be found. I shall try to show that this view of the problem of ampliative induction is mistaken because many laws of nature—or at any rate universal propositions which are supposed by natural scientists to be laws of nature—are not concerned with connexions between causes and effects. Since, however, consideration of ampliative induction has been connected for a long time with the discussion of causation, it is important to examine what has been said about induction from this point of view. It is only when we realize the defects of such an approach that we can hope to understand what is required for a satisfactory solution of the problem. Moreover, some of the points raised in the discussion are of interest for any theory of natural laws.

The doctrine that it is the business of the scientist to search for causes is as old as Aristotle, who maintains in several places that genuine scientific knowledge is always knowledge of causes.[1] But the Greek word αἴτιον or αἰτία which we translate by 'cause' is even vaguer than the English term, for it seems to cover at times all such notions as those of ground, reason, and explanation. Thus in one passage Aristotle's translators make him say that the premisses of a syllogism are the causes of the conclusion,[2] although in ordinary English we should say rather that they were the grounds. Aristotle himself was aware that the Greek word had a number of different senses, and in his account of physics, that is to say, natural science, he tried to classify them.[3] The aim of the natural scientist, Aristotle tells us, is to understand natural change or process, that is, to know why it takes place, and he must therefore have a clear conception of the possible answers to this question. There are four causes to be distinguished, the material, the formal, the efficient, and the final. The first of these is the matter out of which something comes to be, e.g. the bronze of which a statue is made; and the second is the form which the matter receives. The early Ionian philosophers were obsessed by the desire to find material causes. Plato, on the other hand, was interested primarily in forms. But, according to Aristotle, both are required for

---

[1] e.g. *Posterior Analytics*, 71^{b}9 and *Physics*, 184^{a}12.
[2] *Posterior Analytics*, 71^{b}22.
[3] *Physics*, 194^{b}16. The account is repeated at *Metaphysics*, 1013^{a}24 as part of a philosophical lexicon.

a process, which is always the reception of a form by some matter. In contrast with these two, which may be called the internal conditions of the change, we have the efficient and the final cause, which are external conditions. The efficient cause is that which initiates the change. In the making of a statue it is the sculptor. The final cause is that end which is to be realized by the change. In the making of a statue it might be the representation of a man. Clearly none of the causes distinguished here is in itself a complete explanation of any change, but Aristotle considers that all four are required for the explanation of every change. He thinks, for example, that it is always proper to look for the final cause of a process, something for the sake of which it occurs, even although the process may not be initiated by an intelligent being.

Unfortunately Aristotle does not tell us how we are to discover causes. We have seen that he bases all science on induction, the method by which we obtain the universal premisses required for our demonstrations; but he does not try to connect his theory of induction with his doctrine of the four causes. Indeed, he has no theory of induction as it is practised in natural science, since neither the summative nor the intuitive induction which he discusses is of any use for the establishment of natural laws. We must, therefore, turn to later philosophers for the working out of the theory that ampliative induction is a search for causes. We shall find that in their writings the word 'cause' takes on yet other meanings.

§ 12. BACON'S METHOD OF INDUCTION BY ELIMINATION

The first serious attempt to formulate and justify the procedure of natural scientists was made by Francis Bacon. For a proper understanding of his work we must realize that it was intended to provide a method of scientific research at a time when such research had scarcely begun, and that it was written in direct opposition to the doctrine of Aristotle, which he thought responsible for the poverty of natural science in his day. Bacon's programme is announced already in the title of the book on induction which he published in 1620. Aristotle's logical works were commonly called the *Organum*, that is, the instrument for acquiring science, and Bacon named his book the *Novum Organum*.

He writes in one of the early sections: 'As the present sciences are useless for the discovery of effects, so the present system of logic is useless for the discovery of science.'[1] By the 'present system of logic' he means the doctrine of Aristotle. Science, he thinks, should enable us to make predictions which are of use in practical life, but Aristotle's logic has nothing to do with such science. Indeed, 'the present system of logic assists in confirming and rendering inveterate the errors founded on vulgar notions rather than in searching after truth, and is therefore more harmful than useful'.[2] The reason is that devotees of syllogistic reasoning accept as premisses universal propositions which have not been properly established.

'There are and can exist', he says, 'but two ways of investigating truth. The one hurries on rapidly from the particulars of sense to the most general principles and from them as premisses (supposed to be of indisputable truth) derives the lesser laws. This is the way now in use. The other constructs its generalizations from the particulars of sense by ascending continually and gradually till it finally arrives at the most general principles, which is the true but unattempted way.'[3]

He recognizes that Aristotle professed to start from experience, but he will allow him no credit for this. Attacking Aristotle's work in natural science, he writes:

'Nor is much stress to be laid on his frequent recourse to experience in his books on animals, his *Problems*, and other treatises. For he had already decided, without having properly consulted experience as the basis of his decisions and generalizations, and having decided he dragged experience along as a captive constrained to accommodate herself to his decisions, so that he is even more to be blamed than his modern followers, the scholastics, who have deserted her altogether.'[4]

The root of the trouble is that Aristotle has no proper theory of induction for use in natural science. If he ever gets what he considers to be a law of nature, it is only by a method which Bacon calls simple enumeration, that is, by the citing of a few instances which fall under the generalization but neither exhaust its scope nor allow us to intuit its necessity. And so Bacon argues:

'We must invent a different form of induction from that hitherto in use. . . . The induction which proceeds by simple enumeration is puerile, leads to uncertain conclusions and is exposed to danger from one contradictory instance. . . . A really useful induction should separate nature by proper rejections and exclusions. . . . Now this has not been done, except perhaps by Plato, who certainly uses this form of induction in some measure to sift definitions and ideas.'[5]

[1] *N.O.* i. 11.　　[2] *N.O.* i. 12.　　[3] *N.O.* i. 19.　　[4] *N.O.* i. 63.　　[5] *N.O.* i. 105.

When he wrote the last sentence, he was referring, of course, to the Socratic dialectic.

This, then, is Bacon's programme. For a long time he was highly praised because it was thought that the procedure of induction which he outlined had contributed much to the advancement of science which followed. He and Newton were often cited as the two chief exponents of scientific method. Then, after a while, he fell into disrepute, because it was noticed that science had not in fact proceeded as he said it should. Macaulay, for example, belittled his contribution to knowledge. But our recent neglect of Bacon is unfair. He was at least the first philosopher to try to formulate a theory of induction suitable for use in natural science, and his work was better in some ways than that of certain successors who are still studied. Let us see how he tried to solve the problem.

His theory of induction is based on the principle that a generalization cannot be validated by any number of favourable instances but can be invalidated by a single unfavourable instance. This he summarizes in his famous remark, *Major est vis instantiae negativae.*[1] He thinks that by relying on the greater force of negative instances we can indirectly establish laws of nature which we could not establish directly. This is the method of elimination, as opposed to the method of confirmation. The antithesis is still to be found in the writings of Lord Keynes and Nicod. But the method of elimination is bound up with a certain doctrine about the character of natural laws. Bacon assumes that the laws we are trying to discover are laws of connexion between generating and generated natures. It is not entirely clear what he means by 'nature', but he seems to intend an event in that sense in which events may be said to recur, i.e. a kind of phenomenon of which there may be many instances. There are, he tells us, only a limited number of generating natures or causes, and all the complication of the world results from the co-ordination of them in their various possible degrees.[2] The problem of science is to find the generating natures for the various distinguishable generated natures. This task we can hope to complete satisfactorily if we remember that a generating nature or cause must always be co-present, co-absent, and co-variant in degree with its corresponding generated nature or effect. We are to digest the evidence collected by observation into three tables of presence, absence, and degrees and then use the evidence

---

[1] *N.O.* i. 46.　　　　　　[2] *Advancement of Learning*, III. iv.

so arranged to eliminate hypotheses about the cause of that which is under investigation. When only one hypothesis is left, this can be accepted as the true cause.

The example he takes is that of an inquiry to find the cause of heat.[1] In the first table (of presence) we put cases which agree in that they are all examples of heat but otherwise differ widely among themselves. Since, according to his assumption, there is just one cause of heat, we can eliminate from consideration all those circumstances in which the various instances of heat differ from each other. In the second table (of absence) we collect cases which in many ways are like cases included in the first table but nevertheless are not instances of heat. We can then argue that whatever is present in these cases where heat is absent can be ignored. In the third table (of degrees) we collect instances of heat differing in degree, and after inspection of these cases we rule out of consideration all these circumstances which do not vary concurrently with the heat. The conclusion which he reaches by this method is that motion is the cause of heat.

Apparently he thinks he has provided here a sure and certain method for discovering causal laws—almost, one might say, an inductive machine, by the use of which even men without special talent may make useful discoveries.[2] He was not alone in holding this curious view that the adoption of the right method in research would make intellectual differences negligible, for we find a similar doctrine in Descartes's *Discourse on Method*; but he was certainly wrong in supposing it possible to give such a solution to the problem of induction.

Bacon's theory of induction depends on his doctrine of generating natures or causes, which is to be found at the beginning of the second book of the *Novum Organum*. Unfortunately this doctrine is extremely obscure. He agrees with Aristotle's dictum that true science is knowledge of causes, and he apparently accepts Aristotle's distinction of four causes as a correct account of the different ways in which the word 'cause' is used; but he says that consideration of material, efficient, and final causes is useless for science. Except in human affairs the doctrine of final causes is positively harmful. Here Bacon is in agreement with the views of the scientists, such as Galileo, who were at that time re-founding physics. Material and efficient causes are useless because they are variable, i.e. we do not always have the same material and efficient

[1] *N.O.* ii. 11. [2] *N.O.* i. 122.

causes for different instances of the same kind of happening. They are mere vehicles for the form. What we want to know is how we can produce a certain result whenever we wish. To know this is to know the form of that which is to be produced. The form is the *natura naturans* or generating nature. Although in my summary I have used the word 'cause' freely as being sanctioned by Bacon's explanations and likely to convey some meaning to a modern reader, it is important to note that Bacon himself commonly used the word 'form' when referring to that which is to be found by induction, perhaps because he thought that readers of his day, who had been educated in the Aristotelian tradition, might be misled by the use of the word 'cause'. But what he means when he talks of a form is not nearly as clear as he thinks it is.

Bacon's form can scarcely be the same as Aristotle's formal cause. For Aristotle's formal cause is, as we have seen, merely the correlative of matter, that which can have form. In Aristotle's sense to assign a formal cause is only to say in a precise fashion what character is being realized in a certain matter. But Bacon thinks of a form as a generating nature distinct from the generated nature of which it is the form. For him it is certainly not a mere definition of the generated nature, since no knowledge of definitions could give us the power which Bacon frequently says we acquire with the knowledge of forms, and no one could maintain with any show of plausibility that all natural science is a search for definitions. We have seen that in his example of induction he reaches the conclusion that motion is the form of heat. Consideration of this example, and of casual remarks in other places, suggests that he means by the word 'form' the set of physical conditions for a sensation. Perhaps he would say that the form of sweetness was the physical structure shared by all things which taste sweet. In several places he commends the atomic physics of Democritus.[1] But he has not worked out any theory of perception within which he could explain this doctrine clearly, if, indeed, it is what he has in mind. Against this interpretation we have the fact that he usually speaks of the form as something observable and supposes that it can be found by careful examination to be present in all the cases listed in the table of presence, whereas the physical conditions of a sensation are not themselves observable and so not discoverable by the Baconian methods of elimination.

At times Bacon appears to be aware of this difficulty, for he

[1] e.g. *N.O.* i. 51.

speaks occasionally of trying to find the latent (i.e. unobservable) configuration of the particles of things and admits implicitly that we cannot hope to read this off from his tabular statements of the results of observation. In one place he says that after collecting all the evidence we may rightly let the intellect go its own way in speculation about the hidden form.[1] This doctrine of *intellectus permissio* is in effect an anticipation of the hypothetical method in natural science and a confession that we cannot go far by the use of his tables.

Whatever may be the correct interpretation of Bacon's remarks about forms or formal causes, it is clear that natural science·is not all a search for formal causes in any sense which that phrase can bear in his writings. There is, however, another theory about causes which has become prominent since his time in the discussion of induction and still has advocates. To this we must now turn.

§ 13. HUME'S DOCTRINE OF ANTECEDENT CAUSES

There is a usage of the word 'cause' in English in which we suppose a cause to be an event which produces another event later in time but contiguous with the first. Thus we may say that the lighting of a match on a certain occasion was the cause of an explosion. This usage is quite different from any of those noticed by Aristotle,[2] and it differs also from Bacon's usage of 'form', since for Bacon the form and that of which it is the form are apparently contemporaneous. In order to avoid any possibility of confusion I shall call a cause in the new sense an antecedent cause. It is this notion of cause which Hume examines in his *Treatise of Human Nature*. Indeed, he declares that it is the only proper sense of 'cause' and that Aristotle's list is useless.[3] I believe that the attention which he gave to the idea of antecedent causation has made it seem much more important to philosophers than it really is in science.

Hume constantly speaks of causation as a relation between events, and he thinks that it has a special interest for the theory of knowledge because it is only by means of this relation that we can ever make an inference from the observed to the unobserved.[4] He has surely made a mistake here, for we can make inferences to

---

[1] *N.O.* ii. 20.   [2] Aristotle's efficient cause is a substance, not an event.
[3] Book I, Part III, Section xiv. Other references are to the same book and part.
[4] Section ii.

what we do not observe by means of laws of nature which are not causal in form. Thus if I see a male white cat with blue eyes I can infer that it is deaf, although I have not yet tested its hearing. We shall find, however, in a later section that a great deal of what Hume says about the logical character of causal laws may be applied without much modification to other laws of nature.

Having emphasized the importance of the causal relation as he understands it, Hume proceeds to analyse the notion of causation. He finds that it is complex. It involves the notions of precedence, contiguity, and necessitation or production. Of these the first two give rise to no special difficulty. But the third is troublesome, because it is difficult to find any impression from which the idea of necessitation can be derived, although according to Hume's fundamental principle every idea must be derived from some impression. Finding himself at a loss, he proceeds, as he says, to beat about the neighbouring fields in search of what he wants. First he examines the arguments put forward by Hobbes, Locke, and others to prove the principle of universal causation, namely, that every event has a cause. He has no difficulty in showing that these arguments all beg the question. Then he asks himself 'why we conclude that such particular causes must necessarily have such particular effects and why we form an inference from one to another'.[1] To this question he answers that our belief is due to association of ideas, which in turn is to be explained by constant conjunction in experience of those items we now call cause and effect. And here he finds the answer to his original question about the origin of the idea of necessitation. He says that it is derived from the feeling of expectation with which we await the second of the two items that are associated in our minds. Since the necessity we suppose in the connexion of cause and effect is, as it were, projected from our minds, it cannot be said to be part of the connexion considered objectively—if, indeed, we are entitled to use such language at all in expounding Hume. He therefore concludes that, apart from precedence and contiguity, constant conjunction is the most important notion involved in our complex idea of causation.

In the course of his discussion Hume enunciates rules by which to judge of causes and effects, that is, rules by which to determine when we may consistently say that a certain kind of event is the cause of a certain other kind of event.[2] These rules turn out to be

[1] Section iii.   [2] Section xv.

very like the tests which Bacon applies in his search for forms by the method of elimination. We are told that there must be a constant union between cause and effect and, as a corollary, that if they are capable of degrees they must be co-variant. Almost certainly Hume had Bacon's theory in mind when he wrote these rules, but I do not think that he intended to offer them as a new version of induction by elimination, because there is no place in his scheme for such induction. The procedure of elimination was devised by Bacon as an alternative to simple enumeration. He thought that simple enumeration could give only irrational confidence, whereas elimination would yield rational conviction. But Hume was unable or unwilling to make any distinction between rational and irrational belief, and so for him there could be no hope of an escape from irrational confidence to something better. According to his account of belief the practice of induction can be no more than the establishment of associations between ideas, which occurs in animals as well as in men.[1] On the one hand we have the blind confidence which nature teaches, on the other the scepticism to which reason leads, and there is no third course open to us.

Hume's discussion of causation has had the success of a scandal. Very few philosophers wish to deny his contention that we cannot see any necessity in the laws of nature which we assert. For that contention is, after all, undeniable. Even the sober Locke said as much. What shocks us is Hume's assertion that induction can be no more than the association of ideas without rational justification. And because he reached this conclusion by examination of the notion of an antecedent cause, many philosophers suppose that if only they could prove some proposition about antecedent causes which Hume called into question all would be well. In particular a number of philosophers, of whom Kant is the most famous, have tried to demonstrate the principle of universal causation, supposing it to be a premiss indispensable for any rational development of science. I shall not try to deal with such attempts in detail, because I think they involve a mistaken notion of science; but it will be useful to consider briefly J. S. Mill's account of induction,

---

[1] Section xvi. When speaking as an historian rather than as a philosopher, Hume could distinguish very well between science and superstition. The sub-title of the *Treatise*, 'An Attempt to Introduce the Experimental Method of Reasoning into Moral Subjects', shows his respect for Newtonian science. But he understood the character of his own philosophy better than some of his modern disciples, although he naturally said many things inconsistent with scepticism.

since this is the best-known attempt to present the search for ante-cedent causes as a rational undertaking.

§ 14. THE INDUCTIVE METHODS OF J. S. MILL AND THEIR PRESUPPOSITIONS

J. S. Mill's *System of Logic* is a classical work on inductive logic and it is still the foundation of what the elementary text-books have to say about the subject. But it is not a very original book, for on all important points Mill is a disciple of Bacon or Hume.

Like Bacon, he distrusts induction by simple enumeration, and he points out that we cannot hope to justify it by talking about the uniformity of nature.[1] If the principle of the uniformity of nature is supposed to mean that, whenever one phenomenon has been accompanied by another in a few cases, we are entitled to say that the conjunction holds in all instances, it is obviously false and even silly, since it would justify far too much. Many suggestions of law which were originally based on observed conjunctions have later been discredited by negative instances. If we think some such principle necessary for science, we should rather say: 'The uni-verse is so constituted that whatever is true in any one case is true in all cases of a certain description.' But then the difficulty is to find what description is relevant. From these considerations Mill concludes that induction must be a search for causes. He understands causation in the Humean sense, that is to say, as a relation between events involving constant conjunction, and he tries to dispense with the notion of necessary connexion by defin-ing a cause as an unconditional and invariable antecedent. The method he proposes to use for the discovery of causes is an adapta-tion of Bacon's induction by elimination. I shall not consider his exposition in detail, since it has been discussed many times in the text-books, but I think it is worth while to remark that Mill's presentation somewhat obscures the nature of the argument. Instead of talking of three tests to be applied to hypotheses about the cause of a phenomenon, namely, the tests of co-presence, co-absence, and co-variation, he offers a number of independent methods, each conceived as a positive argument, or even as a proof of causal connexion. Thus, corresponding to the rule that nothing can be the cause of a phenomenon which is not present when the phenomenon occurs, he has a canon to the effect that if a number of positive instances of a phenomenon agree in one circumstance

---

[1] *System of Logic*, III. iii.

only (apart from being all instances of the phenomenon), then that circumstance is the cause of the phenomenon. In all he has five such methods, the method of agreement corresponding to the requirement of co-presence, the method of difference corresponding to the requirement of co-absence, the method of concomitant variations corresponding to the requirement of co-variation, and two others which are really superfluous. Instead of considering these further we shall go on to examine what he has to say about the presuppositions of induction.

In the eliminative method we argue that a certain kind of event is the cause of the phenomenon we are investigating because it is the only candidate for the position which satisfies the requirements of a cause, but this argument would have no value at all if it were not already established that there is *some* cause for the phenomenon. Now the proposition that there is some cause for the phenomenon cannot have been derived by deduction from the more specific proposition that such-and-such a kind of event is the cause of the phenomenon, because it is to be used in the establishment of the more specific proposition. It can only have been derived from the principle of universal causation, namely, that every event has a cause. How are we assured of the truth of this principle? Mill is an extreme empiricist, as faithful as he can be to the tradition of Hume, and he will therefore admit no *a priori* proof of the principle which he requires. The only suggestion which he can offer is that the principle is itself established by induction. A similar suggestion is to be found in Hume's *Treatise*. After criticizing the *a priori* arguments for the principle Hume writes: 'Since it is not from knowledge or any scientific [i.e. demonstrative] reasoning that we derive the opinion of the necessity of a cause to every new production, that opinion must necessarily arise from observation and experience.'[1] But this is merely an incidental remark, not part of an attempt to justify induction. For Mill the question is more urgent, because he wishes to show that his procedure for finding causes is valid. Let us examine his argument in detail.[2]

Mill recognizes that his suggestion appears to involve a circle, but he says that the induction used to establish the principle of universal causation is not the same as that which presupposes the principle. That it cannot be the same is evident, for Mill's inductive methods are supposed to be ways of discovering causes and

[1] *Treatise*, Book I, Part III, Section iii.   [2] *System of Logic*, III. xxi.

the establishment of this principle is not the discovery of the cause of anything. But the only alternative is an argument from simple enumeration, and it is rather surprising that he should rely here on a kind of reasoning which he thinks unreliable in the special inquiries of science. The explanation seems to be that he believes the method permissible when the universal propositions to be proved are of vast generality. Thus we find him asserting that it is used to establish the fundamental truths of arithmetic. There are, he says, an enormous number of positive instances confirming the generalization that $2+2 = 4$, and no negative instances such as might be expected if the generalization were false. The example is very unsatisfactory indeed, but it shows at least that in certain other important contexts Mill is prepared to put his trust in simple enumeration and that the method as he conceives it involves no presuppositions about causation. For, whatever arithmetical truths may be, they are certainly not concerned in any way with causal connexions. This is not the place for a general discussion of simple enumeration, but it is easy to show without any such discussion that Mill's attempt to use the method for the establishment of the principle of universal causation is fallacious.

The objection is not that the principle, like the truths of mathematics, needs no empirical justification, being already certain *a priori*, but rather that no empirical justification can be given for it. Mill writes:

'To the law of causation we not only do not know of any exception, but the exceptions which limit or apparently invalidate the special laws, are so far from contradicting the universal one, that they confirm it; since in all cases which are sufficiently open to our observation we are able to trace the difference of result, either to the absence of a cause which had been present in ordinary cases, or to the presence of one which had been absent. The law of cause and effect, being thus certain, is capable of imparting its certainty to all other inductive propositions which can be deduced from it.'

It is untrue, however, that we have always been able to assign causes to the events we have perceived. If this claim were correct, the work of science, as Mill understands it, would be finished, for there would be no unsolved problems, which is plainly absurd. And to say that we have been able to assign causes in all cases sufficiently open to our observation is no improvement; for by 'cases which are sufficiently open to our observation' Mill must mean those cases in which we have been able to satisfy ourselves some-how about a cause, and if we ask how we are supposed to satisfy ourselves about such a matter we find that the attempted proof of the principle of universal causation involves a circle after all. Mere observation will not show that one event is the cause of another, as Mill's language might suggest. According to his own exposition in other places we argue: 'On the assumption that there is some cause this must be it, since no other candidate can pass the tests for a cause.' That is to say, according to his own theory we use the principle of universal causation as a premiss in arguments to establish the propositions from which the principle is supposed to be derived by induction.

Although he thinks he can prove that for every phenomenon there is some cause, Mill is not so sure that for every phenomenon there is only one cause. He admits that there may be a plurality of causes. In ordinary life and in elementary science we often speak of a certain kind of event as a cause of a certain other kind of event, although we cannot say that all instances of the second are preceded by instances of the first. Thus we say that poisoning is a cause of death, although we certainly do not believe that all deaths result from poisoning. Are we entitled to assert that this is only a loose usage, and that for every kind of event we describe as an effect there must be some one other kind of event related to it according to the strict requirements of co-presence and co-absence? We do sometimes assume that there is just one cause, for example, when we ask what is *the* cause of cancer; but is our inclination to ask for a single cause any guarantee that there is one? I shall not try to answer this question for reasons which will become clear in the next section. But I must draw attention here to the fact that if we admit the possibility of alternative causes we cannot eliminate candidates for the position of cause on the ground that the effect has occurred without their preceding. That is to say, Mill's method of agreement becomes useless. He is well aware of this, and prizes his method of difference more highly than the others because he thinks it would survive the admission of a plurality of alternative causes. In the method of difference we argue that because a certain circumstance is the only new feature in a situation where a phenomenon occurs it must be the cause, or at least a cause, of that phenomenon. Our reasoning depends only on the principle that nothing can be the cause of a phenomenon which occurs without being followed by the phenomenon. And I believe that when we look for causes in the way described by Mill we do, in fact, put more faith in his method of difference than in the others. It is the method which corresponds most closely to experimental procedure.

§ 15. LIMITS TO THE USE OF THE NOTION OF CAUSE IN NATURAL SCIENCE

We have seen that the word 'cause' has been used by philosophers in a number of different ways, some of which no longer seem natural at the present day. In modern English we most commonly speak of a cause in the sense of Aristotle's efficient cause or Hume's antecedent cause. But we also use the word sometimes in ways which have not been noticed so far. Thus Newton wrote among the random notes at the end of his *Optics*:

'What I call Attraction may be performed by impulse or by some other means unknown to me. I use that Word here to signify in general any force by which bodies tend towards one another, whatsoever be the Cause. We must learn from the Phaenomena of Nature what Bodies attract one another and what are the Laws and Properties of the Attraction, before we enquire the Cause by which the Attraction is performed.'

It is difficult to determine what exactly Newton had in mind when he spoke of a cause of attraction, but it seems clear that he meant something by naming which we could answer the question 'Why do bodies attract each other?' and such a thing could scarcely be either an efficient cause or an antecedent cause. Again, laws of nature have occasionally been mentioned as causes, although this is a usage which most people would consider strained and unfortunate, because a cause is normally supposed to be something which can be indicated by a noun. If, then, we are to give a definition which will cover all the various usages of the word, we must say that a cause is anything by the thought of which we can render a happening intelligible to ourselves. When, however, a word is used in so vague a fashion as this, it should be suspect in philosophy, and I suggest that we ought to break with the philosophical tradition which says that natural science is concerned exclusively with the discovery of causes. It is, of course, true that scientists try to describe and explain what happens, but their efforts are certainly not directed to finding causes in the sense of Aristotle's doctrine of the four causes, and it is only in certain special cases, important chiefly in the early stages of scientific development, that their work can be called a search for causes in the sense of Hume's doctrine of antecedent causes.

The word 'cause' and the corresponding Greek word αἰτία were probably used first in legal contexts to mean the subject-matter of a dispute. This technical usage still remains in English law, and by a slight extension of meaning we speak in ordinary life of the causes in which men are interested, when we wish to refer to the matters which are of special concern to them. The use of 'cause' in the explanation of natural happenings may seem at first sight very remote from this, but in all its various application the word still retains some mark of its forensic origin. When we look for efficient causes we think primarily of persons whom we can hold responsible for particular events, and when we look for antecedent causes we think primarily of states of affairs which it is important to notice if we wish to influence the course of history to our advantage. In each case the use of the word 'cause' involves an element of anthropomorphism. Although it would be foolish to deny that it is proper to talk of causes in the practical affairs of everyday life, it would be equally foolish to assume that the notion which serves us well enough in these contexts can be so refined that it will serve as the fundamental category of all explanation in natural science. Yet this, in effect, is what Hume and other philosophers have assumed in their discussions of antecedent causes. If, indeed, we try to think out carefully what would be involved in a principle of universal causation as conceived by these philosophers, we find that the notion of antecedent causation seems to dissolve under our scrutiny.

In ordinary speech we often say that one particular event is the cause of another particular event. Thus, I may say that it was the dropping of a smouldering match by someone which caused a fire in a warehouse on a certain day, or I may say that the Air Ministry ought to hold an inquiry to determine the cause of a particular air disaster. This seems to be the most primitive use of the word 'cause' in application to events. In this sense a cause is some happening earlier than the effect on hearing of which we find the occurrence of the effect intelligible. Reflection shows, however, that in such cases we find the occurrence of the effect intelligible only because we have taken a great deal for granted. Thus, in the example of the fire at the warehouse I take for granted a great many singular facts such as that the warehouse contained dry wood-shavings and was normally well ventilated, but I take for granted also a universal proposition that if a red-hot body falls on dry wood-shavings in the presence of oxygen a fire will follow shortly after. When I put all this clearly to myself I can see that my only reason for speaking of the dropping of the match as the cause of the fire was that this striking or unexpected circumstance completed a certain set of conditions from which fires usually follow. If I had approached the problem from a different point of view, i.e. taking different singular facts for granted, I might have said that the cause of the fire was the placing of the wood-shavings in the warehouse or the opening of a window through which a draught of air came. From considerations of this kind we are led on to say that the particular events which in common speech we describe as causes may be only cause factors or vehicles for such factors, and that it would be more precise to reserve the word 'cause' for a type of event, however complex, on which some other type of event always follows.

Many laws of nature formulated by scientists are indeed laws of causal connexion in this sense between types of events, e.g. the generalization that friction causes a rise of temperature. And some, but not all, of them are laws of reciprocal connexion, that is to say, laws which allow us to argue either from cause to effect or from effect to cause. But, as we have already noticed, there are many laws of nature which cannot be expressed as causal connexions, for example, that all mammals are vertebrates, and causal laws appear to be more common in the less-advanced sciences. To anyone who considers the notion of antecedent causation carefully this will not seem surprising.

In the first place, there is a difficulty about temporal precedence and contiguity, which Hume thought so straightforward as to require no comment. We say that the cause must precede the effect and also that there must be no gap between them. It is true we sometimes speak of a cause as preceding its effect by a small interval, but then we assume that there is some causal chain filling the gap between the first and the second event and say that only the proximate cause, i.e. the last link in the chain, is cause in the strictest sense. It is sufficient, therefore, to consider the case where there is supposed to be no interval at all between cause and effect. Now any events which are to satisfy this requirement of having no interval between them must be processes having duration, not instantaneous occurrences. For there can be no contiguous instants, just as there can be no contiguous points. Between any two distinct instants there must be some interval, however small, since an instant is not a part of time but a limit of a part of time. Let us suppose, then, that we are using the word 'event' in the sense of 'process', and that the two events which we call cause and effect adjoin one another in time, the one ceasing in the instant in which the other begins. The former process, since it lasts for a certain time, must have temporal parts each of which is itself a process. Why should we call the whole process the cause, rather than the last half or the last quarter? It seems as though the event called cause must be resolved into a causal chain each link of which can be resolved again in the same fashion, and so on *ad infinitum*. In short, there is no one event of which we can say that it is the unique cause of the event called effect; and by a precisely similar argument we can show that there is no one event of which we can say that it is the unique effect of another event called cause.

Secondly, there is a difficulty about the understanding of the principle 'same cause, same effect' which is presupposed in the search for causal connexions between types of events. When are two particular events sufficiently alike to justify the assumption that for the purposes of this principle they are instances of the same type? If a horse is found eating grass and a donkey is found eating thistles, are we to say that these two particular events are instances of the one type *ungulates-eating-herbage*, or are we to go farther and say that these two events are instances of the type *feeding* of which other instances are to be found in the absorption of mineral solutions by plants? If the kind of event we choose to consider is defined in very general terms, it is impossible to find any other kind of event by which it is uniformly preceded or uniformly succeeded. What, for example, shall we say is the cause or effect of movement? There is no answer, because the notions have no application at this level of generality. On the other hand, it is useless to insist on complete similarity of the particular events which are to be covered by the same causal law, for there will always be some detectable difference between any two particular events we consider, even if only in relational characteristics. One explosion, for example, occurs in a laboratory where the scientists speak English, another may be in a laboratory where the scientists speak French. And if the type of event we choose to consider is described with a great wealth of specific detail it is impossible to name any invariable and unconditional antecedent or consequence, because an event so defined is not repeated.

These considerations must not be supposed to imply a refutation of determinism. There may be some universal scheme of connexion between events according to which what happens later in time could always in principle be inferred from a sufficient knowledge of what happened earlier, and what happened earlier from a sufficient knowledge of what happens later; but the doctrine of universal causation assumed by Mill in his discussion of induction is not an adequate account of any such scheme. On the contrary, the notion of antecedent causation on which he relies cannot be employed profitably except in certain rather special circumstances. It is useful only so long as we are content to stop our analysis at some point and say that the events with which we propose to deal are processes of a certain duration and a certain degree of generality. Now this is a common situation in everyday life, for the customs of language and the needs of practice fix the types of events to which we ordinarily attend. We think of some processes, e.g. explosions, breakages, and actions like the pressing of a bell-button, as natural units because it is psychologically impossible for us to detect parts within them. But this is not the only reason why we select processes for special attention, for we speak also of storms and battles as single events. All that is necessary to secure our attention is that a process as a whole should have some character which we can easily recognize as recurring in various instances. If, then, such a process is uniformly preceded or uniformly followed in our experience by another such process, we say that it is the cause or the effect of that other. It is true that we do not say that day causes night or night day, but this is sufficiently explained by the fact that day and night alternate, i.e. there is not the single irreversible order which we expect when we distinguish cause and effect.

That there should be pairs of processes satisfying these conditions is a fact of great practical importance to us, because when we have formulated the sequences in universal statements we can make predictions with comparative ease; but there is no reason whatsoever to suppose that every process must be an element in such a sequence. Indeed, when we consider things more carefully, it appears somewhat remarkable that there are in nature any recognizable routines of which we can say that particular processes are instances. That there are such routines is due to the fact that the world is resolvable into relatively isolated systems of considerable stability. It is quite possible to conceive a world in which there would be no recognizable routines such as the growth of trees, because nothing stayed put long enough for any routine of that sort to be completed. The surface of the sun is presumably like this. By following up the same line of reasoning we come to the conclusion that there might be a world with no recognizable routines whatsoever. In such a world some principle of determinism might hold, although it would be impossible to formulate any causal laws because there would be no recurring processes which we could regard as causes and effects. A very powerful intelligence which could contemplate such a world might perhaps be able in the end to discover the laws which governed it, but the task of making a beginning in natural science would at least be very much more difficult than it is in the world we know. We may even be tempted to say that it is a fortunate accident for scientists that they find themselves in a world of relatively isolated systems for which they can formulate a number of causal laws. But this is not strictly correct, for our existence as human beings with sense organs and brains would be impossible if there were no relatively isolated, and therefore comparatively stable, systems in nature. We can say, however, that, just because the possibility of formulating causal laws depends on the existence of relatively isolated systems, laws of this kind cannot be ultimate in any scheme of universal determinism. It is therefore a mistake to assume that all science must be a search for causal laws.

§ 16. THE FORMULATION OF NATURAL LAWS IN SCIENTIFIC PRACTICE

The work of scientists is not merely a self-conscious, systematic search for laws of any kind by means of which they can make inferences from the observed to the unobserved; but this is nevertheless an indispensable part of their activity, and we must now consider some of the types of laws they have formulated, apart from the causal laws discussed in the previous section. I understand here by 'laws' any uniformities in nature such as we assume when making inferences to the unobserved, apart from those which can be established by summative induction. In the usage of scientists the term is sometimes reserved for uniformities which are considered especially important because many others can be derived from them, but I am deliberately using the word here in a wide sense. The types of laws to be mentioned in this section are not offered as an exhaustive list, and they may not even be mutually exclusive, but the suggested classification will at least show that some of the older logicians have over-simplified their accounts of induction.

1. A very large number of natural laws are concerned with the *uniform association of attributes*, e.g. the laws that common salt is soluble in water, that all mammals are vertebrates, that all ruminants have cloven hooves. Laws of this kind are extremely important in the classification of things into natural kinds. Thus, our distinction of chemical substances is based on the fact that we find certain attributes of matter uniformly carrying with them certain other attributes, and our distinction of biological species is based on the fact that there are uniform associations of attributes to be discovered in living organisms. It is conceivable that the various determinate characters which we can recognize, e.g. colours, shapes, densities, degrees of hardness, &c., might be so distributed among particular objects that we could not assume any uniformities of association, and if this were so natural science would be impossible. The knowledge that a particular thing had a certain group of characters would then not enable us to predict that it would have any other character. We could, of course, still make such platitudinous remarks as that red things are not green (i.e. we could know the incompatibility of determinates under the same determinable); but we could not classify particular things under such general terms as 'iron', 'salt', 'water', 'cow', 'fish', all of which stand for very complex conjunctions of characters. Each possible combination of characters might perhaps be said to constitute a separate species of natural object, but just because there were no discoverable limits to the possibilities of combination such classification would be pointless.

When the natural scientist begins his work of trying to formulate laws, he finds himself already committed in common with other men to a classification of things into natural kinds; and, although he must certainly improve that classification, it is never necessary, or even possible, for him to go back to the beginning and start as though he were ignorant of all uniform associations of attributes. It is true, as I have said, that we can conceive a world in which there would be no uniformities of association, but in order to do so we must make a rather difficult effort of abstraction. For in such a world there could be no perception of cabbages and men, sticks and stones, earth, air, fire, and water, in short, no awareness of material things, but only something like the variety of sensations we have when recovering from an anaesthetic. Moreover, in such a world there could be no development of intelligences such as ours. In the world we know, on the other hand, the work of the scientist is only a development of an activity already implicit in his recognition of perceptual objects. He finds, for example, that he can carry farther the kind of classification by which sticks and stones have been distinguished, and he tries to carry the process to the limit. If he finds some pieces of matter which are apparently in other respects like lead but have a different density, he does not content himself with recording the anomaly, but coins some new general term, e.g. 'heavy lead', to describe the new material and immediately looks for other characters in which it differs from ordinary lead. That is to say, he assumes in effect that the difference in density must be a symptom of other differences, because to do anything else would be to abandon the principle that chemical substances are natural kinds in which all associations of attributes are determined by law. In biology the norms of size, shape, habit, &c., by which scientists define species are not so precisely stated as the properties of chemical substances; but even there any considerable departure from the standard calls immediately for a new effort to discover associations of attributes. If some new creatures were discovered which looked like house-flies but were three times the size of the largest-known house-fly, biologists would not be content until they had found other differences of the new species or variety.

It will be noticed that among the attributes by which natural kinds are distinguished there are some which can be recognized only by reference to other natural kinds. Thus solubility in water, which we ascribe to common salt, is a dispositional property which cannot be recognized unless water can be distinguished from other liquids. The fact that attributes of this kind are involved in some of our most ancient classifications of things shows the great complexity of the work which has already been done by the time natural scientists begin their deliberate search for laws.

2. Another type of natural law is concerned with the *uniformity of development* to be expected in certain natural processes. We say, for example, that a chemical reaction which requires some time for its completion always involves certain phases, that there is a certain sequence of stages in the development of an embryo, that a disease may be expected to run a certain course. It might be thought that according to the account of causation given in the

previous section we should be prepared to call any distinguishable earlier phase of such a routine the cause of what follows, but we find that scientists do not often use this terminology when the process which interests them looks like a gradual development within a self-contained system. The reason may be that the word 'cause' carries with it still some notion of dramatic intervention, of action by one thing on another, which is lacking in these cases.

We may perhaps include under this head the second law of thermodynamics, that free transference of heat takes place only from a body of higher temperature to a body of lower temperature. It differs from the examples already noticed in its enormous generality and in its simplicity, but it is a law to the effect that a process of a certain sort, namely, a free transference of heat, always takes a certain course, namely, that which tends to the equalization of the temperatures of the bodies in thermal communication.

3. A third type of law is concerned with *functional relations between measurable quantities*. An example is the law that for any gas

$$pv = kT,$$

where p stands for pressure, v for volume, T for absolute temperature, and k for a constant dependent only on the units of measurement chosen. The functional relation need not, of course, be so simple as in this example but may in principle be of any type recognized in mathematics. All that is essential is that for each value of a certain variable or variables there should be one and only one value of another variable, and that the relation between them should be expressible by a formula of mathematical analysis. The requirement that the functional relationship should be expressible by a formula is important, because laws of this kind are used for interpolation and extrapolation in the original mathematical sense of those words. Just as we cannot test all possible specimens of gas to make sure that they conform to the law stated above, so too we cannot test any particular specimen at all possible pressures and all possible temperatures. But we want to use the law for inferring the behaviour of specimens, whether old or new, at pressures and temperatures at which we have so far made no observations. And this we can do only if the law provides us with a means of calculating the value of one variable when the values of others are given. Laws of this type are, indeed, universal in two respects, first, as dealing with all the specimens of some kind and secondly, as dealing with all the values of some variable magnitudes (or at least all the values within some prescribed range of variation).

Some writers on scientific method speak of functional relations between variable magnitudes as though they were themselves laws; but this is to ignore the fact that laws of this kind are always about some special kinds of things or processes which have the variable magnitudes. The formula 'All α things are β' which we have used in talking of laws is, of course, a general pattern which does not exhibit the peculiarities of the various types of natural laws. But it has at least the merit of reminding us that even in quantitative laws there is a reference to all instances of a certain kind, e.g. all specimens of gas, all pieces of copper, all propagations of sound. If we decide to use this formula for the purposes of exposition, we may say that the functional expression used in the statement of a quantitative law is to be thought of as part of the expression to be inserted for 'β'. Thus the gas law we have taken as our example can be written in the form: 'Every specimen of gas behaves in such a way that its pressure, volume, and temperature are in the relation $pv = kT$.'

4. The laws of another group are concerned with *numerical constants* in nature. Such, for example, are the laws about the melting-points of chemical substances. Some laws which are said to deal with constants may, however, be presented as laws of functional relationship between variable magnitudes. The speed of light may, for instance, be described quite correctly as a natural constant; but it is to be defined as the ratio of the measure of the space traversed to the measure of the time taken in any propagation of light, and we can therefore express the law about it in the statement: 'All propagation of light is such that $s = 300,000\ t$, where s is the space traversed in kilometres and t is the time taken in seconds.' Similar remarks can be made about the coefficients of expansion of chemical substances and, indeed, about any constants which are defined as ratios between variables or as parameters of any other kind in functional relationships.

Laws of the last two types, which have to do with measurable quantities, have been formulated only in the later stages of scientific development. Some of them are, indeed, refinements of laws which might be described as qualitative and classified under one or other of the first two headings. That iron could be melted by great heat was well known before the invention of a scale of temperatures, and a quantitative statement about the melting-point of iron differs only in degree of precision from the older qualitative statement. But this difference is of very great importance. In the first place, it makes possible much more detailed predictions about the behaviour of particular pieces of iron; secondly, it enables us to test in a more decisive fashion any hypotheses which may be put forward to explain the phenomenon of melting. I shall have occasion to return to the second point in later sections. Occasionally scientists, and particularly physicists, have been so much impressed by the importance of quantitative laws as to assert that no statement can be scientific which is not quantitative. To say this, however, is to go too far. Not all the qualitative statements which have been put forward as formulations of natural laws can be treated as merely crude approximations to quantitative statements. Some of them, e.g. that all mammals are vertebrates, must stand as formulations which cannot be improved by development of the technique of measurement. And it must be remembered that even quantitative laws have a qualitative aspect; like all other natural laws they are concerned with things or processes of certain kinds, and so can never be assimilated to purely mathematical formulae of functional relationship between numbers.

§ 17. THEORIES ABOUT THE LOGICAL CHARACTER OF NATURAL LAWS

If we reject the view that ampliative induction is concerned always with causal connexions, what are we to say of the logical character of the propositions which it establishes?

There is a belief among some logicians that all precisely formulated laws of nature must be laws of reciprocal connexion, i.e. that if it is true to say 'All α things are β' it must also be true to say 'All β things are α'. This doctrine seems to be a relic of the belief that inductive scientists are always engaged in a search for causes as defined by Bacon or Mill; for it receives no confirmation from an examination of the laws formulated in the more advanced sciences. Some of the universal propositions asserted by inductive scientists are simply convertible, others are not, and there is no reason to describe the first group as more precise, or more fundamental, than the second. I therefore mention this superstition only in order to dismiss it.

A more important question is that of the relation between natural laws and the propositions established by summative, intuitive, and recursive induction. In order to explain the differ-

ences between these types of induction we have found it necessary to distinguish three sorts of universal propositions. The form
of expression 'All α things are β' may, it seems, be used in different
contexts to state truths of quite different kinds; all that the various
usages have in common is the rule whereby from a statement of
this form taken together with a statement which predicates the
first term of something we may derive a statement which predicates the second term of that same thing. We must now consider
whether natural laws resemble in any important respect the
propositions of any one of the sorts we have already distinguished
or require to be treated as distinct from them all alike. Since,
however, the difference between natural laws and universal
propositions about numbers is so evident as to need no further
comment, it will be sufficient to compare natural laws with the
propositions established by summative and intuitive induction.

Natural laws are often said to be concerned with necessary connexions, and it is therefore a plausible suggestion that they may be
principles of necessitation which for some special reason we cannot
hope to establish by intuitive induction. This was apparently
Locke's view. In the fourth book of his *Essay on the Human
Understanding* he says several times that we cannot have insight
into the connexions which we assert in natural science; but he
holds nevertheless that they may be necessary in the same sense
as connexions which we are able to comprehend, and he implies
that a sufficiently powerful mind which was furnished with the
appropriate ideas of what he calls the real internal essences of
things might see the necessity of natural laws. According to his
doctrine the reason why we cannot establish such laws by intuitive
induction is not simply that our intellects are too feeble, but that
our experience does not furnish us with the ideas which would be
required for an understanding of the connexions we assert.

The chief objection to this view was formulated by Hume.[1]
Although he referred only to causal laws, his argument may be
applied to laws of other kinds. Take any supposed law you please,
he says, and you will find that you can conceive the contradictory.
If, for example, it were really a principle of necessitation that salt
dissolves in water, it would be impossible that salt should not
dissolve in water. For if α-ness necessitates β-ness it is impossible
that anything should be α and not β. And what is impossible is
inconceivable. For if anyone tried to conceive the impossible, he

[1] *Treatise*, Book I, Part III, Section vi.

would not succeed in conceiving anything. Nevertheless, we can quite easily conceive of salt remaining in water without dissolving, although we have not found it to do so, and from this it seems to follow that it is not necessary that salt should dissolve in water. This is an extremely formidable objection, and it is not surprising that many modern philosophers have taken it to be a conclusive refutation of the suggestion that natural laws are principles of necessitation. I shall reserve further comment on it until the other possible suggestions have been considered.

It has commonly been assumed that natural laws are propositions of unrestricted universality, and it is, of course, evident that they cannot be established by summative induction. For the sake of completeness we ought nevertheless to consider the suggestion that their universality is restricted, although we cannot hope to enumerate all their instances. Aristotle maintained on *a priori* grounds that the universe must be finite in extension.[1] He thought that we could speak sensibly of infinity only in connexion with possibility, and that there could exist nothing which was actually infinite. In recent times some astronomers have maintained that the universe must be finite, but for quite different reasons connected with the theory of relativity, and Sir Arthur Eddington has even tried to state the number of particles which it contains. It may seem at first sight that if either of these arguments is sound, all laws of nature must be restricted in their universality, because there can be only a finite number of things to talk about. But this is not so. Although laws of nature are commonly expressed in the present tense, they are understood to deal with the future as well as the present and the past, and there is nothing in the arguments which I have mentioned to show that the sequence of future events must have an end. If, therefore, we try to defend the suggestion that the universality of natural laws is restricted, we must suppose that the statements in which we express them are always intended to refer to some finite period of time, although they may contain no explicit limitation.

So far as I know, Professor Whitehead is the only philosopher who has tried to maintain such a view.[2] His argument is based, not on any supposed proof of the finiteness of the universe, but on a peculiar doctrine of his own that laws of nature are, so to say, local and temporary customs established among some constituents of the universe during a 'cosmic epoch'. He holds that we can never

[1] *Physics*, 204^{b}1.   [2] *Science and the Modern World*, ch. iii.

have any warrant for making wholly unrestricted generalizations about what happens in nature, but that we can reasonably make conjectures about uniformities in limited regions of space-time. How large such a region may be he does not explain, and I think he would say that the limits are not to be supposed precisely determined. His idea seems to be that in use every empirical generalization must be restricted, at least implicitly, to some finite region of space-time, and that its trustworthiness will vary inversely as the size of the region for which it is assumed to hold. According to this view, when a universal proposition is tacitly understood to refer only to matter within the solar system during a few centuries, it should be accepted with more confidence than when it is taken to refer to all matter within the galaxy during several millions of years, and *a fortiori* with more confidence than when it is taken to refer to things in distant nebulae during many light-years.

It must be admitted that scientists do in fact show special caution when using some of their supposed laws of nature for the making of inferences to events which are very remote in space or time; but their caution can be explained and justified without reference to Professor Whitehead's theory that laws of nature have only restricted universality. If we have found all α things in our experience to be β, we may assert that all α things without restriction are β and yet presently feel some hesitation in using this proposition as a premiss for inferences about very remote instances of α-ness because we reflect that all the instances we have observed may have been subject to some local or temporary condition (e.g. of temperature or atmospheric pressure) not mentioned in our statement of the supposed law. When we reason in this way, we are not abandoning a belief in laws of unrestricted universality. We are merely admitting that in our attempts to formulate laws we sometimes overlook factors which should be mentioned and say 'All α things are β' when we should say 'All $\alpha\gamma$ things are β'. Indeed, the considerations which make the scientist cautious in such a case cannot be stated without an assumption that precisely formulated laws of nature have unrestricted universality. It seems unnecessary, therefore, to discuss the alternative further.

In order to explain summative and intuitive induction we have made two distinctions: (*a*) between restricted and unrestricted universal propositions, and (*b*) between facts and principles. It is not obvious that these distinctions coincide, and, if we reject both the suggestion that natural laws are principles and the suggestion that they are propositions of restricted universality, we ought to consider next whether we can conceive them as facts of unrestricted universality. This seems, indeed, to be the only remaining possibility, and it is the view adopted by Hume. He allows that we often talk of natural laws as though they were principles of necessary connexion; but he holds that the necessity is, as it were, the projection of our feeling of expectation, which itself is due to the constant conjunction of certain items in our experience. To assert a law of nature is, then, only to assert a constant conjunction without restriction to the field of our actual experience. Some modern followers of Hume speak of this as the regularity theory of natural laws; in order to keep as close as possible to Hume's own phraseology I shall call it the *constancy* theory.

It is often objected against this theory that there cannot be facts of unrestricted universality or, to put the matter in another way, that sentences which purport to state such facts are meaningless. The philosophers who maintain such a view do not deny that we can formulate truisms of unrestricted universality such as 'All coloured things are extended', but they hold that no significant universal statement can be at once contingent and unrestricted. In the past the thesis was often put forward without argument by idealist writers who assumed a connexion between universality and necessity, but in recent times it has been defended by positivists with an argument based on their theory of meaning. It is said that no sentence can express a contingent proposition unless it admits of verification by experience. But an unrestricted universal proposition cannot be verified by experience. Therefore no such proposition can be a contingent truth, and so the constancy theory of laws is refuted. I do not find this argument convincing. It depends on the use of a criterion of significance which I see no reason to accept, and it leads to some very curious consequences. According to the ordinary rules of logic a sentence of the form 'All α things are β' must be supposed equivalent to the negation of a sentence of the form 'There is an α thing which is not β'. Now a sentence of the second form may very well be verified in experience by the discovery of something which is α and not β, and so it must be suppposed to express a contingent proposition. It is surely very strange indeed to say that this sentence has no significant negation, and yet this is the conclusion to which we are led by the argument now commonly urged against the constancy theory. It is true we can never have any good ground for asserting a contingent proposition of unrestricted universality, and there may conceivably be some good argument against the possibility of such propositions, but I have seen none.

The constancy theory of natural laws ought nevertheless to be rejected for another reason. It is impossible to conceive natural laws as facts, whether of restricted or unrestricted universality. In order to make this point clear it will be useful to consider an imaginary example in which the special difficulties connected with unrestricted universality are avoided. Let us suppose for the sake of argument that the term 'dodo' is defined in such a way that nothing can be called a dodo unless it lived on the earth within a certain period of years which ended in the eighteenth century. Then we can say with confidence that the number of dodos is finite. Let us suppose further that it has been established by complete enumeration that every dodo which existed had a white feather in its tail. It is, of course, impossible to establish this proposition now, because most of the evidence has been lost; but we can conceive that there might have been an organization of bird-watchers which kept records of all the dodos from the origin to the extinction of the species. Are we to say that the universal proposition so established is a law of nature which has been proved for certain? Surely not, for laws of nature are normally expressed in the timeless present, and are assumed to be concerned not only with actual instances of some kind, but with anything which might have satisfied a certain description. If on the strength of our records we suggest that there is a law of nature that all dodos have a white feather in their tails, we say in effect that, if there had been any dodos other than those mentioned in our records, they too would have had a white feather in their tails. But an unfulfilled hypothetical proposition of this kind cannot be derived from a proposition which is concerned only with the actual. A contingent universal proposition can always be expressed in the form 'There are in fact no α things which are not β', and from such a proposition it is impossible to deduce that if something which was not in fact α had been α it would also have been β.[1]

Consideration of the objections which can be urged against all the theories so far mentioned has led some philosophers to say that

---

[1] This difficulty is overlooked by some modern philosophers who maintain that Hume was mistaken in thinking his own philosophy sceptical. Cf. R. E. Hobart, 'Hume without Scepticism', in *Mind*, xxxix, 1930.

the sentences in which we profess to formulate laws of nature are not statements of any kind, but prescriptions, or maxims of conduct, by which we guide ourselves in making predictions about particular cases. This suggestion was first put forward by F. P. Ramsey,[1] and has been adopted by a number of positivists who think it the only view consistent with their criterion of significance. Thus Schlick writes:

'Natural laws do not have the character of propositions which are true or false, but rather set forth instructions for the formation of such propositions. . . . Natural laws are not universal implications, because they cannot be verified for all cases; they are rather directions, rules of behaviour, for the investigator to find his way about in reality, to anticipate certain events. . . . The relations between reality and ourselves are frequently expressed in sentences which have the grammatical form of assertions but whose essential sense consists of the fact that they are directions for possible acts.'[2]

The argument might be paraphrased as follows: 'The only significant statements about the world are those which assert matters of fact and are capable of verification in experience. The sentences in which we formulate laws of nature look like statements about the world, but they cannot be verified in experience, because they have unrestricted universality. They must therefore be interpreted as prescriptions of our own making, rather than as statements.'

It is somewhat high-handed to say that sentences which are commonly treated in all respects as though they were statements cannot be such because they do not satisfy the test of being verifiable in experience; and some other positivists have preferred to modify their criterion of significance so as to exclude only sentences which cannot be falsified, i.e. refuted, by experience.[3] This concession allows us to say that sentences which express natural laws are statements, but it leaves unsolved the problem about the logical character of natural laws. No positivist can admit that they are principles of necessitation, and it is evident for the reason already given that they cannot be matters of fact. We must therefore take the prescription theory of natural laws as the only one consistent with positivist doctrine.

[1] *Foundations of Mathematics*, pp. 237 ff.

[2] 'Die Kausalität in der gegenwärtigen Physik', published in *Die Naturwissenschaften*, 1931, and quoted by Weinberg in his *Examination of Logical Positivism*, p. 146.

[3] Cf. K. Popper's *Logik der Forschung*, but I understand that he would not now call himself a positivist.

If the sentences in which we formulate natural laws are to be construed as prescriptions, they must still be supposed universal in scope, e.g. 'Whenever you find a dodo assume that it has a white feather in its tail'. Now the positivists have no reason at all to give why we should adopt such general rules. It is not permissible for them to say that a rule of this kind will enable us to make successful predictions, for such a remark is itself a universal statement about the world and contains all the difficulties they find in those formulations of natural laws which purport to be universal statements. Indeed, such a remark made in recommendation of a prescription amounts in effect to an assertion of the law which the prescription is intended to replace. And, if they are really consistent, the positivists cannot reply that they are content to record the way in which we behave without offering any justification. For to say that we make rules of the kind Schlick describes is to state a law, that is, a proposition of unrestricted universality, about human behaviour. If he is to be true to his own principles, the upholder of the prescription theory must say only that all scientists whose methods he has studied have in fact behaved as though they had adopted rules for the guidance of their own expectations.

But even this modest claim cannot be admitted. The practice of scientists in the formulation of natural laws is not adequately described as the making of rules for the guidance of their expectations. When they have formulated a law of nature, scientists consider themselves entitled, not only to make predictions about the unobserved, but also, as we have already seen, to assert unfulfilled hypothetical propositions implied by the law. If the sentence which purports to formulate a law gives only a general rule, what is derived from it can be no more than a command or injunction. It is absurd, however, to treat an unfulfilled hypothetical statement as an injunction to expect something. I can, of course, advise someone to believe that if a certain thing had been α it would have been β, but then I assume that it is possible to believe an unfulfilled hypothetical proposition, i.e. something which is not a mere matter of fact.

So far as I know, the four theories which we have now examined are the only suggestions concerning the logical character of natural laws which have been put forward by philosophers. All have their difficulties, but the first seems to me not entirely hopeless, whereas the others offer no hope at all. I shall therefore try to deal briefly with objections to the view that laws of nature are principles of necessitation.

§ 18. NATURAL NECESSITY AND PERCEPTION

Hume's discussion of necessary connexion starts from the assumption that all ideas must be derived from impressions. But there is surely something absurd in his search for an impression from which this idea might be derived. The absurdity is like that which Kant and other critics have found in his search for an impression of the self, but it is not precisely the same. In Hume's terminology an impression is what modern philosophers call a *sensum* (e.g. a flash or a noise or a smell in that usage in which flashes, noises, and smells are said to be objects of sensation), and an idea is an image. Now necessary connexion is thinkable, but certainly not imaginable; and there is no reason to suppose that, because it is thinkable, it must also be sensible. On the contrary, the supposition that it might be sensed is clearly mistaken. When we say that α-ness necessitates β-ness, we mean that it is impossible for an α thing not to be β. Our idea of necessitation is, therefore, the notion of a boundary to possibility. How could such a notion be a copy of anything contained as an element in actual experience? When discussing the philosophical relations, Hume admits that we can recognize the contrariety (i.e. incompatibility) of sensible qualities such as redness and greenness, but he fails to see that even in this special case thinking of contrariety is something very different from imagining a possible object of sensation. And the reason for his failure is his uncritical acceptance of the doctrine that 'nihil est in intellectu quod non fuerit in sensu'. Traditional debates about the *origin* of ideas are full of confusion, and this slogan of the empiricists is as misleading in its way as the talk about intellectual reminiscence, innate ideas, and *a priori* concepts in which their rationalist opponents have indulged. The question 'How do we obtain the idea of necessary connexion?' can be answered only by the statement that we know the incompatibility of certain items such as redness and greenness which we have met in experience. The empiricists are right in saying that there can be no thought without experience, but they are wrong in saying (or implying) that thought is the reproduction, or anticipation, of experience in imagination.

When we consider in detail the argument that it is always

possible to conceive the contradictory of a supposed law of nature, we find the same confusion. If the notions involved in the thought of a natural law were such as Hume supposes, this argument would be fatal to the view that natural laws are principles of objective necessitation; but the situation is in fact very different. Hume frequently speaks of natural laws as propositions by the use of which we make inferences from impressions to ideas. It is clear, however, that, except in certain parts of psychology, the laws of nature formulated by plain men and scientists are not about sensa and images, but about sticks and stones, pieces of metal, elephants, and stars, all of which can be perceived but certainly not sensed. The most plausible example which might be offered to illustrate Hume's account of natural laws would be the proposition that lightning causes thunder. But even here reflection shows that Hume's account is inadequate. When I speak of lightning, I do not mean a vivid visual impression occurring as an element in my experience, but rather a public event which can be perceived by other people or photographed. Similarly, when I speak of thunder, I do not mean the noise impression which sometimes, though not invariably, follows a bright flash in my experience, but rather a public event which can be perceived by other people or recorded by a machine. My imagination of a bright visual sensum not followed by a loud auditory sensum does, indeed, enable me to know that I might experience the one without the other. For while imagining this course of experience I can recognize its possibility. But imagination is powerless to prove a lack of connexion between lightning and thunder. For there may well be many truths concerning lightning and thunder which are not open to inspection by me when I imagine the experiences needed for the perception of lightning and thunder.

In any sense of the word 'conceive' which is relevant to the argument, an ability to conceive the contradictory of a supposed law of nature does not disprove the suggestion that the supposed law is a principle of necessitation. This can be seen from consideration of a mathematical analogy. In 1742 Goldbach, an otherwise unknown correspondent of the Swiss mathematician Euler, suggested that every even number greater than two is the sum of two primes. This conjecture has been confirmed for all the even numbers for which it has been tested, but during the past two centuries no one has succeeded in demonstrating its truth. The attitude of mathematicians towards it can, therefore, be expressed by the statement 'Goldbach's conjecture looks like a theorem, but it may conceivably be false'. There is, of course, a very important difference between this case and the case of natural laws, for we do not think that a natural law might perhaps be demonstrated to-morrow. But this difference only makes my argument stronger. If the conceivability of the contradictory is not to be taken as a disproof of necessity in mathematics, where proof is attainable by *a priori* reasoning, why should it be supposed to furnish such a disproof in natural science? What we call conceiving is often little more in fact than readiness to manipulate symbols according to established rules. In mathematics such manipulation may on occasions enable us to discover principles of modality which were not obvious at first. But in natural science there is no such hope, because the linguistic rules which give meaning to the special symbols of natural science are different in character from those which govern the usage of mathematical symbols.

When the misleading associations of old terminology have been eliminated, the contentions of those who oppose the necessitation theory of natural laws reduce to this: 'Since we cannot say what it would be like to know the necessity of a natural law, it is senseless even to suggest that such a law may be a principle of necessitation.' The hypothesis that something we cannot know *a priori* is nevertheless a truth of principle seems curious, I admit, but I think that it seems so only because we fail to notice the peculiarity of the concepts used in natural science. Having once assumed that there is no important difference between the rules which give meaning to such a word as 'lightning' and those which govern the usage of 'red' in the sensum terminology or 'two' in the language of mathematics, we are naturally led on to say that, if there are any truths of principle concerning lightning, they must be knowable *a priori*. Then, since men undoubtedly speak of necessity in nature, we find ourselves driven to say that the word 'necessity' must have a special meaning in this context and cudgel our brains to give an analysis. In fact, the word 'necessity' is the least troublesome of those with which we have to deal in this part of philosophy. For it has the same sense here as elsewhere. A principle of necessitation is a boundary of possibility, and we know quite well how possibility is bounded from consideration of such cases as the incompatibility of redness and greenness. Our real problem concerns words such as 'lightning' with which we describe objects of perception as distinct from objects of sensation. This point is so important that it is worth spending some space to set it beyond doubt.

In ordinary speech we most often use verbs such as 'see', 'feel', 'hear', and 'taste' with nouns such as 'stick', 'stone', 'explosion', and 'sugar' for their grammatical objects. For convenience I shall use the word 'perception' as a generic term to cover seeing, feeling, &c., in this sense, and I shall call the things we perceive, or might perceive, *perceptual objects*. It is interesting to notice that the phrase 'perceptual object' has a wider range than 'material object', for, while we claim to perceive things such as sticks and stones, which are ordinarily called material objects, we claim also to perceive lightning flashes, which would never be called material objects, that is to say, we claim to see these objects in the same sense of the word 'see' as that in which we claim to see sticks and stones. Even the noises and smells mentioned by plain men in ordinary speech are perceptual objects, for they are supposed to be constituents of a public world which can be perceived by other people. It is true that a plain man may occasionally have to report to his doctor that he hears a noise in his head which he cannot suppose to be a constituent of the public world, but it is clearly not a noise in this sense to which a plain man refers when he says to a friend, 'Listen: there's a funny noise coming from that machine'.

Although the usage of words like 'see' which I have just described is by far the most common and is adopted not only by plain men but also by philosophers and scientists during most of their lives, there are certain curious occurrences which make even plain men feel the need of something more. I have referred already to the noises in the head which the plain man may occasionally have to report. We must place in the same category the stars seen by a man who has had a blow on the head and the pressures which a man who has lost his leg may feel in the place where his toes would have been if his leg had not been amputated. These cases are abnormal in the sense that they occur only when something has gone wrong with a man's body; but there are also normal occurrences which make us feel the need for some other way of talking about what we see, feel, &c. A straight stick which is half in and half out of a glass of water looks as though it were bent. This appearance is public, unlike those to which I have just referred, but it does not seem to fit easily into our ordinary way of talking about what we see, because it suggests a difference between what we see and what we assume to exist independently of our perception. The easiest way out of the difficulty, and the one usually adopted, is to say, as I have just done, that the stick looks bent although it is really straight, but this manner of speaking, although useful and perfectly proper, offers no final solution of the problem to anyone who feels puzzled. If the stick looks bent, something, it may be said, must in fact be bent, although *ex hypothesi* not the stick. Considerations of this kind have led philosophers to make a distinction between two senses of words such as 'see', 'feel', 'hear', &c. They maintain that in their new and more fundamental sense of the word 'see' what we see is not a perceptual object but a coloured expanse which they call a sensum or sense-datum. For convenience I shall use the word 'sensation' as a generic term to cover seeing, feeling, &c., in this special usage. The introduction of the new terminology by philosophers is, of course, not a wholly arbitrary innovation.[1] Even the plain man is accustomed to using the word 'feel' in two ways. He says sometimes that he feels a slap on his back or a hole in his sock, where the feeling is what I have called perception, and at other times that he feels a pain in his tooth or a tickling in his throat, where the feeling is distinguished from the first as being only sensation. He may also say sometimes that he sees an after-image, where the word 'see' is used for a mode of sensation.

The purpose of philosophers in distinguishing between sensation and perception is to find a way of stating facts about the given in circumstances where the common way of speaking seems to lead into difficulties, and I do not think it can be seriously denied that the distinction is valuable, but it has unfortunately given rise to some new misunderstandings. Led away by enthusiasm for their new usage of the word 'see', some philosophers have said, for example, that we do not *really see* sticks and stones. It is of course true that we cannot see sticks and stones in the same sense of the word 'see' as that in which we claim to see sensa such as after-images, but it is surely a gratuitous creation of paradoxes to maintain that our ordinary usage of the word 'see' is mistaken. We learnt to speak of seeing sticks and stones long before we thought of using the word to stand for a mode of pure sensation, and we cannot help continuing to speak in this way, however hard we may try. Other philosophers, noticing that perception is more

---

[1] For the history of the distinction see Sir William Hamilton's note on p. 886 of his edition of Reid.

complex than sensation, have said that, while we may retain the ordinary usage of such words as 'see', we ought to treat perception as less trustworthy than sensation. They argue that seeing a perceptual object consists in seeing a sensum and believing at the same time some proposition or propositions about the origination of the sensum or about the possibility of sensing other sensa connected with it by family resemblance. This attempt to analyse perception is less paradoxical than a veto on the use of words according to their ordinary rules, but it is nevertheless inconsistent with those rules. When we say that a man has seen a stone we do, indeed, imply that he has sensed a visual sensum of some sort, but we do not imply that he has had any belief of the kind suggested. A man may quite properly be said to have seen a stone although at the time of sensing the sensum he had no belief of this kind, or only a false belief, e.g. that he was looking at a sheep. On the other hand, according to our rules of usage for the word 'see' in its perceptual sense the statement that a man has seen a stone entails the statement that there was a stone to be seen, whereas according to the suggested analysis of perception there would be no self-contradiction in the statement that a man saw a stone and there was no stone.

In order to avoid confusions of this kind we must recognize that we have to do with two different terminologies and that the problem for the philosopher is to make clear the relations between them. It is not difficult to state the relations in very general terms. Each usage requires the existence of the object said to be seen, felt, heard, &c., but a claim to perception is more far-reaching than a claim to sensation, in that it asserts not only the existence of some sensum sensed in the perception but also the existence of a perceptual object to which that sensum *belongs*, and it may therefore be open to doubt in a way in which a claim to sensation cannot be. The chief difficulty of the branch of philosophy which deals with perception is to explain how sensa can be said to belong to perceptual objects, or in other words how statements about the existence of perceptual objects are related to statements about the existence of sensa. I cannot attempt to discuss this problem in detail or answer the question about belonging; but it is essential for my purpose to ask in what sense we have ideas of the perceptual objects we assume to exist, and this involves some consideration of the relation between statements about perceptual objects and statements about sensa.

It has been suggested that, when a perceptual object is perceived, the sensum which is sensed in the act of perception belongs to the perceptual object as being a constituent of it, e.g. that the elliptical brown expanse which I sense when looking at a penny on the table before me is literally part of the surface of the penny. This answer seems agreeably simple, but it has awkward consequences. Our way of talking about perceptual objects implies that they can exist apart from our acts of perceiving them. If, then, a sensum is a constituent of a perceptual object, it too must be capable of existing apart from the sensation which is involved in perception. Some philosophers have declared that they find no difficulty in admitting the existence of unsensed sensibilia, but the general view of philosophers, with which I agree, is that this supposition involves an absurdity. The question cannot be settled by arguments from physics or physiology, but only by reflection on the way in which we use words. It is naturally somewhat difficult to make the matter clear to ourselves so long as we follow the usual practice of taking our examples from visual sensation; for the use of the word 'see' to stand for a mode of sensation as distinct from perception is a novelty, and our familiarity with the older usage is liable to mislead us. We can escape from this influence of association, however, if we remember that in establishing our distinction between sensation and perception we have taken for our paradigms of sensation such experiences as the feeling of pains and itches and the seeing of after-images. It then becomes clear that it is absurd to talk of unsensed sensibilia.

Another suggestion, which has found more favour among philosophers, is that the sensum which is sensed in an act of perception belongs to the perceptual object as being caused by it. It is very difficult, however, to understand what is meant by the statement that a perceptual object causes a sensum. It may perhaps be meant that some process in which the perceptual object is involved causes the process which is the sensing of the sensum; but this is very vague and does not explain why the sensum should be said to belong to the perceptual object rather than to other things, such as the brain of the percipient, which are also involved in the process assumed to cause the sensing of it. Possibly some refinement would make the suggestion more plausible, but I think it must be rejected in any case because the notion that perceptual objects cause sensa does not seem to be involved in the way in which plain men talk of perceptual objects. We may say that machines make noises, but the noises of which we speak in this connexion are themselves perceptual objects. The suggestion is rather a product of physiological theory than a starting-point for knowledge and opinion about the physical world. Until we have already perceived perceptual objects, we cannot think of causal processes in the physical world, which for the plain man consists of perceptual objects. Although, therefore, there may be some truth in the causal theory, it cannot be accepted as an account of the way in which we use perceptual object terminology.

The boldest and most consistent attempt to explain the relation between perceptual object terminology and sensum terminology is the doctrine called phenomenalism. The philosophers who advocate this doctrine argue that, since perception undoubtedly involves sensation and statements about perceptual objects can apparently be verified in no other way than by the sensing of sensa, perceptual objects should be regarded as logical constructions from sensa. Now to say that things of kind A are logical constructions from things of kind B is not to say that things of kind A are composed of things of kind B in the sense in which houses are composed of bricks, but rather that sentences which are about things of kind A in the sense of mentioning them are about things of kind B in another sense of the word 'about'. The other sense of 'about' is commonly explained by saying that sentences which mention things of kind A can always be replaced by equivalent sentences which do not mention things of that kind but do mention things of kind B. Thus nations are logical constructions from men, because sentences about nations can always in principle be replaced by different but equivalent sentences about men. According to the phenomenalists, then, statements about perceptual objects are in principle reducible to statements about actual and possible sensa. Thus the statement that there is a penny on the table is to be taken as equivalent to a complex statement to the effect that if anyone sensed sensa of certain kinds, e.g. kinaesthetic sensa such as he would have in approaching the table and putting out his hand, he would also sense sensa of certain other kinds, e.g. tactual sensa such as he would have in handling the penny. Berkeley is the author of this suggestion, but perhaps the most famous formulation of it is Mill's definition of matter as 'a permanent possibility of sensation'.[1]

In the form in which it is usually presented, phenomenalism is

[1] *Examination of Sir William Hamilton's Philosophy*, p. 233.

open to the fatal objection that its programme of replacing perceptual object terminology entirely by sensum terminology cannot
possibly be carried out. I am not referring here to the practical
difficulties of replacing a traditional mode of speech by a new-
fangled and very complicated jargon, for what I have called the
phenomenalist programme is, of course, intended not as a policy
for everyday life, but simply as an explanatory device for removing philosophical perplexities. The trouble is that, if any
statement in the perceptual object terminology is to be replaced
by a series of statements in the sensum terminology, the series
must be infinite to allow for all the infinite variety of possible
sensa which are relevant because they could be obtained in certain
conditions, e.g. the different views of a penny obtainable from
different positions or in different illuminations. An infinite sequence
cannot be specified except by giving a rule for its construction,
and there is no possibility here of providing a rule except by saying
that the required hypothetical statements about sensa are those
which would be true if there were a perceptual object of a certain
sort in a certain place.

If, however, the phenomenalist is prepared to abandon his programme of replacing all statements about perceptual objects by
statements which mention only sensa, he may perhaps try to
maintain the substance of his doctrine by saying that the perceptual object terminology is to be accepted as irreducible but
regarded as the appropriate device for referring to all the infinite
variety of sensa obtainable in all the different conditions which are
possible. In favour of this reformed version of phenomenalism it
may be urged that statements about the sensa to be expected in
certain conditions are in fact derivable from statements in the
perceptual object terminology, and that it is not easy to find
anything else which is entailed by statements in that terminology.
The sensum terminology is, of course, a new-fangled jargon, and
plain men do not say to themselves explicitly that statements
about perceptual objects entail statements in this jargon. But
plain men do regard statements about perceptual objects as indi-
cations of the course of sense experience which they may expect,
and in cases in which plain men attribute to themselves or others
unexpressed beliefs in the existence of perceptual objects it is often
impossible to find anything except the tacit expectation of a
certain course of sense experience. When, for example, a man
takes a step too many while going up stairs in the dark and is

surprised by the curious sequence of sensations which occurs on such occasions, we say that he thought there was another step; but our only evidence, and perhaps the only evidence available to the man himself, may be the fact that he is surprised when he experiences a sequence of sensations incompatible with the proposition that there is another step. The new theory seems, then, to give a plausible answer to the question 'How is perceptual object terminology related to sensum terminology?' and I think it is correct as far as it goes. But it cannot properly be regarded as an improved version of phenomenalism.

When the phenomenalist first announces his programme of replacing sentences in the perceptual object terminology by sentences in the sensum terminology, he wishes to show that the matter of fact stated by a true statement in the perceptual object terminology is a conjunction of a host of independent matters of fact which can be stated by hypothetical statements in the sensum terminology. Berkeley was clear about this. He said that God supplies sensa to us according to a plan and that the complex expectations about sensa which we express in the language of the vulgar (i.e. in perceptual object terminology) are justified, but he maintained that God's choice of a plan was arbitrary and that, if God had decided otherwise, some of the propositions about sensa involved in the analysis of a perceptual object statement might have been false. In short, he held it was only by the special grace of God that anything mentioned in vulgar speech had a back. Other phenomenalists, who reject his queer notion of sense experience as a divine language, agree with him in thinking that a perceptual object statement is equivalent to a host of statements in the sensum terminology each of which, if true, states an independent matter of fact. When, however, we reject the programme of reduction which the phenomenalists originally set before themselves, we can admit that statements in the perceptual object terminology entail statements in the sensum terminology without supposing that a matter of fact stated by a true statement in the perceptual object terminology is a conjunction of independent matters of fact about sensa. It would, indeed, be very odd to maintain this, for many of the statements in the sensum terminology which are entailed by perceptual object statements are unfulfilled hypothetical sentences. Such sentences may, no doubt, be used to state matters of fact, but only because they are elliptical. When, for example, I say that if Hannibal had marched on Rome he would have taken it, I intend to convey that there were certain facts which in conjunction with Hannibal's marching on Rome would have necessitated his taking it. So too when I say that if I had had certain experiences, such as those involved in putting out my hand, I should have had certain others, such as those involved in touching a penny, I must apparently mean that there were certain facts, not further specified, which in conjunction with an experience of the first kind would have necessitated an experience of the second kind. This is something for which the phenomenalist can find no place in his scheme.

This short discussion does not provide a full theory of perception, but a statement of some requirements to be met by such a theory. It is sufficient, however, to establish the thesis asserted at the beginning of this section, namely, that we cannot have an idea of any perceptual object in precisely the same sense of the phrase 'have an idea' as that in which we say that we have an idea of red. To have an idea of anything is, no doubt, to be able to use a symbol of some sort appropriately, i.e. according to rules of meaning, but the rules for the use of different kinds of symbols may be very different. A perceptual object is not an element of an experience as a sensum is, and a symbol for a perceptual object cannot be confronted with that for which it is a symbol *in the same way* as a symbol for a sensum may be. We may, if we choose, say that perceptual objects are presented or given to us in perception, but we must admit that this presentation is something quite different from the presentation of a sensum which is an 'internal accusative' of an act of sensing. Whenever we assert the existence of a perceptual object, we are going beyond what is immediately given in sensation, and even beyond what can be so given. Our rules for the use of symbols in the perceptual object terminology determine, at least in outline, what course of sense experience we may expect if the assertion is true, but they do not enable us to give an analysis of the meaning of any symbol of that terminology by showing how sentences containing it can be replaced by sentences containing only symbols of the sensum terminology. Again, if we think fit to defy the philosophical tradition of the last three hundred years, we may perhaps say that we *know* of the existence of some perceptual objects. But when we take this course, we must still admit that such knowledge does not entitle us to say that there can be no laws of necessary connexion concerning perceptual objects of the kind we know to exist. For knowledge of the existence of a perceptual object must in any case be quite compatible with a great deal of ignorance about it even in respect of matters which could be determined by perception, e.g. its internal constitution. If this assertion seems paradoxical, we should try to remove our feeling of perplexity by reconsidering the way in which we use the word 'know' rather than by saying there can be no truths concerning perceptual objects which are not open to inspection.

From all this it follows that the arguments by which Hume's view of natural laws has been supported are themselves based on a mistaken doctrine of perception. In particular, we should not allow ourselves to be impressed by the argument that, since we can always imagine a perceptual object behaving in a manner contrary to supposed laws of nature, these latter can never be principles of necessitation. For to imagine a perceptual object is only to imagine the sensa which one would expect to sense in perceiving the object, and natural laws are not concerned with sensa but with perceptual objects whose existence involves more even than a permanent possibility of sensation. I conclude, therefore, that there is no good reason for denying that laws of nature are principles of necessitation. And, since this is the only account of laws of nature which appears to make sense, I propose to assume that, if there are any laws of nature such as we try to formulate in science, they are principles of necessitation. The subject is full of perplexities, but I think that our troubles arise from a failure to recognize that different parts of our language have meaning in different ways. When we are dealing with perceptual object terminology, we must accept what we find with natural piety and not try to make its rules conform to a pattern derived from sensum terminology or from mathematical terminology. Some light may be thrown on the subject, however, by consideration of the way in which perceptual object terminology is related to the special terminology of the physical theories in which scientists try to explain natural laws.

§ 19. THE EXPLANATION OF NATURAL LAWS

We have seen that the natural laws formulated by scientists are of various kinds, and it is no exaggeration to say that, if we tried to make a list of all the distinguishable laws of these various kinds which have been stated by scientists, we should soon find that we had very many thousands. It is difficult to accept all these laws as independent and ultimate. We wish to know why there are such uniformities, and it is the asking of this question, rather than the search for new uniformities, which marks the beginning of modern science. I do not wish to deny that there has been systematic study of parts of nature which amounted to little more than a search for new uniformities. What we call natural history is just the careful recording of the structures and habits of living organisms. But this example helps to prove my point. There is an obvious difference between the descriptive work of the natural historian and the explanatory work of the modern biologist, and it is customary to date the beginnings of modern biology from the first attempts to explain the generalizations made by natural historians. This aspect of science is so familiar to modern scientists that they sometimes speak of the empirical generalizations which suffice for the making of predictions about individuals as though these were the basic *facts* from which science starts, overlooking the induction by which such generalizations are themselves derived from the singular facts of experience. Thus we find the word 'phenomenon' commonly used in the writings of modern scientists not for what someone observes at a particular place and time, which was the original sense, but rather for a generalization that in certain circumstances something of a certain sort can always be observed. In works on psycho-physiology, for example, there are references to the Purkinje phenomenon, which is really the *law* that in white light of gradually increasing intensity the various colours emerge in a definite order. And after a survey of the various laws of optics two eminent physicists write 'All the optical phenomena we have considered speak for the wave theory'.[1]

In order to make clear what is meant by explanation in natural science it will be convenient to begin by considering those simple cases in which empirical generalizations are explained by other laws that have been established by direct induction from experience. It has been found that the disease called pellagra does not occur among people who eat wheat as their staple cereal but does occur among people who live mainly on maize or certain other cereals. This empirical generalization is said to be explained when it is established that pellagra is due to a deficiency of vitamin B and that vitamin B is present in good quantity in wheat. Again, it is established by common experience that violent effort such as

[1] A. Einstein and L. Infeld, *The Evolution of Physics*, p. 120.

running uphill leads to an involuntary increase in the rate and depth of breathing. This is explained when it is discovered that violent effort leads to an increase in the amount of carbon dioxide in the blood and that this increase in turn causes a little organ in the brain to send impulses through a nervous arc which ends with the muscles controlling respiration. Many such examples can be found in the natural sciences and particularly in biology. Whenever biologists explain generalizations about the behaviour of living organisms by reference to chemistry and physics, they are engaged in this sort of activity. In explaining such a generalization they show that, although it can rightly be called a law of biology, it need not be regarded as independent or ultimate, since it follows from other laws, namely, from laws about the constitution of organisms of certain kinds and laws about chemical substances, which are themselves to be accepted as generalizations from experience.

When we explain a given proposition we show that it follows logically from some other proposition or propositions. But this can scarcely be a complete account of the matter. For if I hear that there is a lion in my garden and demand an explanation of this curious fact, I am certainly not satisfied by a statement that there are two lions in my garden, although the first proposition follows logically from the second. An explanation must in some sense simplify what we have to accept. Now the explanation of laws by showing that they follow from other laws is a simplification of what we have to accept because it reduces the number of untransparent necessitations we need to assume, but this may not be obvious at first sight. The plain man who knows that he has to breathe harder when he climbs a hill may say that this proposition is simple enough for him and that the explanation given by physiologists, so far from removing difficulties, merely imposes a burden on his memory by requiring him to remember some propositions of which he had never thought before. If we are to understand the nature of the simplicity introduced by scientific explanation, we must not dismiss this objection as merely foolish. It is true that in our example the explanation involves a number of new generalizations and that the proposition which satisfies the plain man is simpler for his purposes than the explanation. But the plain man who makes the objection is interested only in laws which have some obvious reference to his practical affairs. The scientist, on the other hand, is interested also in laws of any kind about the subject-matter which he studies and would have considered it his duty to note the existence of the small organ in the brain even if he had not been able to establish any connexion between it and the control of respiration. For him the explanation introduces a simplification because it shows that of a number of laws which he has to assume in any case, one follows from the others and so need not be regarded as ultimate.

When a natural law is explained, we can say that it has been shown to be a necessary consequence of some other proposition or propositions, but the necessity of which we speak here is only relative to those other propositions. We are still unable to see the intrinsic necessity of the law, and it seems clear that we shall never by any advance in natural science reach a point at which we can say that natural necessities have become self-evident. What we can achieve, however, is a reduction of the number of independent laws we need to assume for a complete description of the order of nature. When only a comparatively small number of laws need be accepted as ultimate in a certain field of study, the science of that field can be presented as a system of general propositions entailed by a few postulates of high generality, that is to say, in the same fashion as a system of geometry. Such a system is often called the theory of its field. This use of the word 'theory' was originally similar to the use in mathematics by which we speak of the theory of sets and the theory of functions. But, unlike a theory in mathematics, a theory or system in natural science is to be accepted only if its postulates are confirmed directly or indirectly by experience, and so the word has come to mean a suggestion for a system or, by a further extension of usage, a suggestion for an explanation of any kind. This tendency has been encouraged, no doubt, by the attempts of physicists to make theories with the help of what may be called *transcendent hypotheses*, and to these we must now turn.

When we explain laws by showing that they are logically entailed by other laws, the propositions which serve as postulates in our system are of the same kind as those they explain, and they can be established by the same means, namely, by direct induction from experience. In physics, however, attempts have been made to explain laws by deriving them from postulates of a different kind. The oldest suggestion of this sort is the atomic theory. This was first put forward by Democritus in the fifth century B.C., but did not receive general approval from scientists until the begin-

ning of last century, when Dalton showed that it would provide
an explanation of some simple laws about the constant combining
weights of chemical substances. In its modern form it explains a
host of empirical generalizations, and everyone engaged in physical
science assumes that with further specification it will explain still
more. The novelty of the theory is that it explains laws by means
of postulates which are not themselves established by direct induction from experience and cannot, indeed, be tested directly in
any way. These postulates are hypotheses about the existence of
objects which must, from the nature of the case, be imperceptible.
Another physical theory of the same type is the undulatory theory
of light, first suggested by Huyghens in the seventeenth century
and later developed by Clerk-Maxwell into the general theory of
electro-magnetism. This is obviously not the place in which to try
to expound either of these theories in detail, but it is important
for our purpose to make clear the peculiar nature of the hypotheses
on which they are based.

The peculiarity of the objects and processes assumed by physical
scientists in the formulation of these theories is not merely that
they are small in relation to the sticks and stones about which we
talk in common speech. Indeed, according to later developments
of the undulatory theory electro-magnetic waves may be of very
large dimensions, and it is sometimes argued that in a certain sense
each electron occupies the whole of space. The essential point is
rather that the physical world as described in such theories cannot,
from the nature of the case, be observed as sticks and stones are
observed. I can see a wave passing over the surface of a pond, but
it is merely senseless to speak of seeing or observing in any other
way an electro-magnetic wave.[1] It is even impossible to imagine
these things, for if we try to imagine them we must attribute to
them qualities such as colour or perceptible hardness which they
cannot possess. I propose to call hypotheses about things of this
kind *transcendent*, because I think it is necessary to indicate quite
clearly that they are concerned with things which are not observable even in principle. This is a difficult doctrine, and two questions about it come to mind immediately.

In the first place, if all our ideas are derived from experience,
as it seems plausible to say with Locke and the empirical school
of philosophers, how can we even suppose the existence of things

---

[1] We say, of course, that we observe light, but by 'light' we mean in this
context a perceptual object.

which are in principle unobservable? The answer is that in these hypotheses we suppose only the existence of a set of things having a certain structure which can be expressed in the language of mathematics. The sense in which the word 'structure' is used here can best be understood from an example. A tune which is heard and a musical score which is seen may be said to have the same logical structure although they are sensibly very different. That structure might conceivably be expounded to a person who had neither hearing nor sight but only touch. Structure cannot, of course, exist without content, and, when I say that in transcendent hypotheses we suppose only the existence of a set of things having a certain structure, I do not mean that we suppose the existence of a set of things having only a certain structure, for that would be absurd. What I mean is that, although we cannot even conjecture what the content is that embodies the structure, we can reasonably suppose that there is a set of things of that structure, just as a man deaf from birth can suppose that there are complex objects called tunes which embody the structures about which he reads in books on music. That transcendent hypotheses are concerned only with structure has often been overlooked in the past, because scientists and philosophers have mistakenly allowed themselves to slip some imaginative elements, such as perceptible hardness, into their conceptions of the objects mentioned in the hypotheses. Berkeley pointed out quite correctly that the hypothetical entities of the physicists were unimaginable, but he concluded wrongly that because they were unimaginable they were inconceivable.[1]

Secondly, how can hypotheses of this kind explain laws about observable things? If the hypotheses contained no reference to the world of common sense it would, of course, be impossible to explain laws about observables by their help. The hypotheses are, however, doubly general propositions (universal and existential) of such forms as: 'Wherever light of such-and-such a colour (i.e. a perceptual object) occurs, there is a wave process of such-and-such a wave-length, and vice versa.' They are introduced for the purpose of explaining laws, and, however abstruse they may become in the course of development, they must always remain attached in this way to the world of perceptual objects if they are to achieve their purpose.

---

[1] Locke's distinction of primary and secondary qualities, which Berkeley derided, was an attempt to deal with the notion of structure. The distinction was first suggested by Democritus.

The making of transcendent hypotheses involves the introduction of a new terminology, and it is important to realize how this is related to the sensum terminology and the perceptual object terminology. There is no direct connexion between transcendent object terminology and the sensum terminology, for the physical scientist is not concerned as such with sensa. His aim in formulating transcendent hypotheses is to explain laws about perceptual objects (not sensa), and his new terminology therefore has direct connexion only with perceptual object terminology. In relation to this latter it appears as a more comprehensive language. That is to say, the new terminology of the physicist would, if complete, provide an expression corresponding to every expression of the perceptual object terminology, e.g. 'copper', 'lightning', 'freezing', &c., but contain also expressions, e.g. 'electron', to which there is nothing corresponding in the perceptual object terminology. Natural laws which have been formulated originally in the perceptual object terminology can therefore be translated into the transcendent object terminology. When so translated they naturally appear more complex, because the new terminology is, so to say, of finer grain. Instead of a comparatively simple statement about the melting-point of a chemical substance we have a statement about the average velocity of molecules of such-and-such internal constitution at the time when the attractive forces between them no longer suffice to keep them in a rigid formation. But the greater complexity of the expressions for laws in the new terminology is intended to exhibit the necessity of the laws, and the price paid is small if the new terminology does indeed make it possible to explain the laws within a comprehensive theory.

I have spoken of correspondence between expressions of the perceptual object terminology and expressions of the transcendent object terminology, and I have said that statements of the first can be translated into statements of the second, although the converse is not always true. This way of speaking is not common among scientists, but I wish to indicate that the transcendent object terminology is really a quite new language and not a mere supplement to the perceptual object terminology. We may fall into serious confusion if we try to mix expressions from the two terminologies. Although it is quite correct to translate the word 'table' in certain contexts by the expression 'set of molecules', it is absurd to say that I now perceive a set of molecules. A famous example of confusion of this kind is to be found in the first

sentence of Sir Arthur Eddington's *Nature of the Physical World*.
Instead of talking of two terminologies to be kept distinct, he
speaks there of two tables, one a perceptual object which is solid,
and the other a scientific object which is full of empty spaces, since
it consists of molecules whose volume is small in relation to the
total volume within which they move. The mystery disappears as
soon as we recognize that when the table is said in perceptual
object terminology to be solid, the word 'solid' is to be understood
in the appropriate way, i.e. as a word of the perceptual object
terminology. There is then no inconsistency between the assertion of the plain man and the assertion of the physicist. On the
contrary, the sentence 'The table is solid' can quite well be translated as a whole into the terminology of physics. It would be very
strange if it could not, for the terminology of physics is designed to
explain among other things why some perceptual objects are solid
and others not. When we say that tables and pennies consist of molecules with certain forces between them, we suppose the molecules
and the forces to be such that pennies cannot drop through tables.

When first introduced a transcendent hypothesis may be extremely vague, provided only that it entails the laws which it is
intended to explain. When Huyghens tried to explain the diffrac-
tion and the interference of light by means of his undulatory theory,
he had no clear idea of the nature of the waves he supposed to
occur, but the wave-motion seemed to render some laws of optics
intelligible and there was no rival suggestion which could do as
much. The theory therefore began to win acceptance among
scientists and was gradually developed by greater definition of all
the necessary details. As it developed, it became capable of explaining other known laws of optics and also some laws which had
not been established before by direct induction but which were
verified after they had been deduced from the hypothesis. For
when such a hypothesis has some degree of success, it immediately begins to dominate the interest of scientific researchers.
At first they try to devise additional tests, that is, to discover
more and more consequences which they can verify. Admittedly,
verification of these consequences can never amount to demonstration of the hypothesis, just as the confirmation of a law of nature
in many instances can never amount to demonstration of the law.
But when several uniformities foretold by the theory, that is to
say, deduced from the hypothesis, have been confirmed by direct
induction, scientists soon cease to debate whether the hypothesis

is acceptable in principle. Their interest now is to devise tests by which to decide between alternative developments of the theory in those parts or aspects that have hitherto been left indefinite.

In the earlier stages of its development a transcendent hypothesis may contain assumptions about unobservable objects which are similar to the laws of nature we formulate about observable objects in that they cannot be seen to be necessary. Thus Dalton assumed that the atoms of different elements could combine only in certain fixed ratios. This seemed to explain some laws which had been discovered by chemists, but it was itself something requiring explanation, and hypotheses about valency are still being developed in our own time for the improvement of the general theory. It is felt as an imperfection of a theory that it should assume any laws which cannot be seen to be intrinsically necessary, and attempts are therefore made to specify the hypothetical entities of the system in such a way that any connexions between them required for the purposes of the theory are intrinsically necessary. This does not mean, however, that we can hope to derive laws of nature some day from self-evident truths alone. Although the connexions *within* the world of transcendent entities posited by a theory may all be self-evident, the relations *between* this world and the world of perceptual objects remain opaque to the intellect, and it is only by assuming these relations that we can explain our laws about observables.

§ 20. CRITICISM AND DEFENCE OF TRANSCENDENT HYPOTHESES

Transcendent hypotheses of the kind we have been considering were first introduced into physics by the Greek atomists, but they were of little use for many centuries, because they were very vaguely formulated at the beginning and the philosophers who propounded them were unable to derive from them any new consequences which could be tested in experience. Greek atomism was a programme for the making of a theory rather than a theory, and it was not until the seventeenth century that transcendent hypotheses were employed in a genuinely scientific manner. Huyghens was the first great physicist to attempt this method of explaining natural laws with full consciousness of what he was about.[1] In the

---

[1] Leibniz had stated the programme of explanation by hypotheses as early as 1678 in a letter to Conring (see L. Couturat, *La Logique de Leibniz*, p. 268), but that does not detract from the merit claimed here for Huyghens. Leibniz often compared scientific hypotheses with suggestions for the solution of cryptograms (cf. *Nouveaux Essais*, IV. xii. 13).

preface to his *Treatise on Light* of 1690 we find the following passage:

'There is to be found here a kind of demonstration which does not produce a certainty as great as that of geometry and is, indeed, very different from that used by geometers, since they prove their propositions by certain and incontestable principles, whereas here principles are tested by the consequences derived from them. The nature of the subject permits no other treatment. It is possible nevertheless to attain in this way a degree of probability which is little short of complete certainty. This happens when the consequences of our assumed principles agree perfectly with the observed phenomena, and especially when such verifications are numerous, but above all when we conceive in advance new phenomena which should follow from the hypotheses we employ and then find our expectations fulfilled. If in the following treatise all these evidences of probability are to be found together, as I think they are, the success of my enquiry is strongly confirmed and it is scarcely possible that things should not be almost exactly as I have represented them. I venture to hope, therefore, that those who enjoy finding out causes and can appreciate the wonders of light will be interested in these varied speculations about it.'

From that time onwards there have always been scientists and philosophers to defend the method. Of all who have written about scientific method Whewell is perhaps the most vigorous in his championship of the use of hypotheses. There have been criticisms, however, and to these we must now turn.

In a celebrated General Scholium at the end of his *Principia* Newton writes:

'So far I have explained the phenomena of the heavens and of the sea by the force of gravity, but I have not yet assigned the cause of gravity. . . . I have not yet been able to deduce from the phenomena the reasons for these properties of gravity and I invent no hypotheses (*hypotheses non fingo*). For everything which is not deduced from the phenomena should be called an hypothesis, and hypotheses, whether metaphysical or physical, whether of occult qualities or mechanical, have no place in experimental philosophy. In this philosophy propositions are deduced from phenomena and rendered general by induction. It is thus we have come to know the impenetrability, the mobility, the *impetus* of bodies and the laws of motion and of gravity. It is enough that gravity really exists, that it acts according to the laws we have set out and that it suffices for all the movements of the heavenly bodies and of the sea.'

This is a strange passage and has given rise to much debate. It will be noticed that Newton speaks in a very curious way of *deducing* propositions from phenomena. This expression occurs in other places, and we must assume that Newton used it deliberately; but it obviously cannot mean what is ordinarily called deduction, and I can only conclude that Newton meant that the propositions which interested him were derived from observations in a very strict way. Apart, however, from the peculiarity of its phraseology, the passage is fairly clear. Newton seems to be saying in effect that he thinks it should be possible to find an explanation for gravitation but that this must be discovered by ordinary induction from facts found in experience, because no other method is admissible in natural science. His phrase *hypotheses non fingo* has been used as a slogan by those who distrust transcendent hypotheses.

Newton's doctrine in this passage and in other places where he talks of scientific method is very puzzling, because it does not square with his own practice. He was obviously inclined to favour the atomic hypothesis about matter and the corpuscular theory of light, and he allowed himself occasionally (e.g. at the end of his *Optics*) to make speculations of a transcendent character about the explanation of gravitation. But more remarkable still, his establishment of the theory of motion and of the principle of universal gravitation, which he cites as an example of direct induction from phenomena, is in truth a very notable achievement of the hypothetical method. The so-called law of gravitation is that every body attracts every other body with a force which is proportional to its own mass but varying inversely as the square of its distance from that other. This is indeed a universal proposition, but not one which could conceivably be established by the discovery in experience of instances falling under it. We do not perceive forces of attraction between the bodies we can observe, and we never shall, because forces are objects of a sort we cannot hope to perceive. What we do observe are movements of perceptual objects such as stones, but these give no direct confirmation of the law of gravitation. My chair and my table, for example, are not, so far as I can see, moving towards each other at present; indeed, the law of gravitation does not require that they should, for it deals only with forces, not with actual movements. Even the famous apple did not furnish an instance which directly confirmed the law. For, as Newton himself would insist, the movement of the apple was not determined solely by the attraction of the earth; the resistance of the air and the attraction of the distant heavenly bodies all had some part in determining the course of events. Newton's law of gravitation was, of course, established by an argument from experience, but not by ordinary induction. The true account of the matter seems to be that Newton offered a general theory of mechanics and that the so-called law of gravitation was one of the transcendent hypotheses in this theory. The fundamental principles of his theory are given in his laws of motion:

'(1) Every body continues in its state of rest or uniform motion, except in so far as it is compelled by a force to change that state. (2) Change of motion is proportional to the force and takes place in the direction of the straight line in which the force acts. (3) To any action there is always an equal and contrary reaction, or the mutual actions of any two bodies are always equal and oppositely directed along the same straight line.'

These propositions are not laws in any ordinary sense, but rather postulates which define the idea of force by relating it to that of motion. Given these postulates and hypotheses concerning forces of various kinds such as gravitation, the motions to be expected of bodies in various kinds of situation can be deduced. When these consequences, themselves general in form, are confirmed by observation, as they are, the whole theory is said to be confirmed; but none of the propositions which go to make up the theory has been or can be tested directly. For an explanation of the paths of the heavenly bodies in the solar system Newton had to consider not only the force of gravitation, but also centrifugal force (or inertia). His hypotheses provided together a very satisfactory theory and were therefore accepted, but none of them could have been established separately.

Newton's authority, therefore, should not prejudice us against the use of transcendent hypotheses. His remarks should be taken rather as a somewhat confused protest against the unscientific use of hypotheses. In the past many philosophers, e.g. Descartes, had undoubtedly tried to explain phenomena in a grand manner by the use of hypotheses which they were either unwilling or unable to submit to detailed testing, and I think that for Newton the word 'hypothesis' probably had some of the unfortunate associations which the word 'speculation' now has for natural scientists. The value of an hypothesis is to be judged, however, by its explanatory power and the agreement of its consequences with all the known facts. Hypotheses which survive these tests obviously deserve more respect than dogmas about which their supporters will allow no question or idle fancies which cannot be put to the test because they are consistent with any facts whatsoever. If he were alive to-day, Newton would probably admit without hesitation that hypotheses like that which Huyghens put forward have been amply justified, and that it is inconceivable that physical science should now try to dispense with them.

In more recent times opposition to the use of transcendent hypotheses has come mostly from philosophers and scientists who are influenced by phenomenalism. Berkeley did not discuss the question explicitly, but it is clear from his general attitude to physical science that he did not think it necessary or even possible to find a place anywhere in his theory of knowledge for the atomic hypothesis or anything similar. Since his day the successes of the hypothetical method have been so great that no one would now propose to reject it entirely. The aim of phenomenalists in our time is, therefore, rather to explain away the appearance of transcendence which they find in physical theories. Some of them content themselves with saying that any statement which appears to be about transcendent objects can be replaced in principle by a series of hypothetical statements about sensa. I have never seen any detailed attempt to carry out this programme, but I am quite confident that any such attempt would fail. Since, as we have seen, statements about perceptual objects cannot be replaced by statements about sensa, there is no reason at all to suppose that statements about atoms and electrons can be eliminated in this way. On the contrary, a direct transition from the terminology of physical theory to the sensum terminology is clearly impossible. Other modern phenomenalists argue that to find the meaning of such an assertion as that there are electrons we must consider the method by which it is tested and then identify that method with the meaning. This suggestion is equally unplausible. There is no single method by which such an hypothesis is tested, for it has been introduced precisely in order to co-ordinate a multitude of laws about perceptual objects, and the evidence for the hypothesis is all the evidence for those laws. The observation of X-ray shadows or of vapour trails in Wilson chambers may perhaps seem to bring us nearer to the transcendent objects of which the physicist speaks than any experiment with familiar perceptual objects, but this is mere illusion. The physical theories were formulated before these particular techniques were developed and do not stand or fall by the results obtained from them rather than by the results of any other physical experiments.

These are comparatively crude attempts to explain away the need for supposing the existence of transcendent objects. A more subtle attempt has been made by some philosophers who belong to the phenomenalist tradition although they might disclaim the title of phenomenalist. In the previous section I spoke of the introduction of a new terminology for the formulation of transcendent hypotheses in physics. The philosophers to whom I have just referred argue that all the novelty of those physical theories which appear to be transcendent lies in their terminology. According to their view the physicist is mistaken if he thinks that he has introduced new existential hypotheses in talking of atoms and electrons. He has merely found a new and more convenient way of talking about observables. The new way is more convenient because it makes for what Mach called economy of thought. For expressions of the perceptual object terminology, which are comparatively simple but yield only mutually independent propositions, there are substituted more complex expressions which enable us to present natural laws as consequences of some small number of postulates. This is just a matter of definition. Nothing is asserted about the world in the new terminology which was not asserted in the perceptual object terminology, but what is said is given in a form more convenient for calculation.

This account of the innovation seems to me wholly unsatisfactory. In the first place the new terminology allows the formulation of statements to which there is nothing corresponding in the perceptual object terminology, e.g. statements about what takes place inside a single atom. For the philosophers just mentioned such statements must be very mysterious. They cannot be translated into the perceptual object terminology and therefore apparently say nothing; but they cannot be disregarded because they are framed in accordance with the rules of the new terminology and are even necessary for the development of the theory. Are we to say that they are merely scraps of symbolism with no independent meaning, and that they are related to statements which have counterparts in the perceptual object terminology much as single letters are related to the words in which they appear? This is a very strange doctrine. It is only by allowing for the construction of these new statements that a physical theory can provide any explanation of established laws, and all the development of a theory consists in the attempt to make these new statements more precise in order that the theory may be submitted to new tests and applied in new ways. This brings us to a second point. If the novelty of a new theory lay solely in the new terminology it used for the expression of established laws, it would be quite inexplicable that a theory should make possible the prediction of laws not hitherto established by direct induction. For, according to the view we are now examining, the making of theory is only the introduction of a new terminology and the terminology is chosen freely by human beings for their own convenience in the formulation of laws already assumed. There seems to be no reason why anyone should expect to derive from consideration of such terminology information about anything other than (a) the laws for the expression of which it was designed, and (b) the characteristics of the minds which devised it. Yet all notable hypotheses have in fact provided explanations of some laws other than those for the explanation of which they were originally put forward, and it is now regarded by scientists as obvious that a good hypothesis may be expected to yield interesting new consequences.

I conclude, then, that the statements made by physical scientists in the formulation of transcendent hypotheses are to be taken at their face value, namely, as assertions of the existence of imperceptible objects with certain specified structures. No other account seems to me to do justice to the facts; and I think that, when philosophers and scientists feel difficulty in admitting that transcendent hypotheses are what they seem to be, that is only because, like Berkeley, they have adopted an unduly narrow view of the possibilities of thinking.

§ 21. THE RELATION BETWEEN INDUCTION AND THE HYPOTHETICAL
METHOD

We must now ask whether we should apply the term 'induction' to the kind of reasoning by which transcendent hypotheses are established. This is a verbal question to be settled according to our own convenience; but it has some importance, because in trying to decide what is the most convenient usage to adopt we are led to remark similarities and dissimilarities which might otherwise be overlooked.

If we understand by 'induction' reasoning in which universal propositions are established by consideration of instances falling under them, we cannot apply the term to the reasoning which establishes transcendent hypotheses. For the essential feature of such an hypothesis is that it relates observables of certain kind to some other things which are not observable. The hypothesis is indeed a universal proposition (e.g. about all light), but it is of such a character that cases falling under it cannot be verified by observation. It can be confirmed only indirectly by the testing of its more remote consequences. If any one of these consequences is a universal proposition about observables which is falsified by experience, the hypothesis must be rejected. If, however, all the consequences we can test are universal propositions confirmed by experience, that is to say, propositions established by direct ampliative induction either before or after being deduced from the hypothesis, all the evidence in favour of the consequences is evidence in favour of the hypothesis, although the latter is still in principle capable of being falsified through the falsification of one of its consequences. The best convention is perhaps to extend the use of the word 'induction' to cover the hypothetical method but at the same time to distinguish this new application of the term by adding the adjective 'secondary'. If we refused to call such reasoning inductive, we should ignore the obvious continuity of interest between it and primary or direct induction and make it more difficult to discuss what they have in common, whereas if we omitted to add any qualification when describing the hypothetical method as a form of induction we should slur over an important distinction.

Some logicians have been so impressed by the importance of hypotheses in what we commonly call the inductive sciences that they have confused together the notions of induction and hypothetical method, supposing all induction to be an application of the hypothetical method and every use of hypotheses an instance of induction. We even find the word 'induction' applied sometimes to the use of hypotheses by historians in the tentative reconstruction of the course of past events. This seems to me an unprofitable and even dangerous widening of the meaning of the term, but I think it is interesting to see what has suggested it.

A universal proposition of natural science which is established by induction may reasonably be called an hypothesis, although, of course, not a transcendent hypothesis. The particular cases falling under it are its consequences and the verification of them can be said to confirm the hypothesis but never to prove it conclusively. It is, indeed, precisely because such a proposition can be no more than a well-confirmed hypothesis that I have called the sort of induction which establishes it ampliative. It is natural, then, that logicians should try to treat of induction together with other attempts to establish hypotheses by consideration of their consequences. But the suggestion that every use of hypotheses is a variety of induction is based on a failure to distinguish different kinds of hypotheses. Apart from laws concerning perceptual objects and postulates introduced to explain such laws, natural scientists have sometimes put forward hypotheses which are, strictly speaking, historical in character. Thus the nebular hypothesis about the origin of the solar system is not a universal proposition about the behaviour of all things of a certain kind, but rather a suggestion for the explanation of the special order found among a number of particular things. It resembles an hypothesis put forward by an archaeologist to explain the origin of Stonehenge. In each case we can do no more than look for evidence which will confirm or refute the hypothesis by verifying or falsifying some of its consequences, but in each case the hypothesis is a proposition of the same kind as those we can claim to establish conclusively by observation, differing from them only in that it is about the past. We can conceive the possibility of receiving wireless messages from astronomers in some other part of the universe to the effect that records made by their predecessors over many millions of years confirmed the nebular hypothesis, just as we can conceive the possibility of finding a contemporary inscription about the building of Stonehenge. If such additional evidence were forthcoming, it would have to be treated according to the ordinary methods of historical criticism.

A specially interesting example of the making of historical hypotheses in natural science is to be found in what is usually called the theory of the evolution of species. Many empirical generalizations have been made about the organisms of various species, e.g. that lions are carnivorous, that frogs grow out of tadpoles, that wheat grains contain vitamin B. It is now assumed that these laws are to be explained by biologists in the sense of being deduced from the constitution of the organisms and the general laws of physiology. In so far as biologists are able to carry out this programme they make their study systematic or theoretical in the original sense of that word. There is, however, a further question which they may ask, namely, how there came to be organisms of these various constitutions. There are obvious similarities between species which have led natural historians long since to classify them in genera and families. But species appear to be genetically distinct, that is to say, the individuals of a species reproduce organisms of their own kind only. And so, in spite of the suggestions contained in such words as 'genus' and 'family', natural historians of earlier times felt compelled to assume that species had been established separately at some remote date in the past. The doctrine of the separate creation of species was not an invention of priests, designed to buttress a system of theology, but the best guess that could be given at the time. The theory put forward by Darwin and his successors is simply an hypothesis to the effect that what we call specific differences have come about through the accumulation of many small differences between individuals of successive generations. The laws of genetics show what can be accomplished by selective breeding. Whether, and, if so, by what stages, the organisms we know have been evolved from organisms of simpler types is a question of historical fact. It is extremely unlikely that biologists will ever be able to trace all the steps by which all the known species have been established, but they have apparently found enough to convince themselves that the general hypothesis of evolution is as probable as an historical hypothesis of that kind can be.

It seems unwise to extend the use of the word 'induction' to cover the establishment of historical hypotheses like those we have just considered and those which are put forward in social and literary studies. Historical hypotheses are quite different in logical character from the transcendent hypotheses of physics and also from the laws which are established by primary induction, for the former purport to be matters of fact, the latter to be truths of principle, and we cannot safely assume that the probability we ascribe to historical hypotheses is the same as that we ascribe to the results of induction, whether primary or secondary. I think this point worth making because it has not been realized by many otherwise estimable writers on the theory of induction, e.g. Whewell.

§ 22. THE CONSILIENCE OF PRIMARY INDUCTIONS

Having decided that we may reasonably call the establishment of transcendent hypotheses secondary induction, we must now consider how the results of secondary induction compare with the results of primary induction in reliability. This is a subject on which there has been much confusion. Some writers who recognize a distinction between different stages of induction have supposed that secondary induction, being dependent on the results of primary induction, must inevitably give results which are less reliable than those of primary induction. I think this view is mistaken and that it arises from a misunderstanding of the relation between the two stages. These writers apparently think of secondary induction as the application of induction to the results of induction and assume that, since the results of any ampliative induction must obviously be less certain than the premisses from which it starts, secondary induction will give less certainty than primary induction. A more satisfactory account of the matter was given by Whewell, who laid great emphasis on what he called the *consilience* of inductions. What I have to say is suggested by his work *Novum Organum Renovatum* but is adapted to the phraseology I have used hitherto.

In order to understand what happens when a law is explained it is best to start by considering the explanation of laws by other laws which are also established by primary induction. We have seen that we can sometimes explain empirical generalizations in biology by showing that they follow from certain physical and chemical laws which are already accepted. When such an explanation has been given, the probability of the biological generalization may very well be greater than it was before. For the biological generalization cannot now be less probable than the physical and chemical laws from which it is seen to follow, and, since these laws, being of great generality, have presumably been confirmed in many more instances than those which provide evidence for the biological generalization, it is reasonable to suppose that their probability may be greater than that which the biological generalization had attained before the explanation. This is a very common situation. It often happens that we make a tentative generalization in some field of study without reposing much confidence in the result of our induction but discover later that what we have conjectured is entailed by some well-established laws and immediately regard our generalization as itself established beyond reasonable doubt. Something similar happens when laws are explained by transcendent hypotheses, but the situation is then more complicated.

If a transcendent hypothesis was put forward to explain a single supposed law, it could clearly have no greater probability than the supposed law which it explained, and might be thought to have less, since it could only explain the supposed law by being in some way more comprehensive, and this greater comprehensiveness would lay it open to greater danger of refutation. No transcendent hypothesis, however, is put forward to explain a single law. When we look for explanations we want to co-ordinate and simplify. We must therefore assume that we have a number of supposed laws, say L_1, L_2, and L_3, which are all shown to be consequences of an hypothesis H. Each of these supposed laws has its own evidence, consisting of a number of instances from which it was originally established by primary induction. How does the probability of H compare with the probability of L_1, L_2, and L_3? Clearly H cannot be more probable than L_1, L_2, and L_3 are *after they have been explained*, for it entails them and therefore communicates to them whatever probability it possesses, but it may be more probable than L_1, L_2, and L_3 were *before they were explained*. For the evidence in favour of H is all the evidence in favour of all the consequences that follow from it, and in relation to this mass of evidence H may well attain a higher degree of probability than any one of its consequences, L_1, L_2, and L_3, had in relation to its own special range of evidence before it was explained. After the explanation L_1, L_2, and L_3 may therefore be more probable than they were before, because each of them derives support indirectly from the evidence in favour of each of the others. This is the consilience of inductions which fit together into a theory, and I think it is a consideration which has great weight with scientists when they estimate the value of theories. Only in this way can we explain the undoubted fact that the supposed laws of physics and chemistry seem to scientists better established now than they were a century ago. The mere accumulation of new instances confirming special laws will not explain the increase of probability. For the number of new instances is comparatively insignificant in relation to the number which had been observed already a century ago, and no one supposes that the long-continued accumulation of similar instances adds much to the probability of a generalization. Those philosophers who advocate a coherence theory of truth may perhaps have in mind something like the notion of consilience, but, if so, they are guilty of misusing it. For the notion of consilience belongs properly to the theory of that kind of probability which attaches to inductive conclusions, not to the theory of truth.

So far I have made no mention of a feature of some transcendent hypotheses to which Huyghens drew special attention in the passage I have quoted from his *Treatise on Light*, namely, their entailment of laws not hitherto established by primary induction. Although this is a very striking merit of transcendent hypotheses, it should not be confused with the considerations which determine the probability of an hypothesis in relation to the evidence of experience and the laws which have already been derived from that evidence by primary induction. It cannot affect the probability of an hypothesis whether the laws it entails were established by primary induction before or after the suggestion of the hypothesis. The confirmation of a hitherto unsuspected law which is deduced from an hypothesis must, of course, raise the probability of the hypothesis, but it cannot raise the probability beyond the degree which it would have reached if that law had already been accepted before the suggestion of the hypothesis. The power of prediction is impressive and important rather because it convinces us that the hypothesis is more than a mere rewording of the laws it was introduced to explain. It gives us the assurance that we are not merely playing with symbols but saying something new and interesting about the world. This can be seen from the fact that we are as much impressed by the power of an hypothesis to explain a law which was indeed already established when the hypothesis was first formulated but not then considered as a law to be explained by the hypothesis. In either case the hypothesis must be taken seriously, because it obviously offers a hope of real simplification, without which there can be no explanation worth the name and no increase of probability according to the principles explained in the previous paragraph. If an hypothesis H were equivalent to a mere conjunction of the laws L_1, L_2, and L_3 which it was supposed to explain, there would be no consilience of inductions and the evidence for L_1 would not help in any way to confirm L_2 or L_3. The conjunctive proposition would indeed be only as probable in relation to our total evidence as the least probable of the conjoined propositions, and would have no special interest for us. When, however, a law L_4 is derived from an hypothesis H which was originally intended to explain L_1, L_2, and L_3, it can no longer be supposed that H is merely a rewording of the three first laws.

It may sometimes occur at a certain stage of development in a science that two rival hypotheses appear to explain equally well all the accepted laws of the field to which they apply. It is then of the greatest importance that scientists should try to find some testable proposition which follows from one but is incompatible with the other; for this is the way to make what Bacon called an *experimentum crucis*. In the circumstances I have indicated the proposition by which they decide must obviously be some suggestion of law not hitherto established by primary induction. If, however, they are unable to find any such proposition, and so cannot devise an *experimentum crucis*, they begin to suspect that the two rival hypotheses differ only in their symbolic formulation, and try to prove this by logical analysis. In recent years, for example, Heisenberg's version of the quantum theory and that of Schrödinger have been shown to be equivalent. In any case the uncomfortable situation to which I have referred rarely lasts for more than a comparatively short period.

§ 23. CONFIRMATION AND ELIMINATION

Acceptance of the doctrine about natural laws which has been outlined in the previous sections does not immediately make clear what account we should give of ampliative induction or how, if at all, this kind of argument is to be justified. If we have found a number of α things which are β and none which are not β, we may, indeed, say that we have some evidence to confirm a conjecture that all α things must be β, but such confirmation falls far short of proof. It is merely the absence of conclusive evidence to the contrary where such evidence might conceivably have occurred if the conjecture had been false. It was dissatisfaction with such argument by simple enumeration that lead Bacon to formulate the first modern theory of ampliative induction, and in the later literature his suggestion of inductive proof by elimination has frequently been contrasted with the method of confirmation to the disadvantage of the latter. Is there any hope of progress on the road he indicated?

Historically the notion of elimination has been connected with the doctrine that ampliative induction requires the principle of universal causation as a premiss, and this is not mere accident. For when we speak of a *method* of elimination we are thinking not merely of the refutation of suggestions of law by the discovery of negative instances, but of the establishment of an affirmative conclusion by the rejection of all other alternatives, and we can only use such a procedure when we are sure that one or other of a finite set of alternatives is correct. Now Bacon and his followers believed that all induction was a search for causes and they were at least consistent in treating the principle of universal causation as a presupposition or premiss of induction. Without a guarantee that something or other was the cause of a certain kind of event there could be no reason to assume that a candidate which had survived the purely eliminative tests for a cause was indeed the cause. But we have seen that a great many of our supposed laws of nature are not causal in form, and it is clear that these could not have been established by the methods of Bacon and Mill. Moreover, in view of the vagueness of the notion of causation, even laws that are causal in form can scarcely have been established by an eliminative argument which uses the principle of universal causation as a premiss. The most we can say in favour of the doctrine of Bacon and Mill is that, when we are interested in finding causal laws on account of their great practical utility, we may be led by our interest to discover regularities in experience which would otherwise have passed unnoticed. The eliminative tests for causes have a certain value where they can be applied, but even there the final argument for an affirmative conclusion seems to rest on confirmation.

It may perhaps be argued that the method of elimination can be retained after criticism of the notion of causation because it is not necessarily dependent on the principle of universal causation, but only on some more general principle of determinism which provides a common pattern for all the various types of natural laws. Even within the traditional theory of eliminative induction we find notable differences between Bacon and Mill about the nature of that which is to be discovered by elimination, and in recent times Lord Keynes has based a theory of eliminative induction on a doctrine of generator properties which are apparently to be distinguished from causes in any ordinary sense.[1] Furthermore, there is a widespread conviction among scientists that their study requires determinism of some sort. This shows itself in the uneasiness aroused by the quantum theory. In opposing any attempt to rehabilitate the method of elimination I do not wish to deny that there may be some principle of determinism whereby every matter of fact is necessitated by some other matter of fact. On the contrary, I admit that I am inclined to assume that there is some such principle, although I do not know where to look for a

---

[1] *Treatise on Probability*, p. 253. These generators seem to be somewhat like Bacon's forms.

proof of it or even how to formulate it in a way that is not open to objection. But I do wish to deny that all ampliative induction is reasoning by elimination with a principle of determinism as a premiss. For surely no one who considers carefully the various types of natural laws mentioned in a previous section can suppose that they were all established by such reasoning. How, for example, could anyone prove in this way that the melting-point of tungsten is 3,387° C.? Part of the argument for this proposition consists, no doubt, in showing by systematic experiment that tungsten does not melt at any temperature less than 3,387° C., and we may, if we like, call that a process of elimination; but the logical presupposition of the use of elimination in this case is a special theory of physical chemistry requiring that each substance should have a fixed melting-point, not a general principle of determinism, and that special theory is itself to be accepted only on inductive grounds.

We are therefore left with confirmation as the fundamental procedure in inductive argument. But it would be a mistake to assume that the number of confirming instances is the only consideration to which we need pay attention when estimating the worth of an inductive argument for a law. If we examine the situation more closely, we find that some generalizations are accepted with great confidence although the direct evidence for them consists only of a few observations, whereas others which have been confirmed in very many instances are still regarded as no more than tentative suggestions.[1] When, for example, a new chemical substance such as deuterium, the heavy isotope of hydrogen, is discovered, chemists do not suppose that a vast number of experiments are necessary to determine each of its properties. Many experiments are, of course, made in different laboratories, because many scientists are interested and wish to see for themselves, but no one thinks that the reliability of the generalizations about it depends on a great multiplication of observations. One or two carefully conducted experiments are thought sufficient. On the other hand, generalizations about the mating behaviour of the birds of a newly discovered species may not be accepted until they have been confirmed by many observations. The explanation of the difference seems to be that in the first case scientists consider themselves entitled to assume in advance that there will be

---

[1] Cf. Hume, *Inquiry Concerning Human Understanding*, Section iv, and Mill, *System of Logic*, III. iii. 3.

uniformities of a certain type. In other words, the induction by which a property of deuterium is established does not stand by itself as an argument from simple enumeration. There is a background of accepted theory to be taken into account.

To abandon the doctrine that induction proceeds by elimination is, however, to give up all hope of attaining certainty by induction. When Bacon suggested the method of elimination he was trying in effect to exhibit induction as a form of deduction. But no one now seriously believes in this project, and I have freely assumed in earlier sections that the results of ampliative induction are only probable. It would, indeed, be foolish to lament that we cannot get deductive certainty in induction. For to express regret that we cannot do something is to imply that we are prevented only by an unfortunate accident, whereas the impossibility of demonstrating laws of nature is like the impossibility of seeing an electron. Indeed, there is some reason to believe that the two impossibilities are connected.

Locke was the first to point out clearly that we cannot hope to gain knowledge in the strictest sense of natural laws. He says: 'I deny not but a man accustomed to rational and regular experiments shall be able to see further into the nature of bodies and guess righter at their yet unknown properties than one who is a stranger to them; but . . . this is but judgment and opinion, not knowledge and certainty.'[1] Unfortunately his treatment of what he called judgement and opinion was not very illuminating, and for a long time afterwards there was nothing better forthcoming. When, however, the theory of probability in matters of chance had been considerably developed, some philosophers thought they could show by its help why the conclusions of ampliative induction were worthy of trust. Thus Jevons in his *Principles of Science*, published in 1874, tried to justify induction within the theory of probability expounded by Laplace at the beginning of the century. And attempts of a similar kind have been made in recent times by Lord Keynes and Nicod. We must therefore turn next to the theory of chances and consider the philosophical problems to which it gives rise. In particular, we must ask whether the probability we ascribe to the results of induction is the same as the probability of which we speak when we are concerned with matters of chance.

[1] *Essay on the Human Understanding*, IV. xii. 10.

PART III

THE THEORY OF CHANCES

§ 24. THE NOTION OF CHANCE

THE theory of probability was developed first in reference to matters of chance, and it is with the notion of chance that we must begin our study. But this notion can be understood only in contrast with the notion of necessity. We have seen that one attribute may be said to necessitate another, as redness, for example, necessitates extension, and that laws of nature can be expressed in the form 'Being α involves being β'. But it is clearly not true that every attribute is necessarily connected with every other attribute. If we find that some α things are β and some are not, we are entitled to say that α-ness neither necessitates nor excludes β-ness. This is the situation which we state by saying that β-ness is fortuitous in relation to α-ness, or more colloquially that it is a matter of chance whether an α thing is β. The word 'chance' is derived from the low Latin word *cadentia*, which itself is derived from *cadere*, and the statement that something is a matter of chance was originally a metaphor from dicing. If a die is thrown, its falling with six dots uppermost is one of several results which may happen, i.e. which are possible but not necessary in relation to its being thrown. The metaphor is not quite dead even now, for we sometimes say that it may or may not *fall out* that an α thing is β.

There is indeed a special usage of the word 'chance' in which we contrast chance with design. Thus I may say that I found a penny by chance, meaning that I found a penny when I was not looking for one. Or, seeing a rock shaped like a man's head, I may ask whether the shape is a chance formation or a piece of sculpture. But the special usage can be brought under the general explanation of the notion of chance given above. In the special usage the occurrence of an event by chance is still opposed to its necessitation by something, but now exclusively to its necessitation by the purpose of an intelligent being to bring it about. The general sense of the word 'chance' is then non-necessitation-by-something and the special sense is non-necessitation-by-purpose. When people ask the metaphysical question 'Is everything a matter of chance?' they are usually employing the word in its special sense. What they mean is 'Do all events happen without design? Is there no creator?' And they are not in the least consoled by anyone who expounds a theory of physical determinism.

Now it is clear that chance, as I have defined it, is essentially relational, just as necessitation and exclusion are. When we say, as we sometimes do, that it is a matter of chance whether a certain particular thing is β, we assume that the hearer shares with us the information in relation to which it is a matter of chance whether the thing is β. If we put our statement in full, we should say, 'In relation to all we know about the thing, namely, that it is α, it is a matter of chance whether it is β.' In relation to some other fact which we do not know, e.g. that the thing is γ, it may be necessary or it may be impossible that it should be β. We know, indeed, that the thing must be either β or not β, and it may follow from a principle of determinism that there is *some* character of the thing which necessitates β-ness or excludes it. But we know only that the thing is α, and that things which are α may or may not be β. These two pieces of knowledge are together the justification for our elliptical statement that it is a matter of chance whether the thing is β. And most of our ordinary statements about chance are elliptical in this way.

Furthermore, the relation which is involved in statements of chance has a sense or direction. It may be a matter of chance whether an α thing is β but not a matter of chance whether a β thing is α. If it is a matter of chance whether an α thing is β, it cannot, of course, be impossible for a β thing to be α; but it may conceivably be necessary for a β thing to be α. Thus it is a matter of chance whether an English-speaking person is a member of the University of Oxford, for being English-speaking neither necessitates nor excludes membership of the University of Oxford; but it is necessary that a member of the University of Oxford should be English-speaking, because no others are admitted. If, however, it is not only a matter of chance whether an α thing is β but also a matter of chance whether a β thing is α, we say that the two characters α-ness and β-ness are independent of each other.

The error of supposing that the admission of chance is inconsistent with determinism arises from a failure to notice the relational character of chance. We take an elliptical statement of the form 'By chance this is β' and overlook the fact that the thing's being β is only a matter of chance in relation to the other characters we know the thing to possess. Then, seeing that chance is in some way opposed to necessitation, we conclude that the statement 'By chance this is β' means that the thing's being β is not necessitated by anything whatsoever, which is naturally a contradiction of determinism. But this is not a correct account of the way we use the word in ordinary life. It is true that we can, if we like, talk of *absolute chance* and so define the expression that it means the opposite of determinism. In certain contexts, such as philosophical discussions about determinism, this might be an intelligible usage, but it must be remembered that it is a special convention, not the ordinary rule for the use of the word 'chance'. If I am right, there is no inconsistency whatsoever between chance in the ordinary sense and any plausible theory of determinism. For surely no intelligent determinist wishes to maintain that any two characters we choose to name are connected by a law. It follows from determinism, as I understand it, that every fact about a particular thing is implied by *some* other fact about that thing, including, of course, its relations to other particulars; but it cannot be true that every fact about a particular thing is implied by *every* other fact about that thing. And yet this is what anyone would have to maintain who wished to reject the ordinary relational notion of chance. Some idealist philosophers have, indeed, suggested obscurely in their doctrine of internal relations that every fact about a thing is implied by every other fact about it, but when it has been clearly stated the thesis seems too absurd to require discussion.

That plain men commonly accept determinism even when talking of chance is shown by another and much more common misunderstanding of elliptical chance statements. I am referring to the very old and widespread error of supposing that chance is a mysterious *agency*. This error is due to the fact that in our elliptical chance statements we often insert the word 'chance' where it would have made sense to put a description of a cause. We say, for example, 'It came about by chance that. . . .' Failing to notice the relativity of chance but holding nevertheless to determinism, plain men have often read into statements of this kind the doctrine that chance itself is a determinant of what happens. Sometimes they personify chance and worship it as a god. In Roman times there were altars to Fortuna, and even in our own day there are traces of this curious belief, e.g. in the phrase 'as chance would have it'. It is strange that any intelligent being should be led into these absurdities; but we find even Aristotle speaking of τύχη as a kind of cause,[1] and I believe that this primitive misunderstanding of elliptical chance statements is still a very common source of bewilderment to people when they discuss matters of chance.

§ 25. PROBABILITY RULES IN MATTERS OF CHANCE

The definition of chance given in the last section enables us to understand why probability judgements are especially important in matters of chance. Let us suppose that we know something to be α, and that we wish to know whether it is β. If we have established a universal proposition that all α things are β or that no α things are β, we can answer the question easily. But we may have found that some α things are β and some are not, and so be able to say only that it is a matter of chance in the sense just explained whether an α thing is β. In that case we cannot make any unqualified inference from the evidence at our disposal. If we could obtain some more evidence about the thing, we might be able to answer our question decisively, but perhaps it is impossible to get any more information. What are we to do? We can, of course, say 'It may be β', but such a conclusion is of no use to us if we have to take a practical decision depending on the answer to the question whether the thing is or is not β. And such situations are very common indeed in life. A doctor who is thinking of trying a new method of treatment on one of his patients wishes to know whether it will succeed in this case, but he can scarcely ever assume that all patients treated in a certain way will recover. If in circumstances such as these we manage to take practical decisions, it can be only on grounds of probability.

A probability judgement made about a particular thing in a situation such as I have described may perhaps be expressed elliptically, i.e. without reference to the evidence on which it is based; but it is usually easy to recognize what evidence the speaker has in mind, and there exists in common usage a way by which the speaker may, if necessary, present the nerve of such an argument in a generalized probability statement. A man who, knowing a thing to be α, says it is probably also β may, if questioned about his reason for making the assertion, reply 'Any α thing is likely to be β' or 'The probability of an α thing's being β is high'. Such an answer is a general statement in the sense that it contains no reference to any particular thing but deals with

[1] e.g. in the *Nicomachean Ethics*, 1112ª32.

probability as a relation between attributes, and it may therefore be said to enunciate a *probability rule*. It bears the same relation to the speaker's probability judgement about a particular thing as a universal statement would to an unqualified prediction about a particular thing said to be covered by it, and I use the word 'rule' here in order to suggest an analogy with laws. The statements cited as examples in text-books on the theory of probability are usually of this form, but the fact that they are concerned with relations between attributes or characters is often obscured by unfortunate terminology. Even when they are dealing with probability rules mathematicians and philosophers sometimes use the phrase 'probability of the event' as though they were concerned with probability judgements about particular occurrences. For a proper understanding of probability in matters of chance the most important notion is that of a probability rule. It is natural and useful to speak on occasions, as we did in the first part of this book, about probabilification as a relation between propositions, but this relation cannot be taken as fundamental, because propositions themselves are not fundamental entities. Probability is indeed relational, but the fundamental relation involved is one between attributes (or propositional functions, as they are sometimes called in mathematical logic). It is only when this notion of a probability rule has been made clear that the appearance of mystery dissolves.

In ordinary life we are usually content to state our probability rules in the vague form 'An α thing is likely to be β'. But we sometimes wish to express precise degrees of probability, and we then use statements of the form 'The probability of an α thing's being β is p', where p marks a place for the symbol of some fraction between 0 and 1. In what follows we shall often have occasion to deal with such precise formulations of probability rules, and I propose therefore to write them in the abbreviated form $P(\alpha, \beta) = p$. Although this mode of expression is now familiar to all educated men, it is a technical usage of comparatively recent origin and requires some explanation.

In 1654 Pascal became interested in a mathematical problem connected with gambling, and from that time onwards many such problems were posed and solved by mathematicians. Most of the earlier papers mentioned in Todhunter's *History of the Mathematical Theory of Probability* bear such titles as 'Solution of a Problem in Play'. Now in dicing and other games of chance the conditions of play are supposed to leave open a number of alternatives which are all equally likely, and it is from consideration of such alternatives that we derive our estimates of the risks of play. Thus we say there are five chances in six of throwing more than one with a true die. Here the word 'chances' is obviously used to mean equal chances, i.e. equally likely alternatives, much as the word 'parts' is sometimes used to mean equal parts, e.g. in the statement that a glass of water contains five parts water and one part whisky. Originally the measurement of probabilities by fractions was only a convenient abbreviation for this manner of speaking current among gamblers. De Moivre opens his *Doctrine of Chances*, published in 1718, with the statement:

> 'The probability of an event is greater or less according to the number of chances by which it may happen compared with the number of all the chances by which it may either happen or fail. Thus if an event has three chances to happen and two to fail, the probability of its happening may be estimated to be ⅗ and the probability of its failing ⅖.'

When mathematicians tried to deal with probability in a general fashion, it was natural that they should adapt to their needs the terminology and methods used in connexion with games of chance, and so we find it said in many mathematical text-books that probability is the number of favourable equiprobable cases divided by the total number of equiprobable cases, whether favourable or unfavourable. This way of speaking is useful and unobjectionable as a piece of technical phraseology, but it should not be supposed to contain the answer to all the questions about probability which have puzzled philosophers. If the phrase were intended as a definition of probability it would obviously be faulty, since the notion to be defined is reintroduced by the word 'equiprobable'. But it is rather a convention by which degrees of probability may be expressed as fractions. Admittedly this convention has sometimes been connected with a mistaken theory about the way in which the equiprobability of alternatives can be established, but it will be convenient to defer consideration of that theory until we have examined the main features of the calculus of chances which has been developed by mathematicians.

It will be noticed that according to the convention just explained $P(\alpha, \beta)$ can never be greater than 1 or less than 0. If it is a matter of chance whether an α thing is β, then $0 < P(\alpha, \beta) < 1$. And it is this situation which we usually have in mind when we talk about probability. But it is sometimes convenient to speak also of the extreme or limiting values as cases of probability. We then have $P(\alpha, \beta) = 1$ as an expression for the universal proposition that all α things are β and $P(\alpha, \beta) = 0$ as an expression for the universal proposition that no α things are β. This is an interesting usage, because it allows us to think of the theory of probability as a generalization of the notion of connexion between characters and brings out that analogy between probability rules and laws to which I have already referred.

Statements of probability rules in the form $P(\alpha, \beta) = p$ are more useful in practice than vague statements of the form 'It is probable that an α thing will be β', because they allow a closer adjustment of conduct to circumstances. Let us suppose that a man is considering whether to risk a stake s in the hope of a gain g. If he knows that the probability of his getting g by staking s is p, he can multiply p into g in order to get what is called the *mathematical expectation*. Whether or not it is rational to take the risk depends at least in part on a comparison of this with the stake. If the mathematical expectation pg is less than s which he risks, we say it is obviously irrational for him to undertake the venture. This is the situation in all commercialized gambling. Those who make their living by catering for other people's love of gambling must fix the possible gain of their clients at some figure such that $pg < s$. In a lottery of n tickets each costing s the gross takings of the promoters will be ns. But the prize money will be $ns-d$, where d is a deduction for expenses and profits. On the assumption that each holder of a single ticket has an equal chance of winning the prize money, the mathematical expectation of a ticket-holder will be $(1/n)(ns-d)$ or $s-d/n$. Sometimes, it is true, the notion of mathematical expectation is not strictly applicable, because the stake and the gain are not of a sort to be measured by numbers. The question at issue may be whether it is reasonable for a man to risk his life in the hope of winning glory by climbing Mount Everest. And even where it appears at first sight that the stake and the possible gain are both measurable, closer reflection may reveal that the notion of mathematical expectation is not strictly applicable. Thus if I have only a hundred pounds to preserve me from destitution, it is not reasonable for me to risk that money for a mathematical expectation of two hundred pounds, although it might be quite reasonable for a wealthy person to make the gamble. In all such cases it will, however, be useful to know the relevant probabilities. When I am considering whether to risk my life, knowledge that the risk would be 1/1000 rather than 1/10 may very well determine my decision.

Reasoning of this kind depends on the use of probability rules, but there may be serious difficulties in the application of the rules to particular cases. When we are unable to determine with certainty whether a thing is γ, we naturally try to determine the probability of this proposition in relation to all the available evidence, and so we look for a probability rule which takes account of all the known characteristics of the thing, say α-ness and β-ness. If we have already formulated a rule to the effect that $P(\alpha\beta, \gamma) = p$, we can apply this without hesitation and say that the probability of the thing's being γ is p. Our statement is elliptical in that it omits all reference to evidence, but the idiom gives rise to no real ambiguity. It may be, however, that we have not formulated, and cannot now formulate, any rule about the probability of an $\alpha\beta$ thing's being γ, although we have a rule about the probability of an α thing's being γ and possibly also one about the probability of a β thing's being γ. What is to be done? We shall see presently that there is no simple formula by which we can derive $P(\alpha\beta, \gamma)$ from $P(\alpha, \gamma)$ and $P(\beta, \gamma)$, even when we know both these latter. To rely solely on our rule about the probability of an α thing's being γ might be extremely rash. Let us suppose, for example, that an insurance company is asked to insure the life of a man who is about to attempt a flight to the moon in a rocket. The usual examination reveals that the man is a healthy person of forty years of age (α), and the probability of such a person's dying within the year (γ) is given in the company's tables, but there are no statistics from which the company can estimate the probability of the death of a person who combines with this medical history the interesting characteristic of flying to the moon in a rocket (β). If the company undertakes to insure the man at the ordinary rate for a person of his medical history, it assumes in effect that

$$P(\alpha\beta, \gamma) = P(\alpha, \gamma),$$

and this assumption is, to say the least, quite ungrounded. There are, indeed, some grounds for thinking that the first probability is much greater than the second, because flying to the moon in a rocket resembles in various respects other enterprises which are commonly held to be very dangerous (i.e. to involve a high probability of death); but we have not the material for any precise estimate of the risk and must content ourselves with vague analogies. To ask for more is to misunderstand the situation. The theory of probability does not, and cannot, provide a method for the forming of opinions on all possible questions. Until we have established probability rules we can form no rational opinions; and experience may often be insufficient for the establishment of the rules we require.

It may be thought that the difficulties just mentioned are so great as to make probability rules of very little value in practice. For the particular cases in which we have to take practical decisions can always be distinguished from each other in some way, and if we insist on finding for each case a probability rule which takes account of all the characteristics known to be present in that case we shall rarely, if ever, be able to form any opinions. The answer to this objection is twofold.

In the first place, we often have good grounds for assuming that some characteristics are irrelevant to the question at issue. Having estimated $P(\alpha, \gamma)$ to our satisfaction we may perhaps be able to say that $P(\alpha\beta, \gamma)$ has the same value, because our scientific theories seem to exclude any special connexion between β-ness and γ-ness. Thus, if we find that a candidate for a post has a good record and an appearance of honesty, we do not hesitate to appoint him merely because a motor-car passed down the street at the moment he entered the room for his interview, although having entered the room while a motor-car was passing is a characteristic of this man and we have no probability rule which takes account of it as well as of his other known characteristics.

Secondly, our use of probability rules is often directed by interest in sets rather than individuals. Although an insurance company naturally refuses to issue policies in individual cases which are unusual and may involve very great risks, its main concern is not to avoid paying out money in any cases whatsoever, but to make reasonably sure that there will be a favourable balance at the end of each year's business. For this purpose the company's actuaries consider, not the probability of a given individual's dying within the year, but rather the probability that the death-rate among its clients of a certain general description will exceed a certain fraction. This probability is derived, as we shall see presently, from the probability of such a client's dying within the year, but it may be very much smaller, if the number of clients answering to the description is large. For a calculation of this kind it is essential that the probability rule used as premiss should be of fairly high generality, since otherwise the set of clients answering to the description will be too small for any useful application of the so-called law of large numbers. This is not to say that the actuaries should consider only the broadest class of possible customers, i.e. that of human beings. For if they did so the company would almost certainly lose. There are well-established rules about the probability of death in more narrowly defined classes, and a premium based on a rule about the probability of death in the class of human beings would attract customers only from sub-classes in which the probability of death was higher than this. In practice, therefore, the classification of clients must be carried as far as experience warrants, that is to say, down to the most narrowly defined classes for which there are well-established probability rules. But even these classes must be defined by descriptions of considerable generality, since for a class which is very narrowly defined there can be little statistical information and so no well-established probability rule.

§ 26. FUNDAMENTALS OF THE CALCULUS OF CHANCES

The history of the calculus of chances begins in the middle of the seventeenth century with the inquiries of Pascal to which I have already referred. A certain Chevalier de Méré, who was interested in mathematics but more versed in gambling, put to Pascal a question which had arisen in the course of play, and Pascal exchanged letters on the subject with Fermat. The problem is to determine the probability of getting at least one double-six in twenty-four throws of a pair of dice. The Chevalier argued incorrectly that according to the laws of arithmetic this should be the same as the probability of getting at least one six in four throws of a single die. Then, finding that this conclusion was not borne out by his experience in gambling, he rashly maintained that the propositions of arithmetic must be inconsistent with one another. Although, as Pascal said, he was no mathematician, his problem has brought him fame, for the correct solution of it by Pascal is the first contribution of mathematics to the theory of probability.[1]

The scope of the calculus of chances can be understood most easily from a consideration of de Méré's question. He wanted to have the value of a certain probability calculated from certain

[1] See Todhunter's *History of the Mathematical Theory of Probability*, p. 11.

other probabilities which were supposed to be given. Thus he assumed for the purpose of his problem that the probability of getting six in one throw of a die was $\frac{1}{6}$. With this assumption we are all prepared to say that the probability of getting two sixes in successive throws is $\frac{1}{6} \times \frac{1}{6}$ or $\frac{1}{36}$. De Méré's problem is more complicated, but the reasoning by which Pascal solved it is essentially of the same kind. In short, the calculus of chances is just the procedure for deriving probabilities from others which are supposed to be given, and it is concerned solely with consistency. The mathematician who studies the calculus need not, as a mathematician, concern himself with the question how the given probabilities were determined. Some of the mathematicians whose contributions to the calculus we shall consider held views about the philosophical problem of probability which are now discredited. Thus James Bernoulli thought that probability was the same thing as degree of belief. But this does not invalidate his work, for that can stand by itself as a contribution to mathematics. Consideration of problems in the calculus of chances has, indeed, been the occasion of a number of discoveries in pure mathematics. In particular the theory of arrangements (permutations and combinations) was first developed for the sake of its applications in this calculus.

In the history of the mathematical theory of probability one of the most famous names is that of James Bernoulli, to whom I have already referred. He was one of a family of distinguished mathematicians, and his *Ars Conjectandi* was published by his nephew, Nicholas Bernoulli, in 1713, eight years after his death. In this he proved an important theorem which is sometimes called the law of large numbers. Another famous name is that of Thomas Bayes, an English clergyman of the middle of the eighteenth century. He first enunciated the inversion theorem in an *Essay towards Solving a Problem in the Doctrine of Chances*, which was communicated to the Royal Society in 1763 by his friend the Rev. Richard Price.[1] This was an ingenious piece of work and it inspired an attempt to solve the problem of induction which is sometimes, although incorrectly, called Bayes's theorem. The work done up to his own time was systematized by Laplace in his *Théorie analytique des probabilités*. The first edition of this book was published in 1812 and dedicated to Napoleon the Great. In the second edition, published two years later, this dedication was suppressed and a

---

[1] Price himself was a distinguished writer on moral philosophy.

new paragraph was added saying that the fall of empires which aspired to universal dominion could be predicted with very high probability by one versed in the calculus of chances.[1] Todhunter, writing in 1865, closed his history of the mathematical theory with a chapter on Laplace, as though the *Théorie analytique* marked the end of a period. And so it does. There have been big developments since then in some parts of the mathematical theory, especially in the invention by the biometrical school of devices such as correlation coefficients for dealing with statistical material, but there has been nothing like the theoretical development which took place between Pascal and Laplace. Indeed, some of the claims which were made for the calculus by Laplace and his contemporaries (e.g. Condorcet) have now been abandoned as fallacious.

We shall be able to consider here only a few of the most important theorems of the calculus, namely, those which are of special importance in a philosophical discussion of probability. I shall state them in a symbolism developed from that I have already introduced, but it must be remembered that their discoverers did not always use terminology which made clear the nature of their assumptions.

There are three fundamental theorems in the calculus of chances on which depend all the others. They are the negation theorem, the disjunction (or addition) theorem, and the conjunction (or multiplication) theorem. We could, if we chose, derive either the second or the third from the other two taken together, but it is perhaps more natural to treat them all alike as fundamental.

The *Negation Theorem* is very simple. It merely asserts that

$$P(\alpha, \sim\beta) = 1 - P(\alpha, \beta),$$

where $\sim$ stands for 'not'. The truth of this can be seen immediately from the definition of a probability fraction, and no further comment is necessary.

The *Disjunction Theorem* can be stated in the formula:

$$P(\alpha, \beta \vee \gamma) = P(\alpha, \beta) + P(\alpha, \gamma) - P(\alpha, \beta\gamma),$$

where $\vee$ stands for 'or' and $\beta\gamma$ for 'β and γ'. That is to say, the probability of an α thing's being either β or γ is equal to the probability of its being β plus the probability of its being γ minus the probability of its being both β and γ. In order to understand this

[1] Introduction, p. liv.

theorem let us first consider the special case where β-ness and γ-ness are mutually exclusive. It is easy to see that in this special case

$$P(\alpha, \beta \lor \gamma) = P(\alpha, \beta) + P(\alpha, \gamma).$$

For if a set of equally probable cases can be distinguished under α-ness, the number of such cases which are favourable to β-ness or γ-ness must be equal to the number of those which are favourable to β-ness plus the number of those which are favourable to γ-ness. This is the line of reasoning we follow when we argue that a man who has two tickets in an honestly run lottery has twice as big a chance of winning the prize as a man who has only one ticket. For the probability that the holder of two tickets will win with one or the other is equal to the probability that he will win with the one plus the probability that he will win with the other, since he cannot win with both. Now let us remove the condition that β-ness and γ-ness are mutually exclusive. We may suppose, for example, that our problem is to find the probability that a card drawn at random (α) is either a spade (β) or a king (γ). The probability of an α thing's being both β and γ is already included in $P(\alpha, \beta)$ and also in $P(\alpha, \gamma)$. If we use the special formula appropriate for the case where β-ness and γ-ness are mutually exclusive, we are counting $P(\alpha, \beta\gamma)$ twice. We must therefore write instead the general formula given above. This general form of the disjunction theorem is valid for the special case where β-ness and γ-ness are mutually exclusive, just as for the case where they are not. For if β-ness and γ-ness are mutually exclusive, $P(\alpha, \beta\gamma) = 0$ and the last term in the formula can be neglected.

The *Conjunction Theorem* can be stated in the formula:

$$P(\alpha, \beta\gamma) = P(\alpha, \beta) \times P(\alpha\beta, \gamma).$$

That is to say, the probability of an α thing's being both β and γ is equal to the probability of an α thing's being β multiplied by the probability of an α and β thing's being γ. In order to find the probability of an α thing's being both β and γ we first consider the proportion of equiprobable α cases which are also β cases and then ask what proportion of equiprobable α and β cases are also γ cases. The probability fraction we want is got by multiplying the first ratio into the second. We could, of course, start by considering first the proportion of equiprobable α cases which are also γ cases and so reach the formula:

$$P(\alpha, \beta\gamma) = P(\alpha, \gamma) \times P(\alpha\gamma, \beta).$$

An example will make the procedure clear. Let us suppose that α connotes being a boy, β getting distinction in Latin in the School Certificate examination, and γ getting distinction in mathematics. Then $P(\alpha, \beta\gamma)$ is the probability of a boy's getting distinction in both Latin and mathematics, and it is equal to the probability of a boy's getting distinction in Latin multiplied by the probability that a boy who gets distinction in Latin will also get distinction in mathematics. We may be inclined to assume at first sight that we can use the simpler formula:

$$P(\alpha, \beta\gamma) = P(\alpha, \beta) \times P(\alpha, \gamma),$$

but a little reflection will show that this is a mistake. For, if we say this, we are assuming that a boy who gets distinction in Latin is no more likely to get distinction in mathematics than the common run of boys, i.e. that

$$P(\alpha\beta, \gamma) = P(\alpha, \gamma).$$

It may be that there is in fact no connexion between ability in Latin and ability in mathematics, in which case the equation just stated holds; but we are not entitled to make this assumption without special evidence. The general form of the conjunction theorem is therefore as stated above, and the special or simplified form is to be used only when it is known that the appropriate condition is fulfilled. One of the most common mistakes in arguments about probability is the use of the special form of the disjunction theorem or the special form of the conjunction theorem without justification.

§ 27. THE NOTION OF RELEVANCE AND THE INVERSION THEOREM

We have seen that it is necessary to distinguish between $P(\alpha\beta, \gamma)$ and $P(\alpha, \gamma)$. If we consider the various possible relations between these two expressions, we see that we may have

$$P(\alpha\beta, \gamma) > P(\alpha, \gamma),$$

or
$$P(\alpha\beta, \gamma) = P(\alpha, \gamma),$$

or
$$P(\alpha\beta, \gamma) < P(\alpha, \gamma).$$

In the first case we say that, with α-ness given, β-ness is *favourably relevant* to γ-ness; in the second case that, with α-ness given, β-ness is *irrelevant* to γ-ness, and in the third case that, with α-ness given, β-ness is *unfavourably relevant* to γ-ness. In the discussion of relevance and irrelevance as technical notions in the calculus of chances there are two points of importance to keep in mind. First, these notions always involve three terms. We must not say 'β-ness is favourably relevant to γ-ness' without making any reference to α-ness. It might be found, for example, that distinction in Latin was favourably relevant to distinction in mathematics among boys but not among girls. We might have

$$P(\alpha\beta, \gamma) > P(\alpha, \gamma),$$

but

$$P(\delta\beta, \gamma) = P(\delta, \gamma),$$

where δ connotes the character of being a girl. Secondly, with α-ness given, the relation of relevance or irrelevance is symmetrical as between β-ness and γ-ness, e.g. if, with α-ness given, β-ness is favourably relevant to γ-ness, so, with α-ness given, γ-ness is favourably relevant to β-ness and we may say for short that, with α-ness given, β-ness and γ-ness are favourably relevant to each other. This can be seen by consideration of the conjunction theorem. Since we can consider either $P(\alpha, \beta)$ or $P(\alpha, \gamma)$ first, we have

$$P(\alpha, \beta\gamma) = P(\alpha, \beta) \times P(\alpha\beta, \gamma) = P(\alpha, \gamma) \times P(\alpha\gamma, \beta).$$

And from the right-hand equation we get by cross-division:

$$\frac{P(\alpha\beta, \gamma)}{P(\alpha, \gamma)} = \frac{P(\alpha\gamma, \beta)}{P(\alpha, \beta)},$$

which is a compendious way of stating that relevance and irrelevance are symmetrical in the sense just explained.

The notion of relevance has an interesting application in connexion with the problem of cumulative evidence. Let us suppose that we are considering whether a certain thing is γ, and that we know it is both α and β. How are we to assess the probability of the thing's being γ in relation to the conjunction of α-ness and β-ness, given its probability in relation to each separately? It is often assumed in historical researches and in detective novels that if $P(\alpha, \gamma)$ and $P(\beta, \gamma)$ are both considerable, i.e. greater than $\frac{1}{2}$, $P(\alpha\beta, \gamma)$ must be greater than either. But this is not necessarily true. If the problem is to form an opinion on the question whether a certain picture is by Rembrandt (γ) and we have two pieces of evidence, one that the picture is in a certain style of brushwork (α) and the other that it contains a certain pigment (β), we may conceivably have $P(\alpha, \gamma)$ and $P(\beta, \gamma)$ both very high, but $P(\alpha\beta, \gamma)$

very low or nil. For it may be that Rembrandt altered his style of brushwork during the course of his life and that when he used the distinctive style found in the picture the peculiar pigment found in the picture was not available. If we have reason to believe that this was so, we are compelled to say that the picture is not by Rembrandt. We then have

$$P(\alpha, \gamma) > \tfrac{1}{2},$$

and $$P(\beta, \gamma) > \tfrac{1}{2},$$

but $$P(\alpha\beta, \gamma) = 0.$$

There is, indeed, no solution to the problem with which we started, namely, that of deriving $P(\alpha\beta, \gamma)$ from $P(\alpha, \gamma)$ and $P(\beta, \gamma)$, because the problem is indeterminate. This is not to say that one piece of evidence cannot corroborate another, but only that we have to specify carefully the conditions for such corroboration, and here the notion of relevance is important. Since

$$\frac{P(\alpha\beta, \gamma)}{P(\alpha, \gamma)} = \frac{P(\alpha\gamma, \beta)}{P(\alpha, \beta)},$$

the addition of a new piece of evidence, β-ness, to that we already possess, α-ness, will raise the probability of γ-ness if, and only if, its own probability in relation to α-ness and γ-ness together would be greater than its own probability in relation to α-ness alone. In other words, β-ness will be favourably relevant to γ-ness if, and only if, γ-ness would be favourably relevant to β-ness, with α-ness given in each case. This conclusion has a bearing on the problem of applying probability rules to particular cases. But it is not very helpful. For any statistical information which enabled us to evaluate $P(\alpha\gamma, \beta)$ would presumably enable us to evaluate $P(\alpha\beta, \gamma)$ directly.

The *Inversion Theorem* of Bayes is derived from the same line of reasoning. Starting once more with the formula:

$$P(\alpha, \beta\gamma) = P(\alpha, \beta) \times P(\alpha\beta, \gamma) = P(\alpha, \gamma) \times P(\alpha\gamma, \beta),$$

we divide both sides of the right-hand equation by $P(\alpha, \beta)$ and get:

$$P(\alpha\beta, \gamma) = \frac{P(\alpha, \gamma)P(\alpha\gamma, \beta)}{P(\alpha, \beta)}.$$

This formula is called the inversion theorem, because it enables us by means of the notion of symmetrical relevance to express

$P(\alpha\beta, \gamma)$ as a function of $P(\alpha\gamma, \beta)$. An example will make clear how it is used. Let us suppose that α connotes being a house of such-and-such construction, β being on fire and γ some conjectured feature of a house that may be thought to explain the interesting fact of its being on fire, e.g. its having a defect in the electric wiring. Then $P(\alpha, \gamma)$ is what we call the initial probability of the conjecture, i.e. its probability in relation to the general information that something is a house of such-and-such construction but without regard to the special information that it is on fire, $P(\alpha\gamma, \beta)$ is the probability of fire in relation to our general information and our hypothesis taken together, and $P(\alpha, \beta)$ is the initial probability of a fire, i.e. the probability of a fire in relation to our general information alone.[1] Since we have ourselves put forward γ-ness as an hypothesis to explain our finding β-ness in an α thing, we presumably know $P(\alpha\gamma, \beta)$ or at least assume some value for it. The formula cited above as the inversion theorem enables us to express $P(\alpha\beta, \gamma)$, i.e. the probability of the hypothesis in relation to the total of our information, as a function of $P(\alpha\gamma, \beta)$, which we know. It is sometimes said to deal with the probability of causes, because in many applications γ-ness can be described loosely as a suggested cause of β-ness. If, however, $P(\alpha\gamma, \beta)$ is taken to be less than 1, γ-ness cannot be a cause of β-ness in any strict sense, since it does not necessitate the latter; and in any case the old name for this part of the calculus is unsuitable, because the inversion theorem is not specially concerned with arguments from later to earlier events.

It is important to notice that in formulating the inversion theorem we need three terms. It would be a gross mistake to omit all mention of α-ness and write:

$$P(\beta, \gamma) = P(\gamma, \beta).$$

For, although the relation of relevance is symmetrical in the sense explained above, there is no reason to suppose that the probability relation itself is symmetrical. There is a high probability that an undergraduate of Oxford knows some Latin, but the probability that a person who knows some Latin is an undergraduate of Oxford is comparatively low, because there are many ways of

---

[1] In expounding the inversion theorem some writers use the expression 'a priori probability' where I have spoken of initial probability. This usage is unfortunate and should be avoided. An initial probability may conceivably be established a posteriori. It is only initial in the order of our inquiry.

learning Latin which do not involve going to Oxford. In particular the expressions of initial probability which occur in the
inversion theorem must not be overlooked. If $P(\alpha, \gamma)$, the initial
probability of the hypothesis, were very small indeed, the whole
expression:

$$\frac{P(\alpha, \gamma)P(\alpha\gamma, \beta)}{P(\alpha, \beta)}$$

might have a very low value, although $P(\alpha\gamma, \beta)$ was equal or nearly
equal to 1. If, for example, someone suggested in explanation of a
fire that the house had been hit by a meteorite, we should reply:
'No doubt a house which was hit by a meteorite would almost
certainly catch fire, but the probability of a house's being hit by
a meteorite is so extremely small that we need not take your
suggestion seriously.' On the other hand, the initial probability
$P(\alpha, \beta)$ works in the opposite way, because the expression for it
appears in the formula as denominator. If it is very small, the
value of the whole expression may be very high, although the
value of the numerator is not considerable. In other words, if the
fact to be explained is something very unusual (i.e. having a low
initial probability in relation to our general information), even an
hypothesis of low initial probability may have a high probability
in relation to that special fact and our general information. All
this is surely very good sense.

In certain circumstances the inversion formula can be elaborated
still farther. Let us suppose it to be known that one or other of a
number of mutually exclusive hypotheses must be true, i.e. that an
α thing must be either γ_1 or γ_2 or ...γ_n. Then we can expand the
denominator of our formula as follows:

$$P(\alpha, \beta) = P(\alpha, \beta\gamma_1 \vee \beta\gamma_2 \vee ...\beta\gamma_n)$$
$$= P(\alpha, \beta\gamma_1) + P(\alpha, \beta\gamma_2) + ...P(\alpha, \beta\gamma_n)$$
$$= P(\alpha, \gamma_1)P(\alpha\gamma_1, \beta) + P(\alpha, \gamma_2)P(\alpha\gamma_2, \beta) + ...P(\alpha, \gamma_n)P(\alpha\gamma_n, \beta).$$

And the probability of a particular hypothesis in relation to our
total information will be

$$P(\alpha\beta, \gamma_r) = \frac{P(\alpha, \gamma_r)P(\alpha\gamma_r, \beta)}{\sum_{j=1}^{n} P(\alpha, \gamma_j)P(\alpha\gamma_j, \beta)},$$

where the numerator is one of the terms summed in the denominator. We may take as an example the situation popular with

detective-story writers in which there is a limited number of possible hypotheses about the authorship of a certain crime. It is interesting to notice that these writers often get their effect by arranging things so that $P(\alpha\beta, \gamma_r)$ is very high although $P(\alpha, \gamma_r)$ is very low. But the only case in which we can safely ignore the initial probabilities of the various hypotheses is the case in which we are satisfied that they are all equal (e.g. when all the possible hypotheses about the authorship of a crime are equally likely in relation to our general information about character and records). For then we may cancel out the initial probabilities and write:

$$P(\alpha\beta, \gamma_r) = \frac{P(\alpha\gamma_r, \beta)}{\sum\limits_{j=1}^{n} P(\alpha\gamma_j, \beta)}.$$

This is an agreeably simple formula, but it holds only for the special case just mentioned. We must not put it forward as a general principle, as some writers have done.

§ 28. THEOREMS ON THE COMPOSITION OF SETS

Let us now ask what is the probability of getting just m β things in a set of n α things when it is given that $P(\alpha, \beta) = p$. We are demanding the probability that a set which exhibits a certain character will exhibit a certain other character, and we therefore need some symbols to stand for the characters of sets with which we are to deal. Let $^{\alpha}\sigma_n$ connote the character of being a set of n α things and $^{\beta}\kappa_m$ the character of containing just m β things. The expression we wish to evaluate is $P(^{\alpha}\sigma_n, {}^{\beta}\kappa_m)$, which we can read as 'the probability that an α-set of n members will have a β-content of m'. It is convenient sometimes to think of our set of α things as a succession of trials, e.g. a succession of tosses of a coin. But when we use this illustration we must remember that the order of the trials is immaterial for our purpose and that they must be supposed independent one of another. In particular we must assume that the result of one trial has no influence on the issue of the next, so that, if δ connotes the character of following an α thing which is also β, δ-ness and β-ness are irrelevant to each other with α-ness given, i.e. that

$$P(\alpha\delta, \beta) = P(\alpha, \beta).$$

When we ask the value of $P(^{\alpha}\sigma_n, {}^{\beta}\kappa_m)$ we are looking for a general principle by which to evaluate probabilities about the composition[1] of sets, but our problem is complex and the solution is to be found only by considering first certain special cases. Let us begin by trying to determine $P(\alpha\sigma_2, \beta\kappa_2)$, i.e. the probability of getting two β things in an α-set of two members, on the assumption that $P(\alpha, \beta) = p$. If for convenience we regard the α things as items in a succession of trials, we can say that the desired probability is the same as the probability of an α thing's being both the successor of an α thing which is β and itself β. Then in accordance with the assumption mentioned in the last paragraph

$$P(\alpha\sigma_2, \beta\kappa_2) = P(\alpha, \delta\beta)$$
$$= P(\alpha, \delta)P(\alpha\delta, \beta)$$
$$= P(\alpha, \delta)P(\alpha, \beta).$$

But $P(\alpha, \delta)$, the probability of an α thing's being the successor of an α thing which is β, is clearly the same as the probability of an α thing's being β, for it is already assumed that the second α thing is the successor of an α thing and that the ordering of the α things in a succession is irrelevant to the probability of their being β, and so we have

$$P(\alpha\sigma_2, \beta\kappa_2) = p^2.$$

The important point is, of course, that the trials are supposed to be independent of each other.

By an extension of the same line of reasoning it can be shown that

$$P(\alpha\sigma_m, \beta\kappa_m) = p^m.$$

If, however, the m α things which we consider in this formula are the first m out of the n which we have to consider, there will be $n-m$ α things left, and the probability that all of this remainder will turn out to be *not* β is $(1-p)^{n-m}$. Therefore the probability that the first m of our n α things will turn out to be β and the rest to be not β is the product of these two probabilities, i.e. $(1-p)^{n-m}p^m$. But we are not concerned with the order in which β things occur among the α things. We want the probability of there being just m β things among n α things without regard to order, and, since all the possible orders are equiprobable, we must multiply $(1-p)^{n-m}p^m$ by the number of possible ways in which m things

[1] The word 'constitution' might, perhaps, be more appropriate, but it has been used by some writers (cf. Keynes, *Treatise*, p. 50) in a technical sense and so could give rise to misunderstandings in this context.

may be chosen from among n things, i.e. by ^nC_m or $\dfrac{n!}{m!(n-m)!}$.
We thus get

$$P(^\alpha\sigma_n, {}^\beta\kappa_m) = {}^nC_m(1-p)^{n-m}p^m.$$

It is interesting to notice that this is one of the terms of the expansion of $[(1-p)+p]^n$ according to the binomial theorem in ascending powers of p, namely, that term which involves the mth power of p. There are just $n+1$ terms in the expansion, corresponding to the various possible powers of p from 0 to n inclusive. We can represent each of these terms conveniently by the letter T with an appropriate subscript for the power of p which it involves. Then since $(1-p)+p = 1$, the sum of all the $n+1$ terms is 1. That is to say,

$$\sum_{m=0}^{n} P(^\alpha\sigma_n, {}^\beta\kappa_m) = \sum_{m=0}^{n} T_m = [(1-p)+p]^n = 1.$$

This result is obvious enough, for it only means that the β-content of our α-set of n members must be some number from 0 to n.

So far we have been considering the probability of getting *just* m β things in a set of n α things, but from the result we have reached we can easily calculate the probability of getting *at least* m β things. It is the sum of the probabilities for the several possible β-contents from m to n inclusive. This can be stated shortly in the formula:

$$P(^\alpha\sigma_n, {}^\beta\kappa_{\underline{m}}) = \sum_{j=m}^{n} T_j.$$

Similarly for the probability of getting *at most* m β things we may write:

$$P(^\alpha\sigma_n, {}^\beta\kappa_{\overline{m}}) = \sum_{j=0}^{m} T_j.$$

And for the probability of getting a β-content within s of m, i.e. at least $m-s$ and at most $m+s$, we have:

$$P(^\alpha\sigma_n, {}^\beta\kappa_{\overline{\underline{m\pm s}}}) = \sum_{j=m-s}^{m+s} T_j.$$

From consideration of the binomial expansion it is possible to prove another interesting theorem, namely, that the most probable number of β things in a set of n α things is np or the nearest integer. We must add 'or the nearest integer' because np itself

may not be an integer. The ratio of any term in the expansion to
its predecessor is given by the formula:

$$\frac{T_m}{T_{m-1}} = \frac{n!\,(m-1)!\,(n-m+1)!\,(1-p)^{n-m}p^m}{m!\,(n-m)!\,n!\,(1-p)^{n-m+1}p^{m-1}}$$

$$= \frac{(n-m+1)p}{m(1-p)},$$

and the value of the last expression decreases steadily as m increases. The largest term in the expansion must therefore be that
term T_l after which the ratio of each term to its predecessor sinks
below 1 for the first time. For up to T_l each term will be larger
than its predecessor, and after T_l each term will be smaller than
its predecessor. We have therefore

$$\frac{(n-l+1)p}{l(1-p)} > 1$$

and
$$\frac{(n-l)p}{(l+1)(1-p)} < 1,$$

which can be combined in the formula:

$$np - (1-p) < l < np + p.$$

But since p and $(1-p)$ are fractions which add up to make 1, this
is as much as to say that l must be np or the nearest integer to np.
If $np - (1-p)$ and $np + p$ are both integers, there will be no single
largest term, but two equal terms which are larger than any of
the rest.

This theorem about the most probable β-content can also be
stated as a theorem about the most probable β-ratio or frequency.
Using the symbol ${}^\beta\rho_x$ as an abbreviation for 'having a β-ratio of
x', we can say that $P({}^\alpha\sigma_n, {}^\beta\rho_x)$ has its maximum value when $x = p$
or the nearest permissible fraction. We must add 'or the nearest
permissible fraction' because the β-ratio is equal to the β-content
divided by n.

Although p or the nearest permissible fraction is the most probable frequency of β things among the α things, it need not itself
be highly probable. The probability of getting just this frequency
may be quite low, even much below $\frac{1}{2}$. Let us assume, for example,
that the probability of getting heads in tossing a penny is $\frac{1}{2}$. Then
the most probable number of heads in four tosses is two, but the
probability of getting just two heads in four tosses is only

$${}^4C_2(1-\tfrac{1}{2})^{4-2}(\tfrac{1}{2})^2 = \tfrac{3}{8}.$$

The situation can be explained most easily by means of a figure

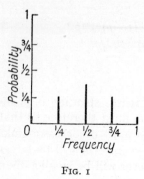

constructed to illustrate this case. There are five possible frequencies to be considered, o, $\frac{1}{4}$, $\frac{1}{2}$, $\frac{3}{4}$, and 1, and their probabilities are respectively $\frac{1}{16}$, $\frac{1}{4}$, $\frac{3}{8}$, $\frac{1}{4}$, and $\frac{1}{16}$. In the figure the probability for each frequency is represented by a vertical line of appropriate length drawn from the point of the base line which corresponds to that frequency. The sum of the lengths of all the vertical lines must, of course, be one unit. What we have proved so far is that in any such diagram there will be the longest line for that frequency which is nearest to p.

Fig. 1

§ 29. BERNOULLI'S LIMIT THEOREM

The theorems stated in the last section are all due to James Bernoulli, but his name is associated especially with a very interesting limit theorem which can be stated in our symbolism as follows:

If $P(\alpha, \beta) = p$, then for any h, however small,

$$\lim_{n \to \infty} P(^{\alpha}\sigma_n, \, ^{\beta}\rho_{\overline{p \pm h}}) = 1.$$

In order to prove this theorem we must consider once more the expansion of $[(1-p)+p]^n$ in ascending powers of p, and it will be convenient to introduce some short descriptions for certain terms in the expansion. Let l be the number such that T_l is the largest term or, if there are two largest terms, that which comes earlier in the expansion; and let $s = nh$ or, if nh is not itself an integer, the nearest integer less than nh. Then all the terms earlier than T_l in the expansion may be called left terms, and all those later than T_l right terms. Similarly all the terms from T_{l-s} to T_{l+s} inclusive may be called inner terms, and all the rest outer terms. The division is shown in the following scheme:

Left		Right	
$\underbrace{T_o \ldots T_{l-2s} \ldots T_{l-s-1}}_{\text{Outer}}$	$\underbrace{T_{l-s} \ldots T_{l-1}}_{\text{Inner}} \; T_l \; \underbrace{T_{l+1} \ldots T_{l+s}}$	$\underbrace{T_{l+s+1} \ldots T_{l+2s} \ldots T_n}_{\text{Outer}}$	

Now the ratio of the largest term to the extreme left inner term is given by the expression:

$$\frac{T_l}{T_{l-s}} = \frac{n!\,(l-s)!\,(n-l+s)!\,(1-p)^{n-l}p^l}{l!\,(n-l)!\,n!\,(1-p)^{n-l+s}p^{l-s}}$$

$$= \frac{(n-l+s)(n-l+s-1)...(n-l+1)p^s}{l(l-1)...(l-s+1)(1-p)^s}$$

$$= \prod_{j=0}^{s-1}\frac{(n-l+s-j)p}{(l-j)(1-p)}$$

$$= \prod_{j=0}^{s-1}\frac{np-lp+sp-jp}{l-lp+jp-j}.$$

Each of the s factors in this product must be greater than 1, since $jp < j$ and sp exceeds jp by at least p whereas l cannot exceed np by as much as p. But, however small h may be, s, which equals nh, can be made as large as we please by taking n sufficiently large. Therefore this product of s factors, which is the ratio of the largest term to the extreme left inner term, can be made as large as we please by taking n sufficiently large. But it has already been proved in the previous section that the ratio of each term to its predecessor decreases steadily throughout the expansion. And so we have

$$\frac{T_{l-s}}{T_{l-s-1}} > \frac{T_l}{T_{l-1}},$$

or

$$\frac{T_{l-1}}{T_{l-s-1}} > \frac{T_l}{T_{l-s}}.$$

Therefore T_{l-1}/T_{l-s-1} can be made as large as we please by taking n sufficiently large. By a similar argument the same can be proved of T_{l-2}/T_{l-s-2} and so on down to T_{l-s}/T_{l-2s}. From this it follows that the ratio of the sum of the left inner terms to the sum of the corresponding number of left outer terms standing next to them in the expansion can be made as large as we please by taking n sufficiently large. But there are in all only $l-s$ left outer terms and of these the s terms from T_{l-s-1} to T_{l-2s} inclusive are the largest. Therefore the ratio of the sum of all the left outer terms to the sum of all the s terms from T_{l-s-1} to T_{l-2s} inclusive must be less than

$$\frac{l-s}{s} = \frac{np-nh}{nh} = \frac{p-h}{h},$$

which is finite. It follows that by taking n sufficiently large we can make the ratio of the sum of the left inner terms to the sum of all the left outer terms as large as we please.

By a precisely similar argument it can be shown that if we take n sufficiently large we can make the ratio of the sum of the right inner terms to the sum of all the right outer terms as large as we please. Therefore by taking n sufficiently large we can make the ratio of the sum of all the inner terms (including the largest, T_i) to the sum of all the outer terms as large as we please. But the sum of all the terms, inner and outer, is 1; and so what we have proved is equivalent to the assertion that as n increases without limit the sum of the inner terms tends to 1, i.e.

$$\lim_{n \to \infty} P({}^\alpha\sigma_n, {}^\beta\kappa_{\overline{l \pm s}}) = 1.$$

A β-content between $l+s$ and $l-s$ corresponds, however, to a β-ratio between $(l+s)/n$ and $(l-s)/n$, i.e. between $p+h$ and $p-h$. And so we have

$$\lim_{n \to \infty} P({}^\alpha\sigma_n, {}^\beta\rho_{\overline{p \pm h}}) = 1,$$

which is the conclusion to be proved.[1]

Understanding of this theorem may be made easier by a consideration of a diagram like that introduced in the last section. As n, the number of trials, is increased we clearly have more possible values for the frequency m/n and therefore more vertical lines. In the accompanying figure there are nine lines corresponding to the probabilities for the various frequencies which may be realized in eight tosses of a coin. As before, the sum of the lengths of all these vertical lines must be one unit, but in order to allow something for the new lines we introduce, the lines drawn from the points in the base line marked '$\frac{1}{2}$', '$\frac{1}{4}$', &c., must be shorter. Whereas the probability of getting a frequency of heads

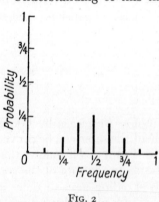

Fig. 2

---

[1] The proof set out above is that given by Bernoulli in his *Ars Conjectandi*, Part IV, ch. v. In most modern expositions it has been replaced by a shorter proof depending on Stirling's formula for approximation to the value of factorials, but for the purpose of this book simplicity is more important than brevity.

equal exactly to $\frac{1}{2}$ in four tosses of a penny is $\frac{3}{8}$, the probability of getting a frequency of just $\frac{1}{2}$ in eight tosses is only $\frac{35}{128}$. But an interesting pattern appears as the number of vertical lines is increased. Those vertical lines which are nearest to the longest line make a figure like a hillock in a gently rising plain. It might loosely be said that the probability was becoming concentrated in the neighbourhood of the most probable value for the frequency. If we take a small interval of the base line about that most probable value, the sum of the lengths of the vertical lines within that interval increases towards 1 as n increases without limit. Naturally this sum can never be made equal to 1, because frequencies outside that interval always remain possible and have their own small probabilities.

Perhaps the best formulation of Bernoulli's theorem in ordinary English is the following: 'In a sufficiently large set of α things it is almost certain that the relative frequency of β things will approximate to the probability of an α thing's being β within any degree of approximation which may be desired.' Here the phrase 'almost certain' is to be understood as a convenient way of saying that there is a probability as near as we like to 1. And it is important to notice that we are talking about the relative frequency of β things, not about the absolute β-content. If I make ten tosses of a penny, the most probable number of heads in my series of trials is five, but there may easily be an absolute deviation of one from that number, i.e. I may easily get four heads and six tails or six heads and four tails. This corresponds to a relative deviation (i.e. a deviation of the frequency from its most probable value) of $\frac{1}{10}$. When I say that this may easily happen, I mean that the probability for it is appreciable. As I increase the number of my tosses, the probability of an absolute deviation of at least one increases. A distribution of at least 51 heads among 100 tosses is, for example, more probable than a distribution of at least 6 heads among 10 tosses. But the probability of a relative deviation of at least $\frac{1}{10}$ sinks rapidly. In short, it is much less likely that I shall get an absolute deviation of at least 10 in 100 tosses than that I shall get an absolute deviation of at least 1 in 10 tosses. This is the gist of Bernoulli's theorem.

Unfortunately there are widespread misconceptions about the theorem. Many people who have heard of it under the name of the law of large numbers, given to it by Poisson, suppose it to be a mysterious law of nature which guarantees that in a sufficiently large number of trials a probability will be 'realized as a frequency'. That this is a misconception I need hardly state. Bernoulli's theorem, like all other theorems in the calculus of chances, allows us only to derive one probability from another. It cannot provide a bridge from probability to certainty. On the other hand what it does state it states as a mathematical necessity, and it is therefore both useless and absurd to try to verify Bernoulli's theorem by any number of tosses of coins. It is as silly to think that Bernoulli's theorem needs verification by experiment as it is to suppose that the proposition that $7+5 = 12$ needs such verification. If we make a million tosses with a coin which we suppose to be truly balanced and get approximately half heads, we should not allow ourselves to be amazed and say 'What a wonderful thing chance is!' Indeed, if we get heads in exactly half of our tosses, we should reflect that this is the most probable single distribution in the light of the assumption we have made about the coin although not perhaps very probable. On the other hand, if we get a proportion of heads which differs considerably from one-half, we should not say that at last we have disproved Bernoulli's theorem. For any distribution of heads from nought to a million is possible. If, however, the distribution which we find is one which would be very improbable on the supposition that the coin was evenly balanced, we may reasonably suspect that hypothesis to be false.

A misunderstanding of Bernoulli's theorem is responsible for one of the commonest fallacies in the estimation of probabilities, the fallacy of the maturity of the chances. When a coin has come down heads twice in succession, gamblers sometimes say that it is more likely to come down tails next time because 'by the law of averages' (whatever that may mean) the proportion of tails must be brought right some time. There is no ground whatsoever for this view. The only ground we have for expecting one frequency of heads rather than another is Bernoulli's theorem, and it is a condition for the correct application of this that the several trials should be without influence on each other. It is absurd to try to prove that the probability of a coin's coming down tails is greater than $\frac{1}{2}$ by use of an argument which starts with the assumption that the probability is $\frac{1}{2}$ each time. There is therefore a fundamental mistake in all gambling systems such as that of betting on black at roulette after red has won twice. In a genuine game of chance there can be no system for improving one's chances of winning. That is part of what we mean by calling it a game of chance.

As an illustration of the importance of the law of large numbers in practical affairs it will be sufficient to mention the business of insurance. Let us suppose that the probability that a man of a certain age and constitution will die within a year is $\frac{1}{10}$. If such an individual considers insuring his life, this is the fraction which he should bear in mind and use in making his decision. But the insurance company which offers to cover the risk of his dying within the year considers another probability derived from this probability. If there are a great many people of the same characteristics insuring their lives with that company, there is a very high probability that the company will not have to pay claims on more than about one-tenth of the policies. If, therefore, the company charges in each case a premium of rather more than one-tenth of the amount of the policy, it is very likely that it will have enough over after all claims are paid to meet its administrative expenses and distribute a dividend to its shareholders. The greater the number of persons insuring with the company, the greater the probability that the company's finances will remain sound, provided always that its premiums are calculated in the way described. This is the all-important consideration which distinguishes the business of an insurance company from gambling.

Bernoulli's theorem has also important applications in science, and here we may take as an example the kinetic theory of gases. According to the hypothesis on which this theory is based a volume of gas consists of a very great number of molecules moving about in various directions and colliding from time to time with each other and with the walls of their container. If we ask what is the probability of a molecule's being in motion towards the right of a certain plane at a certain instant, it seems natural to answer that the probability is $\frac{1}{2}$, whatever the plane and whatever the instant. But, given this assumption, it is very probable indeed that the partition of molecules according to direction of motion will be almost uniform at any time. It is in this way that physicists explain the uniformity of pressure which a gas exerts on the walls of its container, e.g. in a soap bubble. The theory is especially interesting because it involves the explanation of large-scale uniformity by small-scale disorder. A generalization which we were disposed to take as a law of necessitation is now treated as a probability rule in which the probability is very near to 1. This probability rule is itself derived according to Bernoulli's theorem from the random behaviour ascribed to molecules in the transcendent hypothesis at the foundation of the theory.

§ 30. POINCARÉ'S EQUALIZATION THEOREMS

Two other limit theorems of great interest have been formulated by Poincaré.[1] They are both concerned with special conditions which ensure that certain derivative probabilities shall tend towards equality, and they can be explained most easily by means of simple examples in which these conditions are fulfilled.

Let us suppose first that we have an apparatus somewhat like a roulette in which a pointer is made to spin over a circle divided into variously coloured sectors, and that it is required to find the probability of the pointer's stopping within a given sector. Clearly the precise stopping-place of the pointer depends on the total length of its spin. Expressed in radians, this variable x may have any value from 0 up to some maximum m. Within each of the intervals of length 2π into which the total variation may be divided there is a stretch favourable to the pointer's stopping within the given sector; for the pointer may stop there on the first round or on the second round, and so on. The probability of the pointer's stopping within the given sector is therefore equal to the sum of the probabilities for values of x within these stretches. If we knew that the value of x was as likely to lie in any part of the variation from 0 to m as in any other part of equal size, we could infer immediately that the required probability was equal to the ratio of the sum of the favourable stretches to the whole variation, and so approximately equal to the ratio of the given sector to the whole circle. For although m need not be an exact multiple of 2π, it is presumably so large in relation to 2π that its difference from an exact multiple can be neglected. But we are not entitled to assume that the value of x is as likely to lie in any part of the variation as in any other part of equal size. It may perhaps be more probable that x has some value in a middle stretch of the variation than that it has a value in a stretch of equal length at either end. How should we proceed?

Whatever the distribution may be in detail, it seems reasonable to assume that the probability of the pointer's going through a total spin of *not more than* x is some continuous analytic function of x. Let us call this function $f(x)$ and its derivative function (or

[1] *Science et méthode*, p. 78.

rate of change with respect to x) $f'(x)$. The probability of a value of x between a and b is then

$$\int_a^b f'(x)\,dx = f(b) - f(a).$$

This is represented in the accompanying figure by the shaded area

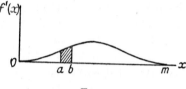

FIG. 3

under the curve between the ordinates at a and b. Now, according to the definition of the derivative function,

$$\lim_{h \to 0} \frac{f(a+h) - f(a)}{h} = f'(a),$$

and when a is fixed, $f'(a)$ is also fixed, being the height of the ordinate to the curve at a. In other words, the smaller the stretch we choose in the neighbourhood of a, the more nearly proportional to the length of the stretch will be the probability for a value of x within that stretch. Although, therefore, we cannot say that the probability for a value of x within any given stretch of the variation is equal to the probability for a value within any other stretch of equal size, we can say that the probability for a value of x within a given stretch must be approximately the same as the probabilities for values of x within other stretches of the same size which together with the first make up a very small part of the total variation of x. This follows from the single hypothesis that $f(x)$ is a continuous analytic function. It is, indeed, intuitively obvious from consideration of the accompanying figure. Whatever the shape of the curve may be, if a and b are sufficiently close together, the ordinate from a point midway between them will inevitably divide the shaded area into approximately equal parts. It is to be assumed, however, that m is large in relation to 2π, i.e. that the stretch of the variation of x corresponding to a single rotation of the pointer is small in relation to the whole. We are therefore entitled to say that if the pointer stops on the first round the probability of its stopping within the given sector is approximately equal to the ratio of the sector to the whole circle; and so on for each other round. From this it follows, as before, that the probability of the pointer's stopping in the given sector on some round or other is approximately equal to the ratio of the sector to the whole circle, although it may perhaps be more likely that the pointer will stop in its seventh round than that it will stop in its first.

To illustrate Poincaré's second argument let us suppose that a man takes a pair of cards and shuffles them repeatedly. Each single shuffle consists of several transpositions made in rapid succession. If it leaves the cards as they were at the beginning (of that shuffle), it is conservative; if it leaves them in the inverse order, it is radical. Whether a shuffle is conservative or radical depends, of course, on the number of transpositions of which it consists, but it is to be assumed that both possibilities are open. We can only say that the habits of the shuffler give some probability c for a shuffle's being conservative and some probability r for its being radical. Obviously $c + r = 1$, but we do not know the value of either. We have now to consider what happens when n, the number of shuffles, is large. According to a formula proved in an earlier section, the probability that a set of n shuffles will contain just m radical shuffles is $^nC_m c^{n-m} r^m$. Now the order of the cards will be inverted at the end of m shuffles if, and only if, m is an odd number; for conservative shuffles make no difference and two successive radical shuffles cancel each other out. The probability that the cards will be in the original order at the end of the whole process is therefore

$$c^n + {}^nC_2 c^{n-2} r^2 + {}^nC_4 c^{n-4} r^4 + \dots,$$

and the probability that their order will be inverted is

$$nc^{n-1} r + {}^nC_3 c^{n-3} r^3 + {}^nC_5 c^{n-5} r^5 + \dots.$$

The difference between these two probabilities is

$$c^n - nc^{n-1} r + {}^nC_2 c^{n-2} r^2 - {}^nC_3 c^{n-3} r^3 + \dots = (c-r)^n.$$

But $|c-r| < 1$, whatever the values of c and r may be, and $(c-r)^n$ must therefore tend towards o as n increases without limit. In other words, the longer the process of shuffling is continued, the more nearly equal become the probabilities for the two possible results.

When we try to construct a similar argument about the repeated shuffling of three cards, we find that the situation is already much more complicated. We have now to consider six different types of shuffle, one of them conservative and five radical in different ways, and we must suppose that each has its own probability. But it is not difficult to see that the same principle applies. Whatever the number of the cards may be, repeated shuffling will make the probabilities for the various possible arrangements of them approximately equal. The only condition is that no conceivable type of shuffle should be absolutely impossible.

Each of Poincaré's arguments proves that certain derivative probabilities tend towards equality, whatever may be the value of certain original probabilities, provided only that these satisfy some very general conditions. The two conclusions are both limit theorems, and might properly be called laws of large numbers. In the first the result depends on the division of the variation of a variable into very many small parts; in the second the most important point is that a mixing procedure is repeated very many times. Although they have not the generality of the theorems treated in earlier sections, their application is not limited to the cases which have been used to illustrate them. Poincaré pointed out, for example, that the first theorem might be used to explain the distribution of stars in the Milky Way and the second to explain the distribution of molecules of different velocity in a gas. He suggested, indeed, that whenever we speak of chance we have in mind one or other of the situations with which the two theorems deal. For, according to his view, the statement that certain events happen by chance means that their causes are either very small or very complex. I do not think that this is a satisfactory definition; but it draws attention to a very important class of cases in which we use the language of chance.

In general, when we say that it is a matter of chance whether an α thing is β, we mean that α-ness neither necessitates nor excludes β-ness; and it may be we have no information about the situation beyond the fact that some α things have been β and some not. But sometimes when we use this phrase we think that we can guess, at least in outline, the type of determination involved in a case where an α thing turns out to be β. We may assume that α-ness covers a very large range of variation some small parts of which necessitate β-ness according to laws of a kind already familiar; then we suppose the situation to be like that considered in our roulette example. Or we may assume that α-ness covers many different possible complexes of factors some of which involve β-ness according to laws of a kind already familiar; then we suppose the situation to be like that considered in our example of shuffling. If we could cope with the minuteness and complexity of the factors assumed to be at work, we should formulate many special laws to the effect that all $\alpha\gamma$ things are β, no $\alpha\delta$ things are β, and so on. Having established these by induction, we should rarely need to make use of a rule about the probability of an α thing's being β. But our powers of analysis are limited, and so we do the best we can by using our general conjectures about the situation to justify a conclusion about the approximation of certain chances to equality. It is a mistake, however, to suppose that all the situations in which we may properly speak of chance are like this, and a still greater mistake to try to define chance by reference to the minuteness or the complexity of causes. Poincaré's theorems are remarkable in that they produce interesting consequences from very meagre postulates, but it must be remembered that, like all other theorems in the calculus of chances, they are hypothetical propositions. When we assume that the probability of a pointer's spinning for an angular distance not more than x is a continuous analytic function of x, we make an hypothesis, though only a little one. But to make an hypothesis of this sort we must already have given some meaning to the phrase 'probability in matters of chance' and so to the word 'chance' itself.

Poincaré's suggestion about the meaning of 'chance' seems plausible because the general use of the word is derived from its use in connexion with games of chance, which usually conform to one or other of his two patterns. But this conformity is not surprising. When men wish to gamble they find apparatus like roulette wheels, well-shuffled packs of cards, and dice especially interesting because it satisfies two conditions: (a) none of the players can hope to gain any advantage from special information about the apparatus, and (b) it is nevertheless possible to form conjectures of probability which may be called relatively *a priori*. I do not wish to suggest that the men who first selected such apparatus had in mind all the considerations set out by Poincaré, but I think his theorems make explicit something which had been dimly recognized long before. When we play with a spinning pointer, we all assume that the equality of the chances of its stopping in various equal sectors depends on the possibility of the pointer's spinning for a longish time. If the pointer were an enormously heavy object which could be pushed only a little way by great effort, or if its bearing had been smeared thoroughly with treacle, we might suppose that it was almost certain to stop in the first half of the first round.

§ 31. EQUIPROBABILITY AND INDIFFERENCE

Most of the writers to whom we owe the development of the calculus of chances held a subjectivist theory of probability. The general objections to any such theory have already been stated, but for an understanding of the history of thought about the subject we must consider how these older writers tried to estimate probabilities.

We have seen that the calculus of chances began with discussions about problems in games of chance and that it was natural for mathematicians to pay special attention to equiprobable alternatives when trying to solve such problems. Now anyone who holds a subjectivist theory of probability must try to explain equiprobability by reference to states of mind. And so we find Bernoulli writing in his *Ars Conjectandi* that of the tickets in a lottery any one is as likely to be drawn as any other 'quia nulla perspicitur ratio cur haec vel illa potius exire debeat quam quaelibet alia'.[1] This is the origin of the famous, or infamous, principle of indifference, according to which alternatives of any kind are equally probable if no reason is known for asserting one rather than another. By older writers the rule was commonly called the principle of insufficient reason, perhaps to suggest some contrast with Leibniz's principle of sufficient reason, but I shall adopt the shorter and more descriptive title introduced by Lord Keynes.

It is easy to show that the principle leads to absurdities. It is supposed to justify the assertion that the probability of a die's falling with the number one uppermost is $\frac{1}{6}$, but it could be used equally well to justify an assertion that the probability is $\frac{1}{2}$. For we may consider as our alternatives the two cases falling-with-the-number-one-uppermost and falling-with-some-other-number-uppermost; and, when our only information is that a die has been thrown, we may say that we know of no reason to assert either of these alternatives rather than the other. From this it should follow that their probabilities are each equal to $\frac{1}{2}$. A precisely similar argument can, of course, be constructed to show that the probability of a die's falling with the number two uppermost is $\frac{1}{2}$, and so on for each of the six possible results, which is absurd. I

[1] Part IV, ch. iv, p. 224.

have deliberately chosen a very simple example to show the in-
adequacy of the principle. Examples of which the absurdity is
less obvious may be found in the chapter which Lord Keynes
devotes to the subject, but it is unnecessary to consider them in
detail. Although the example I have constructed is patently
absurd, it is no more ludicrous than some assertions which have
actually been made by upholders of the principle. It has been
said, for example, in all seriousness that if we know of any proposition only that it may or may not be true we are to take its
probability as $\frac{1}{2}$ because this is in accordance with the equal
distribution of our ignorance between the alternatives.[1] This
statement is in effect a generalization of the absurdity discussed
above.

It is clear that mathematicians and philosophers who professed
to use the principle of indifference for finding equiprobable cases
and so for measuring probabilities must have used some other
principle or principles when they reached results which seem plausible, and many attempts have been made by writers such as
von Kries[2] and Lord Keynes to supply qualifications or additional
requirements which will allow for the determination of probabilities *a priori*.

It has been suggested, for example, that the alternatives to
which the principle of indifference is to be applied must first be
known to be equispecific, i.e. that they should be co-ordinate
alternatives according to some one principle of division. This
condition would undoubtedly save us from some of the paradoxes,
for one of the defects of the crude form of the principle of indifference is that the alternatives which it contemplates need not be
co-ordinate in any way except as being all alike possible. We shall
obviously fall into absurdity if we take being β and being not-β as
our alternatives merely because they are both alike possible attributes for an α thing, although being not-β may cover a multitude of
cases each of which could have been considered as an alternative
to being β. In the paradox about dicing to which I have referred
the alternative of falling with some number other than one uppermost is really a disjunction of cases each of which can be considered as an alternative to falling with the number one uppermost.
The requirement that the alternatives for consideration should be
equispecific would, therefore, rule out some absurd arguments; but

---

[1] W. S. Jevons, *Principles of Science*, p. 212.
[2] *Principien der Wahrscheinlichkeitsrechnung*, 1886.

it does not provide an infallible test by which we can recognize equiprobable cases *a priori*. Let us suppose that we have to deal with a die that is loaded—that is to say, one in which a little piece of lead has been inserted in such a way as to shift the centre of gravity from the geometrical centre of the cube towards that side which is farthest from the number six. Everyone agrees that the probability of such a die's falling with the number six uppermost is greater than $\frac{1}{6}$. But if we try to discover the exact value of this probability, what are the equispecific alternatives to consider? Surely the alternatives of falling with one uppermost, falling with two uppermost, &c., are just as much equispecific alternatives for a loaded die as for an ordinary die, and yet we now refuse to call them equiprobable. No doubt considerations of symmetry may be brought in to explain why we accept the alternatives as equiprobable in the one case and not in the other, but it is not necessary to carry the argument farther here.

The important point to recognize is that any additional requirements which we may introduce in this way are not mere modifications of the principle of indifference, but radically new conditions. That principle, which purports to provide a rule for the determination of probabilities *a priori* from the consideration of our own ignorance, must be rejected entirely. Probability statements may be modest assertions, but even so they cannot be justified by mere ignorance.

In rejecting the principle of indifference we need not reject the suggestion that the measure of probability is to be defined by reference to equiprobable alternatives. They have been confused together in the past because the writers who first talked of equiprobable cases were unable to free themselves from subjectivism and added to their account of the measure of probability an unsatisfactory explanation of probability itself in subjectivist terms. If, however, we are to make any use of the notion of equiprobability, we must distinguish between the definition of the measure of probability and the giving of a rule for the determination of probabilities. James Bernoulli, Laplace, and their followers failed to make the distinction, because they started with the prejudice that probability statements must be concerned in some way with our minds and concluded that such statements should therefore be capable of verification in a direct fashion. Further analysis may show that, while we can define the measure of numerical probabilities by reference to equiprobable alternatives, we cannot hope to determine by inspection what alternatives are equiprobable unless certain special conditions are fulfilled. If this is indeed the real situation, we shall have to admit that the value of an expression of the form $P(\alpha, \beta)$ may sometimes be unknown to us and even unknowable. Laplace himself talked sometimes of unknown probabilities whose values we can only conjecture from empirical evidence; but he did not realize that in order to work out this theory consistently he should have rejected the principle of indifference and given a definition of probability free from all traces of subjectivism.

Before going on to consider further how equiprobability is to be analysed it will be convenient to examine the rival definition of probability by reference to frequency. We shall then be able to understand more clearly what are the issues involved in philosophical discussions about probability.

§ 32. THE FREQUENCY THEORY OF PROBABILITY

The first explicit formulation of the frequency theory of probability is to be found in some casual remarks of Aristotle to the effect that the probable is what usually happens.[1] But there was no serious attempt to work out his theory in detail until last century, and then it was put forward in opposition to the indifference theory. R. L. Ellis suggested it in some papers published in the forties of last century, and Venn expounded it at length in his *Logic of Chance*, published in 1866. There are also some interesting discussions to be found in the *Collected Papers* of C. S. Peirce, who wrote in the eighties and nineties of last century. Some of the earlier upholders of the theory thought it necessary to reject the calculus of chances as worked out by James Bernoulli and other mathematicians of the eighteenth century, because the calculus had been presented in connexion with the indifference theory.[2] But more recent defenders of the frequency definition try to show that they are as much entitled as anyone else to make use of the theorems of the calculus, since these remain true when interpreted according to the frequency definition.

All upholders of the frequency theory agree in condemning the subjectivism of older writers such as Laplace. In particular they object to the claim of Laplace and his followers to derive interesting

---

[1] *Prior Analytics*, 70ª3 and *Rhetoric*, 1357ª34.
[2] See, for example, Venn's *Logic of Chance*, p. 91.

and important results from a recognition of the equal distribution of their own ignorance. Ellis writes: 'Mere ignorance is no ground for any inference whatsoever: *ex nihilo nihil.*'[1] They sometimes admit that from consideration of sets of alternatives whose equiprobability is supposed to be given it may be possible to work out other probabilities. But they say it is a mistake to suppose that we have any special facilities for finding equiprobable alternatives. The indifference criterion for determining probabilities seems plausible, they argue, only because in discussions of probability we often concentrate our attention on examples taken from games of chance, where certain alternatives are always assumed to be equiprobable. But even in games of chance we do not know *a priori* that the various alternatives are equiprobable. The principle of indifference is quite useless as an explanation of our judgements of equiprobability. The real basis for a judgement that certain alternatives are equiprobable is the empirical fact that they turn up with approximately equal frequencies. Indeed, this is all that we can mean when we say that they are equiprobable. Therefore we might as well begin by defining probability in terms of frequency. This is, in brief, the argument of the frequency theorists. They profess to offer a theory according to which probability is something objective about which we may hope to learn from experience. Let us see how they work out their suggestion.

The frequency theory begins with an attempt to conceive the probability of an α thing's being β as the *proportion* of α things which are β, and it must be admitted that this suggestion has an air of plausibility. In ordinary life we often make statements such as 'Most men are honest' or 'Thunder is usually followed by rain', when our intention is to enunciate probability rules, and in scientific contexts we sometimes use this pattern for precise quantitative statements. The sentence 'Four-fifths of the patients treated with this drug recover' is regarded, for example, as an assertion that a patient treated with the drug has four chances in five of recovery. For philosophers who follow Hume the view that probability rules have to do with proportions of instances has a special attraction because of its obvious resemblance to the constancy theory of natural laws. There are, nevertheless, insuperable objections to saying that the probability of an α thing's being β is just the proportion of α things which are β.

If α is a restricted description (i.e. if the class of α things can

[1] *Mathematical and Other Writings*, p. 57.

have only a finite number of members), the proposed definition makes quite good sense. We can then write:

$$P(\alpha, \beta) = \frac{N(\alpha\beta)}{N(\alpha)},$$

where $N(\alpha)$ signifies the number of α things and $N(\alpha\beta)$ the number of things which are both α and β. Indeed, for this case the equation just stated is undisputed. In practice all writers on the theory of probability assume its validity when they deal with problems about finite populations. They say, for example, that if a bag contains w white balls and b black balls the probability of drawing a white ball from the bag is $w/(w+b)$. But such a simple version of the frequency theory is plainly untenable when we have to do with probability rules stated by the use of unrestricted descriptions. For we cannot then say that the total of α things is finite, and it is senseless to speak of a fraction with infinity as denominator. How, then, are we to understand the word 'frequency' in this context? We can still speak of the proportion of α things which are β in some finite sample of α things, and we may, if we like, call this the *relative frequency*; but we certainly cannot assert that it is identical by definition with the probability of an α thing's being β, for different relative frequencies may be found in different samples. In one set of ten tosses of a coin the relative frequency of heads may be equal to $\frac{4}{10}$, whereas in another set of ten tosses it is equal to $\frac{6}{10}$. And if two sets of α things have different numbers of members, it may even be impossible that they should exhibit the same relative frequency of β things. Thus we may get a relative frequency of heads equal to $\frac{1}{2}$ in an even number of tosses, but we cannot possibly get this in an odd number of tosses. There is, in short, no fraction which we can call *the* frequency of heads found in all the various sets of tosses of a coin. Frequency theorists usually try to get out of these difficulties by talking about what happens in the long run, i.e. if we go on increasing the size of our sample. Unfortunately the writers of the last century who put forward this suggestion did not explain it very clearly, and Lord Keynes, writing in 1921, regretted that he could find no careful statement of the frequency theory on which to base his criticism. This gap has now been filled by R. von Mises, and I shall take his account as the best modern presentation of the frequency theory.[1]

[1] The most readily available statement of his views is to be found in his book *Probability, Statistics and Truth* (W. Hodge, 1939). This work was first published in German in 1928.

In order to understand the doctrine of von Mises we must begin by assuming that the open class of α things with which we have to do can be treated as an infinite succession. Apparently it is not essential that the α things considered should be events in fixed temporal order, such as the tosses of a coin; but, if they are not, it is most natural to think of their ordering as introduced by successive acts of observation, and von Mises often uses phraseology which implies this conception. We must next suppose that after inspecting each α thing we write down the proportion of α things which have turned out to be β in the course of our investigation up to date. In this way we can obtain a sequence of fractions of relative frequency which may be represented by the expressions $F_1(\alpha, \beta), F_2(\alpha, \beta)$, &c. For a reason which I have already explained these fractions will differ among themselves. $F_2(\alpha, \beta)$ may be $\frac{1}{2}$, but, if it is, $F_3(\alpha, \beta)$ must be either $\frac{1}{3}$ or $\frac{2}{3}$. The results may be tabulated as follows:

Number (n) of trial	1	2	3	4	5	6	7	8	...
Result of trial	$\sim\beta$	β	β	$\sim\beta$	β	β	β	$\sim\beta$	...
$F_n(\alpha, \beta)$	$\frac{0}{1}$	$\frac{1}{2}$	$\frac{2}{3}$	$\frac{2}{4}$	$\frac{3}{5}$	$\frac{4}{6}$	$\frac{5}{7}$	$\frac{5}{8}$	...

Since the succession of α things is assumed to be unlimited, it is to be supposed also that the sequence of fractions of relative frequency can be treated as infinite, although any part of the sequence which we tabulate must naturally be finite. Now according to von Mises it may happen that such an infinite sequence converges towards a limiting value, say p. If this appears to be the case, it is natural to ask whether the convergence depends on the order in which our α things are presented for observation. It might be, for example, that the infinite sequence of fractions converged to p because every third item in our succession of α things was β while all the rest were not-β. We should then say that our succession of α things and the sequence of fractions derived from it were both regular, i.e. constructed according to a rule, or, in other words, that it was not a matter of chance whether an item occurring in the succession after two not-β things was itself β. Since von Mises professes to be dealing only with matters of chance, he naturally wishes to exclude from consideration all successions which are regular in the sense just explained, and this he does by laying down a condition of irregularity or randomness. Given that the infinite sequence of fractions of relative frequency derived from our original succession converges to a limit, we may say that the succession is random if an infinite sequence of fractions tending to the same limit can be obtained from any partial succession determined by place selection, i.e. from any succession consisting of all the α things whose place numbers in the original succession satisfy some general condition, however fantastic, e.g. that of being divisible by three or that of being prime or that of ending (in the decimal notation) with the same digit as the number of hairs on the head of the Archbishop of Canterbury. A gambler who adopts a system, such as that of betting on red at roulette whenever black has won twice running, may be supposed to believe that he has found a partial succession in which the limiting value for the relative frequency of some attribute is more favourable to himself than that in the original succession; and for this reason von Mises sometimes calls his requirement of randomness 'the principle of the impossibility of gambling systems'.

It is important to notice that this definition of randomness depends on place selection, not on selection by attributes. If we are allowed to form a partial succession by selecting α things for some attribute independent of place, we may very well succeed in forming one in which the limiting value for the relative frequency of β things is different from that in the original succession. We may, for example, select only α things which are already found to be β. Nor is it sufficient, as von Mises suggests in one passage,[1] to say that the question whether a certain member of the original succession belongs to a selected partial succession must be settled independently of the result of the corresponding observation. For when we are forbidden to consider the results of observations before making our selection, we may still succeed in forming a partial succession in which the limiting value for the relative frequency of β things is different from that in the original succession, if only we can find some attribute, say γ-ness, which, with α-ness given, is relevant to β-ness, whether favourably or unfavourably.

If the class of α things satisfies the conditions described in the preceding paragraphs, it is called by von Mises a *collective*, and the probability of an α thing's being β is defined as the limit of the infinite sequence of fractions of relative frequency derived from the collective. In the symbolism explained above his definition may be expressed by the equation:

$$P(\alpha, \beta) = \lim_{n \to \infty} F_n(\alpha, \beta),$$

[1] *P., S., and T.*, p. 33.

provided that the class of α things is understood to be a collective. He has summarized his doctrine as follows:

'It is possible to speak about probabilities only in reference to a properly defined collective. A collective means a mass phenomenon or an unlimited sequence of observations fulfilling the following two conditions: (i) the relative frequencies of particular attributes of single elements of the collective tend to fixed limits; (ii) these limits are not affected by any place selection. . . . The limiting value of the relative frequency of a given attribute, assumed to be independent of any place selection, will be called "the probability of that attribute within the given collective". Whenever this qualification of the word "probability" is omitted, this should be accepted as an abbreviation and the necessity for reference to some collective must be strictly kept in mind.'[1]

The use of the word 'collective' here is apparently intended to suggest that the existence of a certain probability of β-ness (in the sense defined) is a property of the open class of α things considered collectively. Within this scheme all the usual theorems of the calculus of chances can be proved, but they have, of course, a new sense corresponding to the new definition of probability.

The most important novelty in the theory of von Mises is the bringing together of the two notions of convergence and irregularity in his definition of a collective. Both notions had been used by earlier frequency theorists such as Venn, but von Mises was the first to realize the need for working out the relation between them, and I think he is justified in maintaining that there can be no plausible frequency theory which is radically different from his doctrine of collectives. In particular, attempts to simplify his theory, either by abandoning the notion of convergence to a limit or by weakening his requirement of randomness, seemed doomed to failure.[2] The result of his innovation, however, is a very great

---

[1] *P., S., and T.*, p. 38. In my own exposition I have spoken of a succession, rather than of a sequence, of observations, because it seems desirable to reserve the technical term of mathematics for talking about the fractions of relative frequency.

[2] See *P., S., and T.*, pp. 120–54. In *Logik der Forschung* (not discussed in detail by von Mises) K. Popper has suggested that the probability of an α thing's being β should be defined as the sole fraction which is (i) a point of accumulation of the relative frequencies of β things among the α things, and (ii) insensitive to certain kinds of place selection, if there is only one such fraction. But the kinds of place selection which he allows are not sufficient to give full randomness, and it seems that, if he tried to provide this, his definition would become indistinguishable from that of von Mises. For where there is only one point of accumulation, this is also a limit, and the distinction of Popper's definition from that of von Mises is proved only by the *construction* of a sequence which, although not

departure, not only from the simple doctrine of proportions with which we started, but also from accepted mathematical views about infinite sequences.

In order to understand how far removed the theory of von Mises is from a simple doctrine of proportions we must first get clear what it means to say that an infinite sequence is convergent. In popular language, the farther we go along a convergent sequence, the less the terms fluctuate. More precisely, an infinite sequence of fractions F_1, F_2, F_3, &c., may be said to converge to a limit p, if for any number h, however small, there is some term of the sequence, say the nth, after which all the terms are within h of p. This is a triply general proposition (universal, existential, and universal), as may be seen most easily from the presentation of it in the special symbolism of logic:

$$(h)(\exists n)(r) \, . \, r > n \supset |F_r - p| < h.$$

Let us now consider a special case within the theory of von Mises. According to his definition of probability, if we say that $P(\alpha, \beta) = 1$, we mean only that all sequences of the form $F_1(\alpha, \beta)$, $F_2(\alpha, \beta)$, $F_3(\alpha, \beta)$, &c., which are derived in a permissible way from the collective of α things converge to p as a limit. This condition can be fulfilled although infinitely many α things are not β. If, for example, we suppose that a partial succession from which a sequence is derived contains just one α thing which is not β, it is obvious that the existence of this solitary item will not prevent the derived sequence from converging to 1 in the manner just explained. But by successive applications of the procedure of place selection it is possible to obtain from a collective infinitely many partial successions which have no members in common, and so a collective of α things in which there is a probability of 1 for β-ness may nevertheless contain infinitely many α things which are not β. A definition of probability which entails this conclusion is at least mildly paradoxical, because it has been commonly assumed that assertion of a probability of 1 is equivalent to assertion of a law which admits no exceptions. The point has not been sufficiently noticed either by the modern frequency theorists or by their critics.[1] But many frequency theorists like to argue that their doctrine accords well with the rejection of determinism

convergent to a limit, has a sole point of accumulation insensitive to *his kinds* of place selection.

[1] It is noticed by G. H. von Wright in his *Logical Problem of Induction*, p. 14 (Acta Philosophica Fennica, Fasc. III, 1941).

supposed to be involved in the quantum theory, and these might perhaps say that they are content to treat all so-called laws as propositions to the effect that certain relative frequencies tend towards 1. I shall return to this question later. For the moment I wish only to make clear that in its modern form the frequency theory is far removed from primitive simplicity.

On the other hand, the attempt to combine convergence with irregularity involves a revolutionary use of mathematical terminology. For the pure mathematician the notion of convergence is applicable only to infinite sequences constructed according to rule, e.g. the sequence $\frac{1}{2}$, $\frac{1}{4}$, $\frac{1}{8}$, &c. When he says that an infinite sequence is convergent, he means that it follows from the rule of the construction of the sequence that, however small an interval we like to take, all the terms of the sequence after a certain term will presently keep within that interval of the limit. He claims to talk about infinity just because he knows the rule according to which the terms succeed each other. Indeed, it has been said by many mathematicians that to talk about an infinite sequence is the same thing as to talk about the rule of construction by which its terms can be calculated. The sequences which interest von Mises are, however, of a very different kind, as he himself insists. They are ruleless sequences, in which it is impossible to calculate the terms in advance from any general formula and impossible to prove *a priori* that they converge to a limit. It is true that in any of his sequences each term has a denominator greater by one than the denominator of its predecessor, but it is a matter of chance whether the numerator of a term is the same as that of its predecessor or greater by one. In pure mathematics, again, the language of infinity is required only in contexts where we speak of the *possibility* of repeating a procedure *ad infinitum*. Since this intensional notion is unsuitable for his purpose, von Mises has, in effect, adopted an extensional theory according to which a collective is an *actually* infinite aggregate of independent items. If there is a collective from which a convergent infinite sequence of fractions of relative frequency can be derived, its existence is a merely contingent truth, a matter of fact.

Sometimes defenders of the frequency theory say that in speaking thus of collectives they are only following the normal scientific procedure of idealizing what is found in experience.[1] I am not

---

[1] e.g. Lindsay and Margenau, *The Foundations of Physics*, pp. 163–7. Cf. von Mises, *P., S., and T.*, p. 124.

sure what they intend to convey by this remark. If they mean that the passage from finite to infinite successions is something like the passage from figures roughly drawn on a blackboard to figures as they are considered in geometry, I do not think the analogy is at all helpful. It is true that the conceptions of point, line, plane, &c., with which we work in geometry have been suggested by features of experience; but within a system of geometry the meanings of words such as 'point', 'line', and 'plane' are determined by the postulates in which the words occur, and it is no objection to the correctness of a geometrical system that it cannot be applied to experience. In the theory of probability, on the other hand, the business of the philosopher is not to construct a formal system with consistency and elegance for his only guides. His task is to clarify the meaning of probability statements made by plain men, and the frequency theory must be judged as an attempt to carry out this undertaking.[1] If, again, those who speak of idealization mean that the role of collectives in the theory of probability is something like the role of punctiform bodies or frictionless machines in mechanics, their suggestion is no better than that we have just considered. The fictions of mechanics are products of abstraction. With their help scientists are able to simplify the problems posed by experience and so to work out theories of great generality which can later be corrected as necessary for application to the real world. No one wishes to assert that punctiform bodies and frictionless machines exist in nature. The notion of a collective, on the other hand, is made by adding freely in thought to the data of experience (i.e. by the passage from finite to infinite successions); and the peculiarity of the modern frequency theory is that it requires us to assert the existence of collectives whenever we talk about probabilities.

I suspect, however, that those who use the word 'idealization' in this connexion have not thought out very carefully the analogy they wish to draw. Their chief intention may be to apologize for the use of phraseology which they do not take quite seriously. There are undoubtedly many philosophers and scientists who would like to define probability by reference to frequency, but hesitate to commit themselves to the developed theory of von Mises. Although these persons may use the terminology of the theory, they do so with mental reservations. But their

[1] Cf. F. Waismann, 'Die Logische Analyse des Wahrscheinlichkeitsbegriffes', in *Erkenntnis*, i, 1930, p. 233.

position is unsatisfactory. Until some fully reasoned alternative is presented, we must assume that the frequency theory involves the doctrine of collectives precisely as von Mises says it does.

One consequence of the combination of convergence and irregularity in the frequency theory of probability is that probability statements interpreted according to this theory must be both unverifiable and unfalsifiable. They cannot be verified *a priori*, because they refer to irregular sequences; and they cannot be verified *a posteriori*, because they refer to infinite sequences. Similarly they cannot be falsified in any way, because from consideration of a finite stretch, however long, we can never infer with certainty that an infinite but irregular sequence will not converge to some fixed limit. In this respect the frequency theory is no worse than any other theory of probability. For, whatever our theory may be, we must admit that we cannot provide a decisive test of the hypotheses we consider when trying to estimate probabilities from statistics. If we could settle the truth of these hypotheses *a priori*, we should obviously not trouble ourselves with statistics; but when we do use statistics, we must remember that any hypothesis about the probability of an α thing's being β (other than an hypothesis of law) is compatible with any distribution of β things among the α things we observe. This is a reflection which should disturb none but the most simple-minded positivist who believes that every significant statement can be decisively tested. On the other hand, it is important to realize that the frequency theory is no better than any other in this respect. For many of its defenders have claimed that it is more empirical than other theories, and they seem to mean by this that probability statements which are interpreted according to their theory can be tested by experience in some way in which the probability statements of their opponents cannot be tested. This is an illusion. For any theory which is sufficiently developed to be worth discussion, the estimation of probabilities from consideration of statistics must raise problems at least as difficult as those involved in the establishment of natural laws by induction. It may be this point which von Mises has in mind when he writes:

'The results of a theory based on a notion of an infinite collective can be applied to finite sequences of observations in a way which is not logically definable, but nevertheless sufficiently exact in practice.

The relation of theory to observation is in this case essentially the same as in all other physical sciences.'[1]

An objection which seems at first sight more serious has been raised by some mathematicians who argue that the two requirements involved in the definition of a collective, namely, convergence and irregularity, are incompatible. Let us suppose that we have to deal with a sequence of fractions of relative frequency which is said to converge to p as a limit, and that we choose some very small number h. Then according to the definition of convergence there must be correlated with h some number n which is the ordinal number of a term in the sequence after which all the terms remain within h of p. Now this assertion, it is said, implies a restriction on the later terms of the sequence which is incompatible with the notion of chance. For, if it is a matter of chance whether an α thing is β, we can always imagine that in the succession of α things from which the sequence of fractions is derived there might be a run of β things (or not-β things, as the case may be) starting at the $(n+1)$th place and sufficiently long to take the relative frequency outside the prescribed interval. Indeed, since the frequency theory forbids us to assume that the truth of the assertion

$$P(\alpha, \beta) = p$$

depends on the ordering of the α things in our succession, there must be some probability, namely, p^s, which is greater than 0, for the occurrence of a run of length s even at the $(n+1)$th place.

This objection has been answered by von Mises, and his answer is interesting because it puts the essentials of his theory in a clear light. First we must understand that according to his doctrine infinitely many different successions may be derived from the collective of α things. The statement that $P(\alpha, \beta) = p$ means that in each of these successions the relative frequency of β things tends towards p. But we are not to suppose that in each of the successions it tends towards p at the same rate. More precisely, if we choose a small number h, we must not assume that, because in one sequence of relative frequencies all the terms after the nth keep within h of p, therefore the same critical number n will be correlated with h in all the other sequences. To assume this would be to assume regularity in our sequences, and that is forbidden. It is therefore quite possible for very long runs to begin at the

[1] *P., S., and T.*, p. 125. The passage quoted is based on an article by Hempel.

$(n+1)$th place in some of the successions without preventing the relative frequency in those successions from tending ultimately towards p. If we want to find the probability for a run of given length, say s, beginning at any place whatsoever, we must consider a new collective in which the items are not individual α things but groups of s α things. Such a collective may be represented by the scheme:

$$\{\alpha^{(1)}, \alpha^{(2)},..., \alpha^{(s)}\}, \quad \{\alpha^{(s+1)}, \alpha^{(s+2)},..., \alpha^{(2s)}\},$$
$$\{\alpha^{(2s+1)}, \alpha^{(2s+2)},..., \alpha^{(3s)}\}, \quad ...,$$

where $\alpha^{(1)}$, $\alpha^{(2)}$, &c., indicate individual α things and each complex enclosed by brackets indicates an item of the new collective. Some of these groups will consist entirely of α things which are also β, and it is possible to find the relative frequency of such groups in any finite stretch of the new collective. The probability of a run of s β things is just the limit towards which this relative frequency tends in the whole collective. But, when it is given that

$$P(\alpha, \beta) = p,$$

we can prove that $\qquad P(^\alpha\sigma_s, {}^\beta\kappa_s) = p^s$

without recourse to further counting, because the new collective, in which each item is an α-set of s members, has been constructed out of the old collective, in which each item was an individual α thing, and its properties depend on those of the old collective. The proof is not simple, but there can be no doubt of its validity within the assumptions of the doctrine of collectives.

§ 33. THE DEFECTS OF THE FREQUENCY THEORY

Whether it is permissible to speak of infinity in the way required by the theory of von Mises is a question still discussed by mathematicians. Von Mises claims that investigations by Copeland and Wald have furnished a complete proof of the consistency of the calculus built on his conception of a collective, and so dispelled all mathematical objections to the use of his principle of randomness.[1] I do not think the results to which he refers settle the question about infinity that puzzles critics of his theory. On the contrary, they seem to assume a settlement of the question in his favour. The fundamental problem is concerned with the meaning of 'existence' and 'constructibility' in mathematical contexts, and this is still a subject of debate among those interested in the foundations

[1] *P., S., and T.*, p. 142.

M

of mathematics. But it is not necessary to discuss these matters here. While a negative answer to the mathematical question would be fatal to the doctrine of collectives, an affirmative answer would not suffice to establish it as the correct basis for a theory of probability. And I wish to argue that, apart from any considerations about the legitimacy of the extensional notion of infinity, there are two good reasons for rejecting this account of probability.

In the first place, the theory of von Mises does not elucidate the conception of chance, but leads on the contrary to a very strange confusion between chance and law. We have seen already that according to his theory the probability of an α thing's being β may be 1 although infinitely many α things are not β. Let us now consider the situation in which all α things without exception are β, i.e. a situation which would ordinarily be described in the language of law. The class of α things is plainly a collective within the meaning of the theory. For the sequence of fractions of relative frequency of β things among the α things converges to 1, and this convergence is unaffected by any place selection whatsoever. We have therefore the same probability of β-ness in a collective which consists entirely of β things as in a collective which contains infinitely many not-β things. How should this curious conclusion affect our judgement on the theory? We may be inclined at first to suppose that we have discovered here a latent contradiction. But this is a mistake. The theory can never require us to assert that *both* possibilities are realized. The trouble is rather that it assimilates them under one formula in spite of a difference between them which scientific common sense considers very important. In his anxiety to exclude the kind of regularity assumed by inventors of gambling systems, von Mises has produced a definition of randomness which obliterates even Hume's distinction between law and chance.

To some supporters of the frequency theory this consideration may seem to be a recommendation rather than an objection. For it is often represented as one of the merits of the theory that it supplies a rational substructure for the indeterminist interpretation of quantum phenomena. I think this is an unfortunate line of argument. Although the frequency theory may enable us to dispense with the ordinary conception of law, it does so only by introducing laws of a new and very strange kind. According to the definition of von Mises, if we say that the probability of an α thing's being β is *p*, we assert not merely that a single sequence of fractions of the relative frequency of β things among α things converges to p, but that *any* infinite succession of α things will furnish a sequence of such fractions converging to p, provided that it is selected without regard to attributes other than α-ness. Even Reichenbach and Popper, who have tried to formulate less exacting conditions for randomness, are committed to belief in laws of a similar kind. Indeed, any frequency theory which is to be worth consideration must end with such a thesis. For we cannot define probability in general as a proportion found in a finite succession; and, as soon as we introduce the notion of an infinite succession, we have to admit that infinitely many infinite successions may be selected in random fashion from an open class, and that none of them can be disregarded in the formulation of our definition. If, when I speak about the probability of an α thing's being β, I am referring in any way to a succession of α things, I am certainly not referring to a single succession, beginning with some α thing which I observed at a certain time on a certain day, but to all successions of a certain kind. Now enough has been said already about the combination of convergence and irregularity to show that, in comparison with the gnats at which Hume strained, the laws which the frequency theorists require us to swallow are camels of a fairly large size. But for a full understanding of the oddity of the situation it is necessary to compare the assertions of the frequency theorists with the aims of earlier writers on probability.

The comparative stability over many years of certain national statistics, such as the proportion of babies that are boys, has often puzzled people of an inquiring turn of mind. Why, they ask, should we find order on a large scale when apparently there is nothing but disorder on a small scale, e.g. in the distribution of boys among particular families? The importance of Bernoulli's theorem in the history of the theory of probability is due to the fact that it offers us a hope of answering such questions satisfactorily. To say this is not, as von Mises argues, to assume that the theorem is a bridge from probability conceived in some subjectivist fashion to actual frequencies. The theorem has, of course, been grossly misunderstood by many writers, but the hope to which I have referred does not rest on a misunderstanding. If we hold an objectivist theory of probability and can prove it highly probable that the proportion of β things in a large sample of α things will approximate to the probability of an α thing's being β, we have at least the framework for a satisfactory solution of such problems. In order to provide a complete solution of a particular problem of this sort it would be necessary also to determine the probability of an α thing's being β without reference to the frequency of β things among α things in experience and to show that the two fractions were reasonably close together. We think we can do this in some cases, e.g. for games of chance like dicing, but even when we have to admit that our only estimate of the probability of an α thing's being β is based on the frequency of β things among α things in our experience, we still think that we are on the way to an explanation. In cases of this second kind, which are, of course, very common, we do not regard our probability estimate as a compendious statement about frequencies, but treat it rather as an hypothesis which may presently be established, or at least confirmed, by evidence other than the frequency of β things among α things in experience. When, for example, we say that the probability of a baby's being male is 0·52, we think it proper to look for an explanation of this assertion in the physiology of reproduction.

All this the frequency theorist rejects, at least by implication. To the question 'Why should we find order on a large scale combined with disorder on a small scale?' he replies in effect 'Because the larger the scale, the more the order'. If his assertion makes sense at all, it explains what puzzles us only in that Pickwickian sense of 'explain' in which the statement that there are two lions in my garden explains why there is one. He has not, as is sometimes said, repudiated the view that there are strictly universal laws of nature. On the contrary, he is committed to maintaining that there are such laws. But he has to say that they are *laws of chance*, and that the most fundamental among them are concerned with entities which are certainly not fundamental, namely, infinite sequences of fractions of relative frequency. This is surely a mistake.

A second reason for rejecting the frequency theory is that it does not enable us to understand why it is rational to act on considerations of probability. Let us suppose for the sake of argument that the assertions of the frequency theorists are true. What is their relevance to the situation of a man who knows of something only that it is α but has to decide whether or not to act as though it were β? The fact, if it is a fact, that the limiting frequency of β-ness in the collective of α things is greater than ½ seems to have no direct bearing on the particular problem, for it is concerned neither with the individual α thing as such nor yet with the character of α-ness which it is known to have, but solely with the way in which β things happen to be distributed in an infinite succession of α things. It is not necessary to labour this point, for many frequency theorists have themselves stated it very clearly. Thus von Mises writes: 'We have nothing to say about the chances of life and death of an individual, even if we know his condition of life and health in detail. The phrase "probability of death", when it refers to a single person, has no meaning at all for us.'[1] Since practical decisions, e.g. of the managers of insurance companies, always refer to individual cases, this statement, taken alone, would imply that considerations of probability can never be of any use in practical affairs. But frequency theorists usually go on to say that their theory is nevertheless a trustworthy guide in certain fields of practice, such as insurance, where we have to do with many instances of a kind;[2] it is necessary to examine their argument in some detail.

No writer about probability wishes to suggest that a man by basing his action in a particular case on the balance of chances can make sure of success in his enterprise. But it has been maintained that, if a man acted consistently on probability rules as defined by the frequency theory, he would inevitably have more successes than failures in the long run. According to this argument the rationality of acting on considerations of probability in a particular case is derivative from the rationality of the *policy* of acting always on these considerations in cases of the same kind. But what is meant here by 'the long run'? The developed frequency theory does not allow us to predict with certainty the frequency to be found in any finite succession of trials, however long. Even if we knew for certain that $P(\alpha, \beta) = p$, we could not say that in a million trials of α things the frequency of β things would be p or anywhere near p, because any frequency of β things in that million trials would be consistent with the assertion that

$$\lim_{n \to \infty} F_n(\alpha, \beta) = p.$$

Frequency theorists have sometimes talked as though it were a defect of the indifference theory that it did not allow such prediction, but in this respect their own theory is no better off, for

[1] *P., S., and T.*, p. 15.   [2] Ibid., pp. 91–2.

the whole project of trying to predict actual frequencies with certainty is mistaken. It is clear, then, that the general policy of acting on considerations of probability in all cases of a certain kind cannot be justified by a claim that it inevitably leads to success in any finite run, however long. C. S. Peirce recognized this point and therefore concluded that the rationality of such a policy is not to be explained by the profit it brings to any individual agent, but by its advantage to a society of infinite duration.[1] It is surely false, however, that the possibility of rational action in the circumstances we are considering depends on the prospects of survival of the human race. And even if we were sure that the human race would survive for ever and were animated by the most devoted altruism, we could attach no meaning to the promise of an advantage which was to be realized only at the *end* of infinite duration.

It seems clear, then, that frequency theorists cannot justify action based on considerations of probability by showing that it will lead to certain success in some long run. But their case is no better if they fall back on Bernoulli's theorem and speak more modestly of the probability of success in a long but finite succession of trials. If $P(\alpha, \beta) = \frac{2}{3}$ and we consistently take α things to be β, there is a very high probability that in a long run of, say, a thousand trials we shall be right in about two-thirds of the cases with which we deal. This much we can say in accordance with Bernoulli's theorem. But the question at issue is whether the frequency theory can explain the rationality of acting on considerations of probability, and it is important to understand what meaning the frequency theorists assign to this statement. According to their interpretation, it means that, if

$$\lim_{n \to \infty} F_n(\alpha, \beta) = \tfrac{2}{3},$$

then, for a relatively small value of h,

$$\lim_{r \to \infty} F_r({}^\alpha \sigma_{1000}, {}^\beta \rho_{\overline{\frac{2}{3} \pm h}}) = \text{a very large proper fraction.}$$

Why should this consideration justify the policy of betting consistently on the β-ness of α things for a man who knows the truth of the protasis? By the use of Bernoulli's procedure we can only deduce one probability from another, and the probability of which we speak in our conclusion must be interpreted in the same way as the probability of which we speak in our premiss. If, therefore,

[1] *Collected Papers*, vol. ii, p. 398.

our premiss has no relevance to practical decisions about particular α things, our conclusion can have no relevance to practical
decisions about particular sets of a thousand α things. But any
practical decision must be concerned with a particular of some sort.
Even the adoption of a policy for dealing with all the cases of a
certain kind I meet within a year is a decision relating to that
particular set of cases. And so we are no nearer to a solution of the
problem. When frequency theorists claim that they can provide
a justification for the practice of insurance companies by the use of
Bernoulli's theorem, they delude themselves by abandoning their
own definition of probability at a crucial point in the argument.

Although we must reject the frequency definition of probability
because of these serious defects, we should recognize nevertheless
that frequency theorists have done good service by drawing attention to several important points. In the first place, they have
exposed the absurdities of the subjectivist view, and in particular
the absurdity of trying to derive interesting conclusions from the
equal distribution of our own ignorance. It is a gain that the
probability relation is now generally admitted to be something
objective. Secondly, they have made clear that in a great many
cases at least, and those the most important, estimates of probability
can be derived only from records of relative frequency. Thirdly,
in their attempts to define probability by reference to frequency
they have been led to formulate probability *rules* more clearly
than any of their predecessors. A conception of the probability
relation as holding between attributes could have been extracted,
no doubt, from the earlier literature, but this way of considering
the problem was so obscured by talk of events and propositions
that until recently few persons, if any, realized its importance.

§ 34. THE ANALYSIS OF EQUIPROBABILITY

We have seen that in its original conception the frequency theory
of probability corresponded to the constancy theory of natural
laws. It is reasonable to ask whether there are theories of probability corresponding to the other theories of natural laws discussed in an earlier section. I have never seen a prescription theory
of probability, and I doubt whether one could be constructed
which would seem at all plausible.[1] It may be possible, however,

---

[1] The theory of F. P. Ramsey (published in the volume called *The Foundations
of Mathematics*) is concerned only with the consistency of bets and has no resemblance to his account of natural laws.

to develop a theory according to which some at least of our probability statements can be described as truths of principle. Hitherto the frequency theory has had the advantage of being the only fully developed theory in the field which is completely free from subjectivism, and for this reason it has been favoured by the hard-headed in spite of its difficulties. If the alternative just suggested is feasible, we may hope to discover the germ of truth which was in the minds of the older writers when they talked of equiprobable cases. Indeed, the analysis of the notion of equi-probability is the necessary first step in the working out of this suggestion.

In order to simplify our problem let us confine our attention for the present to statements of the form $P(\alpha, \beta) = p$ in which the first term is a restricted description determining a finite class. We may take as an example the sentence 'The probability of an undergraduate's knowing Greek is $\frac{1}{10}$', where 'undergraduate' is understood to mean a person who is at present a junior member of the University of Oxford and 'knowing Greek' being able to pass a University examination in that subject. Apart from some fre-quency theorists who are so devoted to infinite successions that they will not deal with anything else, all writers on probability agree that in such a context the probability fraction is the same as the proportion of members of the first class which belong also to the second class, i.e. that

$$P(\alpha, \beta) = \frac{N(\alpha\beta)}{N(\alpha)}.$$

Indeed, the sentence cited above would ordinarily be regarded as just another way of saying that one in ten of present under-graduates knows Greek. Because of their simplicity, examples of this kind are common in text-books on probability. Very often they are introduced by some such formula as 'A ball is drawn at random from a bag containing w white balls and b black balls'. Here the phrase 'at random' is intended to indicate that the method of selection may be ignored. If the selection of an α thing were not at random but according to a plan, it might involve atten-tion to some character γ-ness such that

$$P(\alpha\gamma, \beta) \neq P(\alpha, \beta).$$

But when we are assured that we need not trouble ourselves about that complication, we consider only $P(\alpha, \beta)$ and assume it to be the same as the proportion of α things which are β.

Why should we identify probability with proportion in these cases? A thing which is α must, we know, be identical with one or another of the members of a finite set. If all these various alternatives are equiprobable in relation to α-ness, the numerical probability of an α thing's being β must be equal to the number of alternatives which involve β-ness divided by the total number of alternatives, i.e. to the proportion of α things which are β. But why should we assume that these alternatives are equiprobable in relation to α-ness? This is the crucial question. In order to get the issue clear and provide a satisfactory answer we must consider once more the relation of probability rules to rational choice.

In our introductory discussion of opinion as a basis for action we found it necessary to distinguish between the original and the technical usages of the word 'probability'. When we speak in ordinary life of the probability of a proposition, we are thinking of its approvability as a basis for action by an agent who possesses only certain limited information. When, however, we discuss the probability relation in which that proposition stands to the available evidence or talk more generally of the probability of an α thing's being β, the word no longer has any reference to human interests. We are now thinking of the objective conditions which are supposed to justify judgements of approval. Clearly a similar distinction can be drawn between usages of the word 'equiprobability'. It is true that this word does not occur in common speech, but if we heard a man speak in ordinary life of the equal probability of various alternatives we should understand him to mean that they were equally approvable as bases for action by an agent possessing only certain limited information. On the other hand, in technical discussions about the theory of chances the word is often used without this implication. The two senses are connected, of course, for, if the technical usage is to be helpful, it must enable us to justify the usage which is nearer to the etymology of the word. But it is important to distinguish them. Our immediate task is to analyse the technical usage with reference to probability rules such as that about the knowledge of Greek among undergraduates, and we must be careful to avoid falling into the subjectivism which has often accompanied talk of equiprobability in the past. Any analysis we offer must be judged ultimately by its ability to explain and justify our usage of the word 'probability' in the ordinary affairs of life, but there should be no reference to human choice in the analysis itself.

In the older literature the technical sense of 'equiprobable' was sometimes rendered by 'equipossible'. Thus Laplace wrote in his *Essai philosophique sur les probabilités*:[1]

'The theory of chances consists in reducing all events of the same kind to a certain number of equipossible cases (*cas également possibles*), that is to say, cases such that we are equally undecided about their existence, and determining the number of cases favourable to the event of which the probability is sought. The ratio of this number to that of all the possible cases is the measure of the probability.'

Von Mises has pointed out that Laplace sometimes used the word 'possibility' instead of 'probability' when the nature of his problem obviously demanded an objectivist theory,[2] and I think that, when he wrote of equipossible cases in the passage I have cited, Laplace may have had in mind something better than the principle of indifference, but, if so, he immediately cancelled his suggestion by the explanation which he added. I wish to take this suggestion seriously and to work out, if I can, a theory according to which the numerical probability of an α thing's being β may be described as the degree of possibility of β-ness in relation to α-ness. A similar definition is to be found in the work of some older writers who tried to escape from subjectivism.[3] If the theory is worth consideration, it should be possible to state it in a thoroughly objectivist fashion, and the first test must be made with the relatively simple example we have chosen.

We do not often speak of one alternative as more possible than another in relation to α-ness, and we may even be inclined to say that possibility does not properly admit of degrees. But we do sometimes say that one alternative under α-ness covers more possibilities than another. We may say, for example, that there are more possibilities of an undergraduate's being a member of University College than of his being a scholar of that college. For every scholar of the college is a member, but not every member is a scholar. This use of the word 'possibility' corresponds to one use of the word 'chance'. For we often say that there are more chances of an α thing's being such-and-such than there are of its

---

[1] Printed as the introduction to the second edition of his *Théorie analytique des probabilités*, 1814.   [2] *P., S., and T.*, p. 316.

[3] Cf. Cournot, *Exposition de la théorie des chances et des probabilités*, 1843, pp. 437–8, quoted by von Kries, *Principien der Wahrscheinlichkeitsrechnung*, p. 283.

being so-and-so, i.e. more distinguishable ways in which it may be such-and-such. When we use either of these idioms we apparently intend it to be understood that the possibilities or chances of which we speak are in some way equal, although at other times we may talk of large and small chances, e.g. when we say that there is only a very small chance of an undergraduate's knowing Hebrew. Now there is, I believe, a very good sense in which the alternatives of being this, that, or the other individual undergraduate can be called equal possibilities or equipossible cases under the concept of a present undergraduate. It is not merely that they are all alike possible in relation to that concept. For the alternatives of being a member of University College or a member of Balliol College or a member of Merton College, and so on, are alike possible, but we do not wish to say that they are equipossible. The important point is that being identical with a certain individual is an *ultimate* alternative under the concept we are considering, that is to say, an alternative which has no sub-alternatives. Alternatives which are not of this kind can be regarded as disjunctions of such alternatives, and for that reason may be said to differ in size. These, however, being ultimate, are the natural units in terms of which we measure all other chances. In examples of the type with which we are now dealing equipossibility can therefore be defined in an objectivist fashion. When we say that two alternatives covered by a restricted description are equipossible, we mean that they are alike either (a) in being both ultimate or (b) in being disjunctions of the same number of ultimate alternatives. On this foundation the ordinary doctrine of numerical probabilities can be elaborated; but we must still ask whether our apparatus enables us to explain the ordinary usage of the word 'probable' in relation to propositions, i.e. the usage which implies a connexion with rational choice.

Let us suppose a man to know that α-ness covers a number of alternatives which are equipossible in the sense just defined. If he learns that a particular thing is α but is unable to discover any more about it, his knowledge of the equipossibility of the alternatives entitles him to say at least that the available evidence gives no reason for assuming any one of the alternatives to hold of the particular thing rather than any other. This is a very modest claim, but in certain circumstances it may be a useful guide to action. If, for example, he can expect to gain some advantage by guessing correctly which of the alternatives holds, and the disadvantages to be expected from an incorrect guess are no worse than the results of not guessing at all, he can put his claim in a more positive form and say that all the alternative hypotheses are equally approvable as bases for action. Rather than behave like Buridan's ass and take no practical decision at all, he may in such circumstances allow himself to be determined by some consideration which he knows to be wholly irrelevant, e.g. by the result of the tossing of a coin, but, if he does so, he shows his rationality in that decision. For a choice is rational when it is made with a good reason, and this agent has such a reason. Here, then, we have the notion of equiprobability which is used in the ordinary affairs of life, but for a full explanation of the rationality of action based on consideration of numerical probabilities we must go a step farther.

Let us suppose that the man we are considering knows the balance of equipossible alternatives under α-ness to be in favour of β-ness, and that he has a sufficient motive for venturing a guess on the question whether the particular α thing he has discovered is or is not β. Since *ex hypothesi* he knows that the alternatives represented by $\alpha\beta$ and $\alpha\sim\beta$ are not equipossible, it would be irrational of him to approve them equally. On the contrary, he should approve the first and disapprove the second. For from the set of equipossible alternatives covered by the first it is possible to select a proper sub-set the disjunction of which is equipossible with the second, as being of the same size, and therefore also equally approvable. If we represent the disjunction of this sub-set by $\alpha\beta\gamma$ and the disjunction of the remainder under $\alpha\beta$ by $\alpha\beta\sim\gamma$, we have $\alpha\beta$ equivalent to $\alpha\beta\gamma \vee \alpha\beta\sim\gamma$ and the probability represented by $\alpha\beta\gamma$ equally approvable with that represented by $\alpha\sim\beta$. Now the probability represented by $\alpha\beta$ must be more approvable than that represented by $\alpha\beta\gamma$, since, when one has the choice, it is obviously rational to stake on a disjunction rather than on any of its members. But this is as much as to say that the possibility represented by $\alpha\beta$ must be more approvable than that represented by $\alpha\sim\beta$, and since the two possibilities exhaust the field, the first may be said to be approvable simply and the second disapprovable. By an extension of the same line of reasoning it is easy to explain why a larger balance of equipossible alternatives in favour of β-ness would justify a greater measure of approval.

I have discussed this matter in some detail because I wish to show clearly how the view I am defending differs from the indifference theory. I have argued that we are entitled to treat alternatives as equiprobable if, but only if, we know that the available evidence does not provide a reason for preferring any one to any other. According to the principle of indifference we may call alternatives equiprobable if we do not know that the available evidence provides a reason for preferring any one to any other. Instead of *knowledge of absence* Laplace and those who agree with him accept *absence of knowledge* as a sufficient ground for judgements of probability. This change accords with their subjectivism. For 'absence of knowledge' signifies only a fact about a mind, whereas 'knowledge of absence' signifies not only a fact about a mind, but also a truth about something independent of that mind. The same point can be put in another way by distinguishing two senses of the word 'indifferent'. According to the principle of indifference alternatives are equiprobable if I am indifferent in my attitudes towards them. According to the theory I have put forward it is necessary that the alternatives themselves should be indifferent, i.e. without difference in a certain respect. When we have to do with examples such as that about the probability of an undergraduate's knowing Greek, we may easily overlook the distinction, precisely because it is then easy to know what alternatives are equipossible. For if a truth is obvious we do not think of mentioning it as an item of our knowledge. This reflection explains also why the upholders of the principle of indifference were sometimes better in their practice than in their theory. When dealing with simple examples of the kind we have considered so far, they often used knowledge for which they made no allowance in their theory.

§ 35. THE NOTION OF RANGE

Our conclusion, then, at this stage of the argument is that the numerical probability of an α thing's being β may be defined as the proportion of equipossible alternatives under α-ness which involve β-ness, if α-ness is known to determine a finite class. We must now inquire whether the same definition can be used in those very important cases where the class of α things is open. Can we say, for example, that a statement about the probability of rain after clouds of a certain kind is to be analysed in this way? If the number of α things is not finite, it is clearly useless to try to work with the alternatives of being this, that, or the other α thing as our equipossible alternatives under α-ness. For the formula:

$$P(\alpha, \beta) = \frac{N(\alpha\beta)}{N(\alpha)}$$

is now meaningless, and there is nothing to be gained from the
ingenious refinements which frequency theorists have introduced
in order to allow themselves to talk in a Pickwickian way of the
proportion of α things which are β. How, then, shall we proceed?
Instead of concentrating attention on the denotation or extension
of our general term, i.e. on the set of individuals which happen to
be α, we must think rather of its *range*. This is an important
notion which requires careful explanation.[1]

If I say of some particular thing that it is an apple, I do not
thereby determine its nature in every detail or exhaust what may
be said about it. An apple may be a Blenheim or a Bramley
seedling or a Ribston pippin or a specimen of some other variety;
it may be green or yellow or red; it may have been grown in a
garden or in a commercial orchard; and so on and so on. There
are, in short, a host of possibilities left open by the character of
being an apple. Some of them, such as being a Ribston pippin,
can be described as specific varieties of the generic character; but
others, such as being an apple which has come half-way round the
world in a ship, are merely conjunctions of characters which include that of being an apple. Moreover, by consideration of still
more complex conjunctions we can always conceive sub-possibili-
ties under any possibilities such as those already mentioned. Indeed, for a knowledge of all the alternatives we should need to
know not only the customary definition of the word 'apple', but
also all the laws of nature. For the alternatives of which I speak
here are supposed to be real possibilities, that is to say, possibilities
permitted not only by principles of formal logic but also by laws
of nature, and nothing less than a knowledge of all the laws of
nature would enable us to decide in every case whether a suggested conjunction was possible. It would not be enough to know
only the laws that would commonly be said to be about apples,
since some of the characters we should have to consider together
with that of being an apple would themselves involve conjunctions
of characters in other things, e.g. that of having been brought
half-way round the world in a steel ship driven by steam. Let us

---

[1] The notion of range (*Spielraum*) was first introduced into the theory of
probability by von Kries in his *Principien der Wahrscheinlichkeitsrechnung* of
1886, but my usage is nearer to that of Wittgenstein (*Tractatus Logico-Philosophicus*, 4.463) and Waismann ('Logische Analyse des Wahrscheinlichkeitsbegriffes', in *Erkenntnis*, i, 1930). It differs from theirs in that I speak of the range
of a character or attribute rather than of the range of a proposition, but this is a
minor point.

suppose, however, that the process of finding sub-alternatives under some character α-ness were carried to the limit. We should then have a set of ultimate alternatives, that is, alternatives without sub-alternatives, each of which was a complex character of such specific detail that any attempt to qualify further an individual to which it belonged would result only in redundancy or self-contradiction. To use the language of Leibniz, each would be the complete nature of a possible instance of α-ness. When in future I speak of the range of α-ness or use the convenient abbreviation $R(α)$, I intend to refer to the whole set of such ultimate alternatives under α-ness. Sometimes, in order to remind the reader more vividly of the explanation given here, I shall use as a synonym the expression 'field of possibility left open by α-ness'. In the special case in which α-ness determines a closed class its range may be identified with its extension, but when we are concerned, as at present, with characters which determine open classes, the two concepts must be distinguished.

It is obvious that, according to this definition, if we take any two characters whatsoever, there must be some relationship between their ranges. Either the first is included in the second, or there is a partial overlap, or the two are mutually exclusive. The various conceivable relationships can be represented easily by the geometrical analogy which Euler introduced for explaining the Aristotelian classification of general propositions. For a pair of characters, α-ness and β-ness, we have the following scheme:

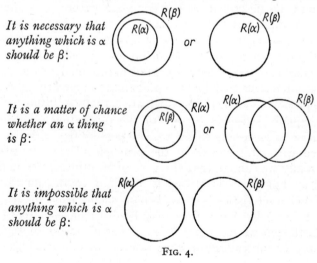

It is necessary that anything which is α should be β:

It is a matter of chance whether an α thing is β:

It is impossible that anything which is α should be β:

FIG. 4.

The relationship represented by the two diagrams in the second row can be expressed also by the statement 'There are some, but only some, ways of being α which are also ways of being β'. This is the situation in which we are interested when we speak in ordinary life of the probability of an α thing's being β, and consideration of the diagrams by which it is illustrated suggests immediately that for the case where α-ness determines an open class we should try to define the probability of an α thing's being β as the proportion of the range of α-ness which belongs also to the range of β-ness. But a little further reflection shows that we cannot hope to develop a satisfactory theory of probability on this basis unless we can find a way of explaining what we mean by a comparison of ranges in respect of size. We know, of course, what it means to say that $R(\alpha)$ is greater than $R(\alpha\beta)$. This signifies only that there are ways of being α which are not ways of being both α and β. But so far we have no justification for talking of a ratio between $R(\alpha\beta)$ and $R(\alpha)$. If we talk in this way, we use the symbol $R(\alpha)$ to signify, not the range of α-ness, but the measure of that range. Such a development may be permissible, but we have still to explain what we mean by 'measure' in this connexion.

Since we have defined the range of a character as a set of ultimate alternatives, it is natural to inquire whether the measure of a range may not be simply the number of members it contains. But here we come on an insuperable difficulty. We have seen that in the terminology of Leibniz each ultimate alternative under α-ness may be described as the complete nature of a possible instance of α-ness. If Leibniz's principle of the identity of indiscernibles is correct, there must be at least as many such ultimate alternatives as there are actual instances of α-ness, for no two actual things can have exactly the same nature in all details. And, since it is impossible to define the probability of an α thing's being β as the proportion of α things which are actually β, it must therefore be equally senseless to talk of the proportion of ultimate possibilities under α-ness which are also possibilities under β-ness. But even without recourse to the principle of the identity of indiscernibles we can see that the variety of ultimate possibilities is infinite. For there is obviously no limit to the number of relational characteristics (such as being 3 inches from the nearest hydrogen atom) by which they may be distinguished from each other. Although we must not base our argument on an analogy which may be misleading in some respect, we can elucidate the

situation by referring again to the geometrical diagrams introduced above. According to definition an ultimate alternative has
no sub-alternatives, and so it must be represented in such a
diagram by a point rather than by an area. This suggests that an
attempt to measure ranges by counting the ultimate alternatives
they contain would be as foolish as an attempt to measure areas
by counting the points they contain.

Although we cannot define the measure of the range of α-ness
as the number of ultimate alternatives under α-ness, we can
nevertheless obtain the measure we need if we can find some way
of defining equal sub-ranges by reference to the ultimate alternatives they contain. For divisibility into equal parts is the essential
condition of measurement. Such equal sub-ranges, if they exist,
must of course be the ranges of alternatives under α-ness which
are equipossible, although not ultimate. What we require, then,
is something like the geometrical notion of congruence. It is true
that the range of one alternative under α-ness cannot be literally
superposed on that of another, but even in geometry the idea of
the literal superposition of figures is felt to be inappropriate.
Euclid used it in the fourth proposition of his first book, but elsewhere he took great trouble to avoid it, and modern writers on the
foundations of geometry have tried to eliminate it altogether.[1]
Fortunately, however, our task is easier than that of the metrical
geometer, since we have not to provide *directly* for the notion of
distance. We can say that two mutually exclusive ranges are equal
if the ultimate alternatives they contain can be set in one-one
correspondence according to a certain kind of rule. It is not enough
that there should be a one-one correspondence of any kind whatsoever, since, as Cantor showed, it is characteristic of an infinite set
that its members can always be put into some sort of one-one
correspondence with the members of a proper sub-set (e.g. the
natural numbers with the squares of the natural numbers), and it
would be foolish to introduce a definition of the equality of ranges
according to which an alternative under α-ness might be said to be

---

[1] It is interesting to notice that the statement 'Things which fit on one another
(τὰ ἐφαρμόζοντα ἐπ' ἄλληλα) are equal to one another' appears in our text of Euclid,
not as a special postulate (αἴτημα) of geometry, but as one of the presuppositions
common to all sciences (κοιναὶ ἔννοιαι). For this reason among others its authen-
ticity has been doubted by Tannery, and probably with justice (cf. Heath, *The
Thirteen Books of Euclid's Elements*, i, p. 225), but it might conceivably be taken
as a definition of 'equality' in a sense wide enough to cover the equality of ranges,
as that is explained here.

equipossible with one of its own sub-alternatives. In order to avoid this absurdity we must lay it down explicitly that the correspondence we require is to be of such a kind that no range can correspond in this special way with a proper sub-range. But it is not difficult to show that there can be correspondence such as we need.

Having first agreed to call two characters independent if neither necessitates nor excludes the other, let us suppose that α_1-ness, α_2-ness, &c., are a set of alternatives under α-ness which have no sub-alternatives except such as are constituted by conjunction with characters independent of all the alternatives alike. Then for any sub-alternative under α_1-ness there will be a corresponding sub-alternative under each of the other alternatives, i.e. a sub-alternative which corresponds as being constituted by the conjunction of that other alternative with the same independent character, say, θ-ness, as has been conjoined with α_1-ness. And there cannot be more than one sub-alternative under each of the alternatives which corresponds in this way with the sub-alternative under α_1-ness which is represented by $\alpha_1\theta$. For if there were two such under any alternative, say, under α_2-ness, they would have to be distinguished by mutually exclusive characters, say, ϕ-ness and ψ-ness, and the characters represented by $\theta\phi$ and $\theta\psi$ would both have to be independent of all the alternatives. But this consequence contradicts the assumption from which it is derived. The sub-alternative represented by $\alpha_2\theta\phi$ would not then correspond in the prescribed way with that represented by $\alpha_1\theta$, but rather with that represented by $\alpha_1\theta\phi$. It is obvious also that in this sense of 'correspond' none of the alternatives can correspond with any of its sub-alternatives. Finally, the conditions stated above cover all sub-alternatives, whatever their degree of complexity. It is therefore established that the alternatives of the original set must have equal ranges, that is to say, be equipossible.

If a set of equipossible alternatives satisfies the condition stated in the last paragraph, it may be described as primary. This description is useful to distinguish it from secondary sets, in which the alternatives do not satisfy the condition and are equipossible only because they are all disjunctions of similar sub-sets of the members of a primary set. Thus if α_1, α_2,... α_{2n} represent the members of a primary set of equipossible alternatives under α-ness, $\alpha_1\vee\alpha_2$, $\alpha_3\vee\alpha_4$,..., $\alpha_{2n-1}\vee\alpha_{2n}$ will also represent equipossible alternatives under α-ness, but the set formed by these latter may be only secondary because they do not satisfy the condition stated above. There may, however, be several different ways of dividing the range of α-ness so as to produce sets of equipossible alternatives, whether primary or secondary. When we are interested in the probability of an α thing's being β, we are concerned only with sets of equipossible alternatives under α-ness which have reference to β-ness in the sense that each necessitates or excludes that character. But among these latter there must be one primary set whose members are not themselves sub-alternatives under alternatives of a set satisfying the same conditions. Let us call this the principal set of equipossible alternatives under α-ness with reference to β-ness. Its importance is that it is the smallest primary set of equipossible alternatives by which the probability of an α thing's being β can be defined. On the one hand, all other primary sets with reference to β-ness are derivable from it by subdivision of the ranges of its alternatives. On the other hand, any secondary set which may be needed for the definition of the probability of an α thing's being β must be derived from it by the grouping of its alternatives in similar sets. Admittedly it is impossible to produce an example of a principal set of equipossible alternatives covered by an unrestricted description from natural science. For in order to do so we should need to know, not only all the laws of nature, but also that they were all. Nothing less would enable us to decide whether a set of alternatives had no sub-alternatives except such as were constituted by conjunction with characters independent of all the alternatives alike. But to say this is only to admit that we cannot in such cases determine the probability of an α thing's being β *a priori*. Our present concern is not to provide a method of determining probabilities, but rather to work out a definition of probability, and for this purpose it is sufficient to show that the existence of primary sets of equipossible alternatives is entailed by our ordinary beliefs about chance.

The fundamental notion in the account of equipossibility given above is that of independence between characters. According to some followers of Spinoza and Hegel this notion has no application in the world, for they maintain in effect that every fact implies every other fact. If this were true, there could be no equipossible alternatives, since there would be no mere possibilities and so no alternatives whatsoever. On the other hand, some Logical Positivists have maintained that there is no necessitation or exclusion except the formal necessitation and exclusion studied in logic. If this were true, nothing could be easier than finding equipossible alternatives, since all simple characters (i.e. those which were not conjunctions or disjunctions of other characters) would be independent of each other and the probability of an α thing's being β would always be one-half, provided only that α-ness and β-ness were simple. This can be shown easily by the following table of possibilities:

	θ	$\sim\theta$
$\alpha\beta$	P	P
$\alpha\sim\beta$	P	P

α {

Here θ represents any character by which it may be proposed to divide the ranges of the two relevant alternatives and P the possibility of the conjunction corresponding to the cell in which it occurs.[1] These two extreme doctrines are both mistaken, but the working out of their consequences is interesting, because it throws light on the real situation. The probability we are now investigating is concerned only with matters of chance, and we speak of chance when we believe that some characters are connected by law but others not. If our assumption is correct, there must be primary sets of equipossible alternatives, because for any character determining an open class there must be some division of its range which leaves no possibility of further subdivision except by the conjunction of the alternatives with characters independent of all alike. What we have called a principal set of equipossible alternatives is, so to say, a set of alternatives *ultimate in the realm of law*.

This implies, however, that the notion of equipossibility is not a far-fetched innovation, introduced only in order to provide a scale for the measurement of probabilities, but rather a fundamental conception in the whole theory of chance. Its importance

---

[1] In his *Tractatus Logico-Philosophicus*, 5.152, Wittgenstein stated explicitly that any two elementary propositions give to each other the probability $\frac{1}{2}$. For the sake of argument I have assumed that it is possible to give a meaning to negation within this system, but in fact, with no mutual exclusion except that of propositions which are formally contradictory, there would be no use for the word 'not'. The system is really as unthinkable as that of the Absolute Idealists mentioned above. In a later paper called 'Some Remarks on Logical Form' (*Aristotelian Society Proceedings*, sup. vol. ix, 1929, p. 168) Wittgenstein came near to admitting this. Since then the theory of elementary propositions has been abandoned by Positivists, and with it Wittgenstein's account of probability, but no stable doctrines have taken their place.

has been recognized in a dim way from the very beginning of the theory, for the *chances* of which gamblers and theorists alike have spoken so often in the plural are simply equipossible alternatives. But thought about the matter has been obscured until recently by the subjectivist prejudices with which theorists have approached the problem of probability. When equipossible alternatives are defined in the way suggested here, it can be seen that they must be equispecific and symmetrical, as some of the older theorists asserted, but there is no longer any temptation to think of these two requirements as additions to the principle of indifference which will enable us to determine probabilities *a priori*.

Although primary sets of equipossible alternatives are basic in the theory of chance, we cannot safely define the probability of an α thing's being β as the proportion of the alternatives in such a set under α-ness which involve β-ness. For we have no guarantee that even the principal set under α-ness with reference to β-ness will be finite. On the contrary, we have good reason to believe that in very many cases this principal set must be infinite. For it cannot be finite if its alternatives involve different values for any continuously variable magnitude. And we commonly assume that some physical magnitudes which are involved in the definitions of most of our general terms, e.g. distance and duration, are continuously variable. To illustrate the difficulty let us take a comparatively simple problem of a kind frequently discussed by believers in the principle of indifference. When a pointer is set spinning on a vertical axis in a well-lubricated bearing, what is the probability of its coming to rest within a given sector of the circle described by its rotation? It may be that the equipossible alternatives of the principal set correspond to the various degrees of force with which the pointer can be set spinning. If so, the desired probability cannot be the proportion of such alternatives which involve the pointer's coming to rest within the given sector; for there is no such proportion. Clearly the only way out of this difficulty is to allow that the range of the character with which we are concerned may be a continuum. The introduction of this notion marks the transition from arithmetical to geometrical probability. Whereas the first is concerned with probability conceived as a ratio between the numbers of items in certain sets of equipossible alternatives, the second is concerned with probability conceived as a ratio between regions of a configuration space. The distinction was made originally by mathematicians who believed in the indifference theory, but it does not depend on any special assumptions of that theory. On the contrary, it first acquires a good sense within the range theory of probability which we are now considering.

If the equipossible alternatives of the principal set under α-ness differ as involving different values for some one variable only, the range of α-ness can be represented as a line of finite length in which each point is one alternative. It may be, however, that the specification of each alternative involves the assignment of values for several unconnected variables. The range of α-ness will then be a region of two, three, or more dimensions, according to the number of mutually independent variables that are involved. Each point in such a region represents one of the equipossible configurations of values for the variables; hence the term 'configuration space' for the system in which they are ordered. If all the variable magnitudes in question are ordinary distances, the configuration space will be identical with the space of common speech; but this is not to be assumed without special warrant. For all we know, there may be in nature continuously variable magnitudes which are not spatial in the ordinary sense. Indeed, duration is commonly taken to be such.

When a range is conceived in this way as a continuous region, it is natural to think of its measure according to the analogy of ordinary measures of distance, area, and volume. The possibility of dividing ranges into equal sub-ranges seems to follow directly from the way in which they are constituted, for the essentials of measurement are supplied already in the assignment of dimensions to the configuration space. And in any such division each of the equal sub-ranges should itself be the range of an alternative in a secondary set of equipossible alternatives. For, although each contains an infinity of points of the configuration space (i.e. alternatives from the principal set), the assertion that they are equal implies that their contents are in one-one correspondence of the required kind (i.e. such that the contents of a range cannot correspond in this way with the contents of a proper sub-range). Unfortunately things are not quite so simple. If for any given character there were only one configuration space in which the equipossible alternatives of the principal set could be ordered, there would be no more to be said; but in fact there may be many different ways of ordering the alternatives, and the ratio between two ranges may vary according to the system adopted. This can be illustrated most easily by reference to a one-dimensional range.

Let us suppose that the equipossible alternatives of the principal set under α-ness differ in the values they involve for some continuous variable x, and that there is no variable unconnected with x which should be considered. It then seems reasonable to say that the alternatives can be represented by the various points in a line AB and that, if M is the centre point of AB, the lines AM and MB will represent equipossible alternatives of a secondary set under α-ness. It may be, however, that each distinct value for x necessitates a distinct value for some other continuous variable y, according to a functional relationship: $y = f(x)$. The equipossible alternatives of the principal set under α-ness can then be represented equally well by the points in another line CD. In the accompanying figure the functional relationship between x and y is represented by the projection of the points of AB into the points of CD. To every point of AB there corresponds one and only one point of CD, but the figure is so drawn that the point N which is the projection of M is not the centre point of CD. Having assumed that AM and MB represent equipossible alternatives (of a secondary set), we must allow that CN and ND, in spite of their inequality, represent the same alternatives. This is as much as to say that there is a bias in favour of values of y which correspond to points nearer to D. But if we had begun by taking the length of CD as the measure of the range of α-ness we should have been led to say that there was a bias in favour of values of x which correspond to points near to A. From the point of view of mathematics there is no reason for choosing either way of describing the situation rather than the other, because there is no reason for preferring either of the two lines as representative of the range of α-ness. And yet to admit two different ways of measuring the range would be to abandon all hopes of formulating an objectivist theory of probability.

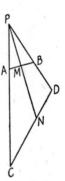

FIG. 5.

When we consider a concrete case, this difficulty does not appear so great. Let us suppose, for example, that our diagram illustrates a game of chance in which a pointer pivoted at P is made to oscillate between the boundaries PC and PD until it comes to rest, and that the alternatives of the pointer's stopping in this, that, or the other position are the equipossible alternatives of the principal set. Then to each possible resting-place of the pointer there corresponds a point on the line AB and also a point on the line CD. Indeed, there is no limit to the number of lines which would satisfy the condition of containing just one point for each possible resting-place of the pointer. But in practice we should not be worried by this consideration. For without special evidence we see no reason for taking any of these lines to represent the range of alternatives in which we are interested. If we found it convenient to select some perceptual representation of the range, our first inclination would be to use the angle between the lines PC and PD or, what comes to the same thing, that arc of a circle about P which is intercepted by the lines PC and PD. I do not mention this suggestion because I think that such problems can be solved *a priori*, but in order to show that common sense assumes certain physical variables to be more fundamental than others. If experience seemed to indicate that there was a bias in favour of certain parts of the angle CPD, we should naturally cease to think of the angle as representing the range in a way suitable for measurement; and in any case we should be inclined to suppose on further reflection that the pointer's stopping within a certain part of the angle depended on some more fundamental fact, e.g. about the degree of force originally applied to it.

The same point can be illustrated more fully by reference to a famous problem in geometrical probability which is known as Bertrand's paradox.[1] It is required to find the probability that a chord chosen at random in a circle will be longer than the side of an equilateral triangle inscribed in the same circle. There appear to be three different solutions, all equally plausible: (1) A chord is determined uniquely when its two end points are specified. Let the first end point be selected; then the chord will be longer than the side of the inscribed equilateral triangle if, but only if, the distance of the second point from the first, measured round the circumference by the shortest route, is greater than one-third of the whole circumference. But the second point is as likely to be in any part of the circumference as in any other of equal size. Therefore the probability of a chord's being longer than the side of

---

[1] It is one of three problems formulated by Bertrand in his *Calcul des probabilités* of 1889, pp. 4–5, in order to show that it is senseless to speak of choosing at random from an infinity of alternatives. As Bertrand pointed out, it is easy to multiply examples of the difficulty. The name 'Bertrand's paradox' was given to this particular problem by Poincaré.

the inscribed equilateral triangle is $\frac{1}{3}$. (2) A chord is determined uniquely when the position of its middle point is specified, and it will be longer than the side of the inscribed equilateral triangle if, but only if, the distance of this middle point from the centre of the circle is less than half the radius. But the middle point of a chord is as likely to lie in any part of a radius as in any other part of equal size. Therefore the probability of a chord's being longer than the side of the inscribed equilateral triangle is $\frac{1}{2}$. (3) A chord is determined uniquely when the position of its middle point is specified, and it will be longer than the side of the inscribed equilateral triangle if, but only if, this middle point lies within a circle concentric with the given circle but having a radius only half that of the given circle. But the middle point of a chord is as likely to lie in any part of the area of the given circle as in any other part of equal size. Therefore the probability of a chord's being longer than the side of the inscribed equilateral triangle is $\frac{1}{4}$.

If any additional argument were required to refute the indifference theory of probability, this paradox would be conclusive. For all three of the suggested solutions are justified by the principle of indifference, although they cannot all be true. But the paradox does not discredit the range theory, unless that is wrongly conceived as a method for determining probabilities *a priori*. As Bertrand remarked, the problem is really indeterminate. A chord is said to be selected at random, but there are various ways in which this may be done, and each imposes a different configuration space for the measurement of ranges. If we are asked to determine the probability that an α thing selected at random will be β and we know that the principal set of equipossible alternatives under α-ness with reference to β-ness is finite, we can say that the required probability is the proportion of such alternatives which involve β-ness. For in this context the phrase 'selected at random' can be understood to mean that the method of selection may be ignored. But when the principal set of equipossible alternatives is not finite, the problem is not determinate, unless nature itself imposes one method of measurement rather than another. Now I wish to maintain that in all empirical problems this condition is in fact fulfilled, and I shall therefore try to show that the puzzles of Bertrand's paradox disappear when a practical method for selecting a chord at random is specified.

Let us suppose, then, that a circle has been drawn on a piece of paper and consider the following directions for selecting a chord: (1) A well-balanced pointer is to be placed with its axis at the centre of the circle and spun twice. The two places on the circumference where it comes to rest are then to be taken as the ends of our chord. With this procedure we think it reasonable to assume that the required probability is $\frac{1}{3}$. (2) The paper is to be laid on a table and a sheet of smooth glass ruled with parallel lines at intervals equal to the diameter of the circle is to be slid over it from some distance. That part of a ruled line which comes to rest within the circle is then to be taken as the chord. With this procedure we assume that the probability is $\frac{1}{2}$. (3) The paper is to be laid out of doors until a raindrop falls in the circle. The centre point of the spot is then to be taken as the middle point of the chord. With this procedure we assume that the probability is $\frac{1}{4}$.

When I say that we find a certain assumption natural in each of these cases, I do not mean that we can determine the probability *a priori*, but rather that we regard one, and only one, of the solutions as plausible even before we have gained any special information about frequencies. Why we should favour *any* solution before we have such information is a question to be discussed later; the point of importance for our present argument is that we have no hesitation in dismissing the other solutions as irrelevant. In each case the selection of a chord is merely incidental to a natural process which could be described adequately without reference to a chord, and the estimate of probability which seems appropriate is that based on consideration of the variables involved in the specification of the natural process. When we spin a pointer twice, the length of the arc between the two resting-places may very well depend on something more fundamental, such as the difference of the two forces applied to the pointer, but it would be fantastic to choose instead as our measure of probability the cosine of half the arc. And yet that is what we should do if we adopted the second solution after the problem had been made determinate by the first experimental procedure.

In order to state the position in general terms we must first make clear what we mean by calling one of two connected variables *more fundamental* than the other. According to the usage I shall follow x is a more fundamental variable than y if, and only if, there is at least one distinct value of x for every distinct value of y, but the converse is not true. When this condition is fulfilled, we can say that every value of y is determined according to law by a value of x with which it is in fact associated but not vice versa. Sometimes in natural science and common speech we express the situation by saying that x is the independent variable and y the dependent. This is a useful way of talking, but it may give rise to misunderstanding, because the words 'dependent' and 'independent' have different meanings in pure mathematics.[1] Clearly there are a number of different ways in which one variable y may be less fundamental than another x, e.g. (1) y may have no value at all for some values of x; (2) y may have a constant value for some stretch of the variation of x; (3) y may have the same value for those values of x which are separated by a certain interval, i.e. y may be a periodic function of x.

Let us now suppose that the equipossible alternatives which form the principal set under a given character α-ness with reference to some other character β-ness differ from each other in that they involve different configurations of values for a number of unconnected variables, and that one of these variables x has another variable y connected with it by a non-linear functional relationship. This is the situation in which paradoxes are supposed to arise. For it is said there can be no good reason why the variation of x rather than the variation of y should be taken as a dimension of the configuration space in which the range of α-ness is to be measured, although the value to be assigned to $P(\alpha, \beta)$ may depend on the choice. Once the distinction of more and less fundamental variables has been stated, some part of the difficulty vanishes, because it becomes clear at least that the variation of a less fundamental variable cannot properly be taken as a dimension of our configuration space.

No one, indeed, would think of suggesting that the variation of a less fundamental variable could be taken as a dimension for the measurement of the range of α-ness, if this variable revealed itself as less fundamental than x by its behaviour within that stretch of the variation of x which is covered by α-ness. For in general the

---

[1] In pure mathematics the distinction of dependent and independent variables follows the direction of the speaker's interest. Thus a mathematician who is studying the trigonometrical function

$$y = \sin x$$

may call x the independent variable, whereas a mathematician who is studying the inverse of this function, namely,

$$x = \text{arc} \sin y,$$

may call y the independent variable.

configurations which could be distinguished in this way would not be equipossible; either some alternatives under α-ness would be omitted from consideration altogether or some which should be distinguished would be improperly run together. But this is not the most important use of the distinction between more and less fundamental variables. If $P(\alpha, \beta)$ is a probability of the sort we try to evaluate by empirical methods, α-ness must be some character exemplified in nature, and it is proper to think of the range of α-ness as part only of a larger configuration space. This implies, however, that no variable y can provide a dimension for the measurement of the range of α-ness if it is less fundamental than some other variable x, even although it reveals itself as such only by its behaviour *outside* the stretch of the variation of x which is covered by α-ness. Here we have the principle which explains and justifies our action in rejecting some of the suggested solutions of the Bertrand problem when that has been made determinate by an experimental procedure. If a chord is to be selected by the falling of a rain-spot to mark its middle point, we think very properly of a configuration space which includes possibilities outside the range of chord-selecting, and we therefore refuse to accept as a dimension for the measurement of that range the variation of any variable such as the length of the arc intercepted by the chord or the distance of the chord from the centre of the circle.

In this way many unacceptable suggestions may be eliminated, but I do not claim that the distinction of more and less fundamental variables suffices to solve our problem completely. For it has not been shown that of any two connected variables in nature one must be more fundamental than the other. So far as I can see, there may conceivably be two variables x and y connected by a non-linear functional relationship which provides for one-one correspondence between their values over the whole possible variation. This is a serious difficulty; for if there is no unique system of measurement for the range of a character α-ness it is useless to speak of the proportion of that range which belongs also to the range of another character β-ness. But I do not think the objection is fatal to the range theory of probability; for here we may, if necessary, fall back on an argument of Poincaré which was noticed in an earlier section. Our present concern, of course, is not to justify the assumption of equal chances required for an *a priori* estimate of probability such as he had in mind, but rather to show that in those cases where we try to estimate $P(\alpha, \beta)$ from statistics we are entitled to assume that there is some single value for this expression.

In this connexion it is important that the characters for which we try to formulate probability rules by the help of statistics are always relatively specific, i.e. have relatively small ranges according to any system of measurement which might conceivably be appropriate. This is as much as to say in Poincaré's language that differences which are very small on the cosmic scale produce results which are large for our interest. But if, as seems reasonable, it can be assumed (a) that of any two connected variables which are equally fundamental each is a continuous analytic function of the other and (b) that by either scale of measurement the range of α-ness is a small part of the configuration space in which it lies, we are entitled to say that metrical relations *within* the range of α-ness will be approximately the same, whether the variation of *x* or that of *y* be chosen as a dimension of the configuration space. This statement is a reformulation of Poincaré's first theorem on the equalization of chances, but it can be understood most easily by the help of a simple analogy from map-making. When two maps of a continent are made according to different projections, regions represented by equal areas in one map may be represented by markedly unequal areas in the other. If, however, we consider only those parts of the same two maps which correspond to a single county, we find that the differences introduced by different methods of projection are negligible; parishes which are represented in the one by equal areas are represented also in the other by approximately equal areas.

These considerations are sufficient to dispose of the main objection to the range theory of probability, but they lead to a conclusion which may be thought curious. If our analysis is correct, we cannot assert that for every pair of characters α-ness and β-ness there must necessarily be some fraction which can be called the probability of an α thing's being β. There must, indeed, be some topological relation between any two ranges we choose to mention; either one contains the other, or there is a partial overlap, or they are mutually exclusive. But further conditions must be fulfilled to ensure that ranges shall be comparable in size. In the cases which specially interest us we have reason to believe that these conditions are fulfilled; but we have still to admit that it may be possible to formulate an expression of the form $P(\alpha, \beta)$ which denotes no single ratio. Is this really shocking? I think not. On the contrary, it seems wise to allow that there may be limits beyond which the notion of numerical probability is not applicable even in matters of chance.

§ 36. THE VARIETY OF THE PROBABILITY RULES COVERED BY THE RANGE DEFINITION

It seems, then, that we are entitled to define the probability of an α thing's being β as the proportion of the range of α-ness which belongs also to the range of β-ness. For convenience I shall sometimes use the formula:

$$P(\alpha, \beta) = \frac{R(\alpha\beta)}{R(\alpha)},$$

in which $R(\alpha)$ stands for the measure of the range of α-ness and $R(\alpha\beta)$ for the measure of the range of the conjunction of α-ness and β-ness. In trying to make clear what is meant by range we have had to distinguish different kinds of measurement. If α-ness determines a closed class, the measure of its range is the number of individuals belonging to that class. If, on the other hand, it determines an open class, the definition of the measure of its range is more complicated. First we must introduce the notion of a primary set of equipossible alternatives, and then we must allow for two distinguishable cases. If the smallest primary set of equipossible alternatives is finite, the measure of the range is the number of items in this set. If, however, the smallest set is infinite, because each alternative involves a different value for some continuous variable or variables, the measure of the range is to be conceived as the measure of a region in a configuration space. The fact that we have had to make these distinctions should not be regarded as a weakness of the range theory of probability. All the various cases fit into one general scheme, according to which the probability of an α thing's being β may be conceived as the degree of possibility of β-ness in relation to α-ness. The demand for an objectivist definition of probability in the technical sense is therefore satisfied, and satisfied moreover in a way which justifies the suggestion of approvability conveyed by the use of the word 'probable' in common speech. On the other hand, the distinctions are necessary, because without them we could not do justice to the variety of the circumstances in which the language of probability may be used.

Just as universal propositions may be of different kinds and require different methods for their establishment, so too statements of probability rules differ in kind according to the nature of the general terms they contain. The analogy is not complete in all details, for there are certain distinctions among universal propositions to which there is nothing corresponding among probability rules. But these failures of analogy are as instructive as the correspondences, and it will therefore be useful to consider probability rules under the heads of division we found it necessary to introduce when considering universal propositions.

First we may take probability rules which are analogous to the propositions of restricted universality established by summative induction. Here the first term (α) in a statement of the form $P(\alpha, \beta) = p$ determines a finite class, and the probability of which we speak is simply the proportion of α things which are β. We have already considered rules of this kind in some detail, but there is one point to be added here. A restricted description is always one which determines a finite class, but we may or may not know the membership of that class. Thus I know that there cannot be more than a finite number of men walking down Whitehall at the moment at which I write, but I do not know who they are or even how many there are. We have seen that some propositions of restricted universality can be established *a priori* because they are concerned with finite classes whose membership we can know *a priori*. For the same reason some probability rules can be established *a priori*, e.g. the rule that the probability of a digit's being prime is $\frac{4}{9}$. It is difficult to imagine circumstances in which we should need to base a practical decision on a rule of this kind, but the language of probability is sometimes used in the theory of numbers, and it is interesting to see that this usage is covered by our definition.

It will be convenient to consider next whether there are any probability rules corresponding to the universal propositions established by recursive induction. If there were a rule of this kind, it would presumably be concerned with the probability of a natural number's having some property or other, e.g. that of being prime; but we cannot, without some special convention, talk of the probability of a natural number's having a property. For the equipossible alternatives under the notion of natural number are being this, that, or the other number, and they do not form a finite set. It is therefore meaningless to speak of the proportion of the alternatives which involve the property of being prime. With the definition of probability we have adopted, the most we can say is that, as n tends towards infinity, the probability that a number not greater than n will be prime tends towards 0. This is, indeed, a theorem whose proof depends in the last resort on recursive induction; but the theorem is a universal statement about probability rules of a certain kind, and not itself the expression of a probability rule. If a mathematician chooses to say that the probability of a number's being prime is 0, we can attach a meaning to his remark, but only by supposing that he has given a special sense to the word 'probability' in this context. Writing ν for 'natural number', $\nu_{\bar{n}}$ for 'natural number not greater than n', and π for 'prime', we can define his new usage by the equation:

$$\mathscr{P}(\nu, \pi) = \lim_{n \to \infty} P(\nu_{\bar{n}}, \pi).$$

A more usual way of speaking about the matter is to say that *almost all* natural numbers are composite. Here the phrase 'almost all' is a technical abbreviation of the same kind.

All the usages of the word 'probability' considered so far have this in common, that they involve no reference to natural laws. They are concerned only with logical possibility. This is obvious enough in the case of statements about numbers, but it is true also of probability statements with restricted descriptions whose range of application cannot be known *a priori*. If I try to determine the probability of an undergraduate's knowing Greek, the fact that I cannot discover all the laws of nature and know that they are all presents no difficulty. It is true that such statements cannot be established without empirical information, but all that is required may be obtained from suitable statistics. Probability statements about numbers are in a sense simpler, since they can be established without any empirical information whatsoever, but this feature is not peculiar to them. In order to determine the probability that a playing-card drawn at random from a standard pack will be a spade it is sufficient to know the meaning of the terms involved in this expression. If it were possible, as many writers have thought, to formulate problems in geometrical probability which were at once abstract and determinate, they too would be soluble *a priori*. The fact that the attempt to formulate such problems must be abandoned need not disturb us. To admit this is only to say that the conditions for speaking significantly of a proportion of possibilities are not fulfilled.

Are there any probability rules corresponding to the universal propositions established by intuitive induction? If this question is taken to mean 'Are there any probability rules concerned exclusively with characters about whose necessary connexions or incompatibilities with other characters we have some knowledge by intuitive induction?', I think the answer is 'Yes'. It seems to me that in certain circumstances I might have occasion to speak of the probability of a square sensum's being red. But if there are any such propositions, they are not of a kind which can be established by intuitive induction. The fact that we can apprehend necessary connexions or incompatibilities between certain characters is no reason for supposing that all truths of principle concerning those characters must be open to inspection. In the domain we are now examining chances are not merely logical possibilities, but alternatives which are equipossible because their only sub-alternatives are constituted by conjunction with characters independent of all alike. If we said that we had intuitive knowledge of probability rules in this domain, we should be claiming, in effect, that we knew all the laws of nature and also the truth that they were all. To put the matter in another way, the most important distinction among universal propositions is between those which do not involve the notion of necessity and those which do. Corresponding to the first group we have probability rules which can be established in the same way, i.e. by enumeration. For here the difference between the universal proposition and the probability rule is simply that between 'All α things are β' and 'A proportion p of α things are β'. Corresponding to the second group we have probability rules which are themselves truths of principle; but we cannot possibly know any of these *a priori*, because they are all much more complicated than the truths of principle which can be apprehended in intuitive induction. In short, there is no distinction among probability rules corresponding to the distinction between universal propositions established by intuitive induction and those for which ampliative induction is required.

Apart from probability rules which can be established by a kind of enumeration, there remain, then, only rules which resemble natural laws in that we cannot hope to establish them *a priori*. These are, of course, the most interesting and the most important for practice. The frequency theorists are right in maintaining that such rules are inferred from observed frequencies, but they are wrong in maintaining that probability is to be defined in terms of frequency, and their error is the same as that of the philosophers who advocate the constancy theory of natural laws, namely, that of confounding evidence with that for which it is evidence. The confusion can be seen very clearly in a passage of von Mises where he criticizes the *Spielraum* theory of von Kries. Having remarked that a believer in ranges cannot hope to determine their equality except from consideration of frequencies in a long series of observations, he concludes: 'In this way we revert to my definition of probability.'[1] If the use of frequencies as evidence for probability rules were sufficient to prove the frequency theory, there would be no room for dispute; but it is a mistake to suppose that the conclusion of an inference must necessarily be a proposition of the same type as the premisses. My evidence for stating that another man is in pain may be that he winces and says he is in pain, but this is not what I mean by my statement.

A similar confusion between evidence and that for which it is evidence is, I believe, one reason for the popularity of subjectivist theories of probability. In natural science we try to obtain precisely recorded frequencies on which to base our estimates of probability, but in ordinary life we can rarely afford to wait for statistics. An employer who has to appoint a person to a position of trust must content himself with the reflection that nearly all men with testimonials as good as those of the candidate before him have proved satisfactory. And fortunately we have a capacity for forming impressions of the relative size of groups or sequences whose members we have not counted. These impressions are usually vague, and, when they relate to the past, they may be grossly inaccurate. For the depth of the trace left in memory by an experience depends on the degree of attention it received at the time of its occurrence; and attention itself is determined by interest. But they provide a substitute for statistics without which we should be helpless in the practical affairs of daily life. Supporters of subjectivist theories remark correctly that the making of an estimate of probability may involve a process of introspection; but they confuse what is discovered by introspection, namely, an inclination to say 'Most α things have been β', with what is inferred immediately from this rough analysis, namely, a probability rule, and say that probability statements merely report feelings of confidence.

The argument by which our most valuable probability rules are

[1] *P., S., and T.*, p. 113.

established is fundamentally the same as that by which natural laws are established, and I propose to regard it as a form of ampliative induction, although the conclusion is not a universal proposition. So long as our attention is confined to universal propositions, we may be tempted to think that ampliative induction goes beyond its premises only in the sense that it proceeds from 'some' to 'all'. But this is an incorrect account of the matter. By consideration of a fanciful example about dodos we saw in an earlier section that natural laws cannot properly be treated as matters of fact with accidental universality. In order to allow for the kind of inference by which probability rules are established it now seems desirable to redefine ampliative induction as the argument from matters of fact to truths of principle other than truths of compatibility (which are entailed by matters of fact). This new definition involves a break with tradition, since from the time of Aristotle the word 'induction' has always been applied to arguments with universal conclusions. But the conception which I now wish to take as fundamental has been attached to the word during the past few centuries by writers such as Whewell, and it seems better to use the old word with a new definition than to try to invent a new term.

In ampliative induction our conclusions, whether they take the form of natural laws or that of probability rules, are no more than probable. We shall have to consider presently whether second-order probability can be explained within the theory of chances. There is, however, another reason why we should be modest in the claims we make on behalf of our inductions about probability. We cannot reasonably pretend that the probability fractions we suggest are ever precisely correct. We may say that, if a spinning pointer is as likely to stop in any sector as in any other of equal size, the probability of its stopping within a given sector of one radian is equal to $1/2\pi$; but this is only an hypothetical statement, and should not be taken to imply that we need ever consider irrational numbers when we try to determine probabilities empirically. It would be absurd, indeed, to claim for any empirical estimate of probability the exactitude implied by a distinction between rational and irrational numbers. The reason is not merely that we must always content ourselves with approximations to an unknowable value, but rather that we are not always entitled to assume the existence of a single true value. I am not referring here to the special difficulties of geometrical probability noticed at the end of the last section, but to a further consideration which could not have been introduced earlier without danger of confusion.

I have spoken so far as though every unrestricted description had a precisely delimited range; but this assumption is not justified by the facts of language. To take a simple example, when we speak of a middle-aged man we have no clear conception of the limits within which our term is applicable. We may be sure that men of twenty are not middle-aged, whereas men of forty-five are, but if we are asked to say where the boundaries should be drawn, we feel that no exact delimitation of the range would render our ordinary usage correctly. Similarly we cannot say how many hairs a man may have while still qualifying to be described as bald. If, then, we talk of the probability of a middle-aged man's being bald, we must not suppose that we have to do with some one fraction, and that by collecting a great deal of empirical evidence we may make an estimate which is very close indeed to the true value. It is sensible to say that baldness is more probable in middle age than in youth, or that a middle-aged man is more likely to be bald than to be bashful; but it would be foolish to say that the probability of a middle-aged man's being bald is exactly $\frac{3}{5}$ or any other fraction. An analogy may help to make the situation intelligible. If a small object such as a pencil is held between a lamp and a sheet of paper at a suitable distance from either, the shadow cast on the paper has a dark central portion surrounded by a lighter fringe which shades off into the whiteness of the paper, so that we cannot say exactly where it ends. With two lamps and two small objects it is possible to arrange for two shadows of this kind to overlap in a region which is noticeably darker than all the rest of the paper. If we now try to determine what ratio this region of overlap bears to one of the shadows, we see that there can be no exact solution to the problem, although it may perhaps be clear that $\frac{1}{7}$ would be too small and $\frac{2}{7}$ too large a fraction.

The descriptions 'middle-aged' and 'bald' are notorious for their vagueness; but in a less obvious way even the technical terms of science may be vague. There are, for example, cases in which the applicability of a biological term such as 'leaf' is left open to doubt. In physical science also there is sometimes room for doubt about the applicability of a term, although here the fringe may be very narrow in comparison with the undisputed range. When chemists speak of hydrogen, they do not always trouble to specify how much of the isotope deuterium may be included in a specimen of gas which qualifies to be described as hydrogen for their purposes. It has been maintained, indeed, that all terms of empirical science must be vague in some degree.[1] Whether or not vagueness could be eliminated from language entirely is a question we need not discuss here. It is sufficient for us to notice that claims to complete precision may be inappropriate even in the scientific formulation of probability rules. If the ranges of our terms are not precisely delimited, an expression of the form $P(\alpha, \beta)$ indicates no single fraction, but only an interval within which any suggested value is as good as any other. This *tolerance*, as an engineer might call it, can be very small when our terms have relatively well-delimited ranges, and it would be tedious to refer to it in every statement we make about probability. In the later sections of this book I shall therefore follow the ordinary practice of speaking as though every expression of the form $P(\alpha, \beta)$ which may be used in ordinary life or science had a single determinate value; but it is important to realize that this practice is rather like the usage of an engineer who says that the piston for a certain engine must be exactly 3 inches in diameter.

§ 37. THE DETERMINATION OF PROBABILITIES *A PRIORI* AND *A POSTERIORI*

While expounding the range theory of probability in matters of chance I have distinguished sharply between the problem of definition and that of evaluation. I have also tried to show that according to the definition which I favour all our most important estimates of probability must be based on experience. But for a proper account of probability estimates in science it is necessary to say something about the use of *a priori* reasoning in this connexion.

When we speak of the determination of probabilities, we may be thinking either of the derivation of probability rules from others which are supposed to be given or of the evaluation of probabilities from evidence which does not include probability rules. Reasoning of the first kind, which provides the subject-matter of the calculus of chances, is certainly *a priori*, but we need say no more about it here. Reasoning of the second kind cannot be absolutely *a priori* except in the solution of such special problems as that of finding the probability of a digit's being prime, but

---

[1] Cf. what F. Waismann says about the *open texture* (*Porosität*) of empirical concepts in *Aristotelian Society Proceedings*, sup. vol. xix, 1945, p. 121.

it would be a mistake to suppose that in all other cases we must wait to learn the frequency of β things in a long run of α things before venturing on any estimate of the probability of an α thing's being β. It is sometimes possible to make conjectures which are at least relatively *a priori*. Thus for each of the concrete situations we imagined when discussing Bertrand's paradox we found it natural to adopt such a conjecture in advance of special information about the results of a succession of trials. And we normally proceed in this way when dealing with games of chance. If, for example, we are satisfied that a die is a cube of homogeneous material, we assume in advance of all evidence from observed frequencies that the probability of its falling with the number six uppermost is $\frac{1}{6}$. It may perhaps be said that we have plenty of evidence about the frequency of sixes in the falling of similar dice. This is certainly relevant, but I do not think it suffices to explain our conjecture. If an intelligent man who had never heard of any regular solid other than a cube were asked to bet on the fall of a regular icosahedron of homogeneous material, he would have no difficulty in reaching the conclusion that the probability of its falling with a certain face uppermost was $\frac{1}{20}$. There is admittedly something puzzling in this, for we seem to be claiming that we can discover interesting truths about nature by *a priori* methods; but it is surely false to suggest, as some frequency theorists have done, that we should abandon all use of *a priori* conjectures in such situations. We should rather try to explain their status and the way in which they can be used legitimately.

In the past *a priori* estimates of this kind have usually been justified by the principle of indifference; and conversely, the fact that we make such estimates has been adduced as an argument in favour of the principle. But the situation is much more complex than it appears at first sight. Sometimes, for example, the argument requires one or other of Poincaré's theorems about approximation to equality of chances. In any case it must always involve some assumptions about the world. Presented in full, the reasoning in favour of a relatively *a priori* conjecture of probability about the fall of a die would be as follows: 'If the laws of nature governing the fall of dice are what I assume them to be in the light of my previous experience with various other bodies and this die is a cube of homogeneous material, as it seems to be, the probability of its falling with six uppermost is $\frac{1}{6}$, because according to my assumptions this result is one of six equipossible alternatives. I admit that there may be some undetected irregularity in the die, and even that there may be laws of nature of a kind quite incompatible with current theories of mechanics, e.g. a law that if a die of platinum is cast at the moment at which a comet strikes a planet of an extra-galactic star, it must fall with a prime number uppermost; but I will dismiss such speculations for the present.' If, after making a conjecture of probability in this way, I find that the frequency of sixes in a long run of trials is considerably greater than $\frac{1}{6}$, I do not hesitate to adopt a new estimate based on the observed frequency, and I justify my change of estimate by saying: 'Apparently the conditions I assumed in making my first conjecture are not fulfilled. Either there is some irregularity in the die or there is some hitherto unsuspected law of nature favouring the fall of a die with six uppermost.' From this it is clear that the original thesis was strictly speaking an hypothetical proposition with the suggested probability rule as apodosis. This hypothetical proposition is absolutely *a priori*, and cannot be refuted, or even rendered unplausible by experience; but, just because it is hypothetical, it must not be confused with probability rules which have been inferred directly from experience.

Once the distinction has been made clear, relatively *a priori* conjectures of probability may be used with perfect propriety. On occasions they may be the only estimates we can make, i.e. when no special information about frequencies is available. But they are most useful when they can be compared with estimates inferred directly from frequencies; and for this purpose it is essential that they should be recognized for what they are, namely, the apodoses of hypothetical propositions. If an *a priori* estimate is confirmed by experience, we say that the assumptions on which it is based are also confirmed and that they explain the frequency found in experience. If, however, the frequency found in experience is notably different from the previously estimated probability, we think it necessary to revise our assumptions. We have not in either case a conclusive argument. For any suggestion of probability (other than o or 1) is compatible with any observed frequency. But we have at least an indication of great value. If a die which appeared to be a regular cube of homogeneous material nevertheless turned up six in ten successive throws, I should be prepared to bet a very large sum that it was loaded. If further examination with the best possible instruments revealed no fault and the die turned up six in a hundred successive throws, I should be prepared to consider the suggestion that a hitherto-unnoticed law of nature favoured the fall of dice with six uppermost in certain special circumstances. The second supposition is fantastic, but arguments which are essentially of the same kind play an important part in some scientific inquiries. When, for example, psychologists examine the evidence for telepathy, they compare the frequency of right answers given by their subjects in certain tests with what they call pure chance or the *a priori* probability of a subject's giving the right answer, i.e. the probability which there would be if there were no factors favouring right answers as such. If in a long sequence of trials the frequency of right answers is notably higher than the *a priori* probability, they argue that it is reasonable to assume some favourable factor not yet identified. Such an argument does not by itself enable scientists to formulate a new law of nature in precise fashion; but it indicates that it is worth while to look for a law of a certain sort, and in some fields of inquiry which are of great complexity it may be the only profitable way of starting a search for uniformities.

The justification of this line of reasoning is part of the general problem of induction, but it is interesting to notice that there can be no place for relatively *a priori* conjectures in the frequency theory of probability. If a supporter of that theory wishes to explain the procedure of a scientist inquiring about telepathy, he must say that the so-called *a priori* probability is really the empirically ascertained probability of getting a right answer from some non-human source, e.g. from a machine which registers a card name each time a card is exposed to the agent. But, so far as I know, statistics about right answers from such a machine have not been collected by any inquirer who talks of pure chance or *a priori* probabilities. And, even if they were, precisely the same argument could be applied to them as to the statistics about replies from human beings, i.e. we could still ask whether the observed frequency agreed with the *a priori* probability of a right answer from such a machine. Furthermore, the fact, if it were a fact, that human beings gave more right answers than machines in the test conditions would have no theoretical interest for a person who lacked all ambition to *explain* empirically ascertained probability rules by showing how they could be derived from principles of possibility and impossibility. If a frequency theorist were consistent, he would content himself in such a case with recording the difference of frequencies.

§ 38. ATTEMPTS TO JUSTIFY INDUCTION BY USE OF THE INVERSION
THEOREM

The earliest attempt to justify induction within the calculus of
chances is that of Laplace, and it is concerned with the estimation
of probabilities rather than with the establishment of laws. Laplace was interested in the practical applications of the theory of
probability, but he realized that no probabilities of any great importance can be determined *a priori*. He therefore proposed to
show how probabilities could be derived from frequencies by an
inversion of Bernoulli's theorem. It must be admitted that an
attempt to invert Bernoulli's theorem looks at least plausible. In
a letter of 1703, addressed to Leibniz, Bernoulli said he thought
such an inversion possible. Leibniz admitted that men seemed to
argue as though the inverse of Bernoulli's theorem were true, but
did not admit that such reasoning was legitimate.[1] In the fourth
part of his unfinished *Ars Conjectandi* Bernoulli promised to show
how probabilities could be derived from frequencies,[2] but he did
not fulfil his promise. When Laplace offered a proof of the inversion a century later he used the inversion formula of Bayes, which
had been enunciated after the time of Bernoulli, and this supposed
proof of Laplace has become so closely associated in the minds
of mathematicians with the use of Bayes's formula that the work
of Laplace is sometimes fathered on Bayes. The supposed inversion of Bernoulli's theorem is often described as Bayes's theorem.
This is unfortunate, because it is not the work of Bayes and, as I
shall try to show, it is not a genuine theorem.

Bernoulli's theorem may be described loosely as an argument
from probability to frequency, and this no doubt is why a number
of distinguished persons, including Bernoulli himself, have supposed that the argument from frequency to probability which they
want can be got by an inversion of the theorem. But there can be
no simple inversion of Bernoulli's theorem, since it is properly
speaking an hypothetical proposition in which both protasis and
apodosis are propositions about probability. In order to state the
argument of Laplace precisely and at the same time make it look
plausible we must rewrite Bernoulli's theorem in some new symbolism. First, let us introduce the notion of an ordered dyad of
characters, that is, the notion of a couple of characters, say, α-ness

---

[1] Leibniz, *Gesammelte Werke*, ed. Pertz and Gerhardt, Dritte Folge (Mathematik), vol. iii, pp. 71–97.   [2] p. 224.

and β-ness, considered in a certain order, and agree to use the symbol δ as a general term for such dyads. Next let us suppose that if $P(\alpha, \beta) = p$, this truth can be regarded as the possession of a character by the dyad of α-ness and β-ness. The symbol π_p will serve to connote this character. Similarly if $F_n(\alpha, \beta) = f$, we may try to express the fact by saying that the dyad has a character connoted by the symbol ${}^n\phi_f$. It is not easy to define the meanings of our new symbols shortly in words, but the way in which they are to be used should be clear from the explanations I have given. The important thing to remember is that they are all supposed to connote characters of ordered dyads. With this apparatus we can now rewrite Bernoulli's theorem as follows:

For any h, however small,

$$\lim_{n \to \infty} P(\delta\pi_p, {}^n\phi_{\overline{p \pm h}}) = 1.$$

Here the theorem no longer looks like an hypothetical proposition, and it seems reasonable to talk of inversion. Written in the same symbolism, what Laplace tries to prove is the proposition:

For any h, however small,

$$\lim_{n \to \infty} P(\delta^n\phi_f, \pi_{\overline{f \pm h}}) = 1.$$

Relying on the developed form of the inversion formula of Bayes, he first asserts that

$$P(\delta^n\phi_f, \pi_f) = \frac{P(\delta, \pi_f)P(\delta\pi_f, {}^n\phi_f)}{\int_0^1 P(\delta, \pi_x)P(\delta\pi_x, {}^n\phi_f)\, dx}.$$

Here the integration sign must be used in the denominator instead of the ordinary symbolism for addition, because there are infinitely many values between 0 and 1 which a probability may have and we cannot list them all. Next Laplace assumes on the strength of the principle of indifference that there is the same initial probability for each of these various values and cancels out all terms of the form $P(\delta, \pi_x)$. In the resulting expression there remain only terms of the form $P(\delta\pi_x, {}^n\phi_f)$ which can be calculated by Bernoulli's procedure. But there are infinitely many of them to be summed in the denominator, and, although $P(\delta\pi_f, {}^n\phi_f)$, which appears as numerator, is the largest of them all, it tends towards 0 as n increases (except in the special case where $f = 0$ or 1). Laplace therefore considers the value of $P(\delta^n\phi_f, \pi_{\overline{f \pm h}})$. This is, of course, the sum of the probabilities for all the various alternatives covered by $\pi_{\underline{f\pm h}}$ and may be expressed as follows:

$$P(\delta^n\phi_f, \pi_{\underline{f\pm h}}) = \frac{\int_{f-h}^{f+h} P(\delta\pi_x, {}^n\phi_f)\, dx}{\int_{0}^{1} P(\delta\pi_x, {}^n\phi_f)\, dx}.$$

Here each of the terms covered by the integrations is of the form:

$${}^nC_{fn}(1-x)^{n-fn}x^{fn}.$$

The factor ${}^nC_{fn}$ can be cancelled throughout, and we then get:

$$P(\delta^n\phi_f, \pi_{\underline{f\pm h}}) = \frac{\int_{f-h}^{f+h} (1-x)^{n-fn}x^{fn}\, dx}{\int_{0}^{1} (1-x)^{n-fn}x^{fn}\, dx}.$$

This can be shown to tend towards 1 with increasing n, however small h may be, and so it seems Laplace has proved the inverse of Bernoulli's theorem.

Not content with this result, Laplace tries to evaluate exactly the *total probability* that the next α thing examined will turn out to be β when the number of α things examined up to date is n and m of these have turned out to be β. He argues that to get this total probability we must multiply each possible value of $P(\alpha, \beta)$ by the probability which it has in relation to the observed frequency and then add the products together by integration. This procedure gives the surprisingly simple result:

$$\frac{\int_{0}^{1} (1-x)^{n-m}x^{m+1}\, dx}{\int_{0}^{1} (1-x)^{n-m}x^{m}\, dx} = \frac{m+1}{n+2},$$

which is called Laplace's Rule of Succession.

If this rule were sound it would be extremely useful. Nor is authoritative support lacking. De Morgan, Jevons, and Karl Pearson have all given it their blessing. But even last century, when Laplace's reputation as a writer on probability was higher than it is now, there were critics such as Boole. And to-day it is generally admitted that the rule must be a mistake, since it leads to absurdity and self-contradiction. Let us suppose, for example, that we have a game something like roulette in which any trial must give one of three possible results, say, red, white, or blue. We do not know what the probabilities are for these different results, but we try to apply Laplace's rule of succession after we have made three trials and got a different result each time. We can argue that, since red has occurred once in three trials, the probability that it will occur next time is

$$\frac{1+1}{3+2} = \frac{2}{5},$$

and so for each of the other colours. But the sum of these probabilities should be 1, since one and one only of the colours must occur, whereas the sum according to Laplace's rule would be $\frac{6}{5}$. Again, the rule of succession leads to conclusions which are in flat contradiction with the premises from which it is supposed to be derived. Laplace assumes that initially $P(\alpha, \beta)$ is as likely to have any value as any other. That is why he cancels out terms like $P(\delta, \pi_x)$ in his application of Bayes's formula. But if we try to apply his rule in the case in which we have observed no α things at all, we get as the probability for the first α thing's being β $(0+1)/(0+2)$ or $\frac{1}{2}$, which is in contradiction with the assumption that apart from reference to frequencies any value of $P(\alpha, \beta)$ is as likely as any other.

It is clear that we must abandon the rule of succession, attractive though it may appear at first sight. And it is not difficult to discover one place where Laplace has gone wrong in his attempt to prove it. He has relied on the notoriously fallacious principle of indifference. But his use of this principle occurs already in his supposed proof of the inverse of Bernoulli's theorem and should therefore bring that supposed proof into discredit. Some writers on probability are nevertheless reluctant to give up Laplace's project entirely, and so attempts have been made to show that his inversion of Bernoulli's theorem does not require the principle of indifference. It has been argued that with increasing n the value of $P(\delta^n \phi_f, \pi_{\underline{f \pm h}})$ tends to 1, whatever the values of initial probabilities such as $P(\delta, \pi_f)$ may be. But this reform of Laplace's procedure does not meet all the difficulties. Laplace assumes that it is initially possible for $P(\alpha, \beta)$ to have any value from 0 to 1 inclusive, and it is on this assumption that his use of the integral calculus rests. But this is as much as to say that there are infinitely many hypotheses whose initial probabilities add up to 1 although all are greater than 0, from which it follows that some at least of the initial probabilities must be infinitesimal, i.e. less than any assignable fraction. According to Laplace's further assumption that these various hypotheses are equally likely at the beginning, *all* the initial probabilities must be infinitesimal, but we have already condemned his use of the principle of indifference and may therefore neglect this complication. Now in certain contexts it may be possible to give a meaning to the phrase 'infinitesimal probability', but Laplace has not justified his usage, and according to his own definitions the way in which he talks of infinitesimal probabilities is strictly without sense. This is fatal to his argument; for no amount of mathematical ingenuity in the use of integration can derive a valid result from senseless premisses.

It may be remarked in passing that Laplace's use of integration in the numerator of his fraction

$$\frac{\int_{f-h}^{f+h} (1-x)^{n-fn} x^{fn}\, dx}{\int_{0}^{1} (1-x)^{n-fn} x^{fn}\, dx}$$

prevents him from applying his formula to the justification of universal induction, i.e. the induction of laws. For if all α things have been found to be β, i.e. if $F_n(\alpha, \beta) = 1$, we can only argue from this by Laplace's procedure that $P(\alpha, \beta)$ is very probably near to 1, whereas what we normally wish to argue is that $P(\alpha, \beta)$ probably equals 1 exactly. This point has been overlooked by Jevons and others who see in Laplace's work the solution of all the problems of induction, including the establishment of laws.

Lord Keynes has tried to state in his *Treatise on Probability* the conditions which would have to be satisfied for a legitimate application of the inversion formula to the problem of induction. He does not himself put much faith in this use of the formula, but his treatment is the most satisfactory I have met. His fundamental notion is that in any valid application of the inversion formula there must be finite initial probabilities for the hypotheses to be considered. This requirement in turn involves the consequence that in any problem to be solved by the formula there should be only a finite number of possible hypotheses. It will be sufficient for our purpose to notice how he considers the inversion formula might be applied in the induction of laws.[1] For convenience of comparison I shall try to express the argument in the symbolism which I have used for expounding Laplace's theory, although it is somewhat more complicated than the symbolism used by Lord Keynes himself in this connexion.

If the number of α things examined is n and they have all been found to be β, we may ascribe the predicate $^n\phi_1$ to the dyad of α-ness and β-ness. Similarly the hypothesis that all α things are β, i.e. a suggestion of law, may be expressed by the ascription of π_1 to the dyad. Using the inversion formula we can now write:

$$P(\delta^n\phi_1, \pi_1) = \frac{P(\delta, \pi_1)P(\delta\pi_1, {}^n\phi_1)}{P(\delta, {}^n\phi_1)}.$$

But $P(\delta\pi_1, {}^n\phi_1) = 1$, since a law obviously entails a regularity in experience, and our equation can therefore be reduced to the form:

$$P(\delta^n\phi_1, \pi_1) = \frac{P(\delta, \pi_1)}{P(\delta, {}^n\phi_1)}.$$

In other words, the probability of the law in relation to the observed regularity is the initial probability of the law divided by the initial probability of the regularity. The denominator of this expression can be expanded, however, as follows:

$$\begin{aligned}
P(\delta, {}^n\phi_1) &= P(\delta, {}^n\phi_1\pi_1 \vee {}^n\phi_1\sim\pi_1) \\
&= P(\delta, {}^n\phi_1\pi_1) + P(\delta, {}^n\phi_1\sim\pi_1) \\
&= P(\delta, \pi_1)P(\delta\pi_1, {}^n\phi_1) + P(\delta, \sim\pi_1)P(\delta\sim\pi_1, {}^n\phi_1) \\
&= P(\delta, \pi_1) + P(\delta, \sim\pi_1)P(\delta\sim\pi_1, {}^n\phi_1).
\end{aligned}$$

We therefore have

$$P(\delta^n\phi_1, \pi_1) = \frac{P(\delta, \pi_1)}{P(\delta, \pi_1) + P(\delta, \sim\pi_1)P(\delta\sim\pi_1, {}^n\phi_1)},$$

and it is clear that the value of $P(\delta^n\phi_1, \pi_1)$ must tend towards 1 as n increases, provided only that $P(\delta, \pi_1)$ has some finite value and that the value of $P(\delta\sim\pi_1, {}^n\phi_1)$ decreases as n increases. But the value of this last term should decrease as n increases, because on the supposition that there is no law the probability of finding all the α things examined to be β should become smaller and smaller as we examine more α things.

[1] *Treatise on Probability*, ch. xx. His discussion of the inversion of Bernoulli's theorem, which is a good deal more complicated, will be found in ch. xxxi.

The merits of this argument have been developed at length by Nicod in his *Foundations of Geometry and Induction*. He suggests that for a complete solution of the problem of the induction of laws we need only to prove that $P(\delta^n\phi_1, \pi_1)$ can be raised *as near as we like* to 1, which he thinks not yet established. He also suggests that this argument, which is essentially the method of induction by simple enumeration, does not involve any difficult assumptions such as those required by the eliminative argument which Lord Keynes favours. This point can be discussed most conveniently when we have examined the eliminative argument within the calculus of chances.

§ 39. THE ARGUMENT FROM RESTRICTION OF ALTERNATIVES

We must now notice another attempt to justify induction within the theory of chances. I shall call it the argument from restriction of alternatives. Just as the use of the inversion formula is supposed to provide a justification for induction by simple enumeration, so this argument is supposed to provide a justification for induction by elimination. We have already seen that induction cannot be reduced to a method of elimination, but it is interesting to examine a modern version of the doctrine.

Lord Keynes has a low opinion of induction by simple enumeration, especially as used for the establishment of probability rules. He writes:

'Let the reader be clear about this. To argue from the *mere* fact that a given event has occurred invariably in a thousand instances under observation, without any analysis of the circumstances accompanying the individual instances, that it is likely to occur invariably in future instances, is a feeble inductive argument. . . . Nevertheless an argument of this kind is not entirely worthless. . . . But to argue, without analysis of the instances, from the mere fact that a given event has a frequency of 10% in the thousand instances under observation, or even in a million instances, that its probability is $\frac{1}{10}$ for the next instance or that it is likely to have a frequency near to $\frac{1}{10}$ in a further set of observations, is a far feebler argument; indeed it is hardly an argument at all. Yet a good deal of statistical argument is not free from this reproach.'

He proposes to apply his own method both to universal induction which establishes laws and to statistical induction which establishes probability rules. 'The analysis of statistical induction', he says, 'is not fundamentally different from that of universal induction. . . . But it is much more complicated.'[1] I shall confine myself to expounding the account of universal induction which he gives in the third part of his work, for this includes all the questions of principle which are involved and exhibits them in a relatively simple form.

The ideal of scientific reasoning as represented by Lord Keynes is an argument somewhat like Mill's method of agreement for the discovery of causes. It is supposed that we have a number of α things which are all β. If we could say that there were no resemblances between the instances except in α-ness and β-ness, then, apparently, we should have the best possible grounds for making the generalization that all α things are β. There would be a perfect argument from analogy.[2] But we are never in a position to say that there are no resemblances between our cases except those included in the scope of our generalization. The best that we can do is to look for varied instances. The greater the variety of our instances, the less likely it is that they resemble each other in some unnoticed way. Indeed, the multiplication of instances is valuable only in so far as the instances are varied. A new instance which differed only numerically from one already observed would add nothing to the probability of our generalization. But new instances may be varied even when we cannot see them to be so, and it is therefore proper to allow something for the number of confirming instances although they may seem alike in all respects. It may perhaps be objected that, however varied our instances may be, they are all alike in being drawn from a certain finite region of space and time which we have been able to observe up to date, and that this resemblance, which is not included in the scope of our generalization, can never be eliminated by any method at our disposal. To this Lord Keynes replies that we are able to eliminate absolute position in space and time by an *a priori* judgement of their irrelevance to natural laws. It is this possibility of eliminating spatial and temporal position, he thinks, which philosophers have in mind when they speak of the uniformity of nature as an *a priori* principle required for induction.

Although Lord Keynes maintains that the best scientific reasoning follows the pattern he has described here, it is not at all clear to me what his method is supposed to establish. Apparently he

---

[1] *Treatise on Probability*, pp. 407–8.
[2] Lord Keynes's use of the word 'analogy' is peculiar. For him it means apparently the same as 'likeness'.

does not think of all scientific generalizations as simply convertible, for he often stresses the increase of probability to be obtained by making the first term of an hypothesis of law more specific and the second less specific. And yet, according to his exposition of the method of analogy, the information obtained by analysis of a number of things which are both α and β would be just as good evidence for the generalization that all β things are α as for the generalization that all α things are β. In the limiting case where the proposition that all α things are β is established by perfect analogy it is said to be all-important that there are no resemblances between the instances except those included in the scope of our generalization. But we should presumably wish to reach exactly the same position if we were trying to establish by this method that all β things are α. Discovery of some β things which were not α would, of course, rule out the hypothesis that all β things are α, but then the argument by which Lord Keynes thinks we can establish that all α things are β would also collapse. For the sort of eliminative reasoning he favours would be useful only in a search for reciprocal connexions. If we try to show that α-ness necessitates β-ness by eliminating other characters which might at first be supposed to necessitate β-ness but are not in fact found in all our instances of β-ness, we need two premisses. First we must assume that some character found together with β-ness in our instances necessitates it. And secondly we must assume that nothing which is absent in any instances where β-ness is present can be a character necessitating it. But this second assumption is just the doctrine that all necessitation is reciprocal.

However this may be, it is clear that the argument is supposed to depend on the reduction of the number of hypotheses which need be considered. We start with a number of possible suggestions about characters which may necessitate β-ness and we assume that whenever one of them is eliminated the probabilities of the remaining suggestions are raised. How is this assumption to be justified? Only by the further assumption that the number of possible hypotheses is finite. If there were infinitely many possible hypotheses, elimination of some would not raise the probabilities of those that remained. But if the number of hypotheses is restricted in some way, induction by elimination may be supposed to give us higher and higher probabilities. We cannot expect more than this; for we do not know how many possible hypotheses there are to be considered, and, although we may on some occasion eliminate all but the true hypothesis, we can never know that we have done this. Our situation is something like that of a man who buys a ticket in a lottery, knowing that the prize will go to the holder of the ticket which is left in the urn after all others have been drawn for cancellation. At the beginning the man has some finite chance of winning the prize, since the number of tickets is finite, but he cannot say what the chance is, not knowing how many tickets there are. It is always possible that his own ticket may be drawn at some time for cancellation, but so long as other tickets are being cancelled and his own remains uncancelled he can be sure that his chance of winning is improving. For the range of alternatives which was originally restricted has been restricted still further.

We therefore reach the conclusion that in order to justify the inductive procedure which Lord Keynes favours it is necessary to assume what he calls the limitation of independent variety. His simplest formulation of this postulate is contained in the following statement:

'We can justify the method of perfect analogy, and other inductive methods in so far as they can be made to approximate to this, by means of the assumption that the objects in the field, over which our generalizations extend, do not have an infinite number of independent qualities; that, in other words, their characteristics, however numerous, cohere together in groups of invariable connection, which are finite in number.'[1]

From this assumption he thinks he can derive the consequence that 'if we find two sets of characters in coexistence there is a finite probability that they belong to the same group, and a finite probability also that the first set specifies this group uniquely'.[2] When once this has been granted, he says, we may hope to increase the probability and make it large.

It is interesting to notice that the justification of induction within the theory of chances by the use of the inversion formula seems to require Lord Keynes's doctrine of the limitation of independent variety just as much as the theory of induction by elimination. We have seen that in a legitimate application of the inversion formula the hypotheses to be considered must have finite initial probabilities. Such finite initial probabilities can be obtained, if at all, only from a principle such as Lord Keynes enunciates in the passage quoted. It is not unplausible, therefore, for Lord

---

[1] *Treatise on Probability*, p. 256.　　　　[2] Ibid., p. 253.

Keynes to suggest that his principle is a fundamental postulate of induction. But, as he remarks, Bacon is alone among the older writers on induction in saying anything explicit about a limitation of the number of possible hypotheses. And in recent literature he discovers only some articles of Professor Broad to support his contention that induction presupposes a limitation of the variety of nature.[1] Perhaps this neglect is not very surprising. For when Lord Keynes comes to ask himself what grounds there are for accepting his principle, he can discover none which are satisfactory. He will not pretend that he knows its truth *a priori*, and he is driven to saying that it is itself made probable by the success which attends its use in induction. This is a suggestion of the same sort as that which Mill made about the principle of universal causation. And, although it is more subtle in form, it is no more sound. I do not propose to discuss it here, because I am going to put forward a fundamental objection to all attempts to justify induction within the theory of chances and, if my argument is correct, criticism of detail is unnecessary.

§ 40. A FUNDAMENTAL OBJECTION TO ALL ATTEMPTS TO JUSTIFY INDUCTION WITHIN THE THEORY OF CHANCES

It is now time to discuss the fundamental question whether the probability which attaches to the conclusion of an induction can be brought within the theory of chances. I wish to maintain that it cannot. If this is the right answer to the question, all such attempts to justify induction as those we have just considered must be mistaken exercises of ingenuity.

Let us first consider the nature of the propositions which we try to establish by ampliative induction. They are either laws or probability rules. Both kinds of propositions have received varying interpretations from philosophers, but I have argued that laws are to be regarded as principles of necessary connexion between characters and that probability rules are to be analysed in terms of necessitation and independence between characters. It is important to realize that philosophers who try to justify induction within the theory of chances accept these interpretations implicitly if not explicitly.

---

[1] 'The Relation between Induction and Probability' in *Mind*, xxvii (1918) and xxix (1920). Although their argument is, I believe, mistaken, these articles are extremely interesting and contain the most intelligible presentation of the view with which we are here concerned.

When, for example, Lord Keynes and Nicod talk of the initial probability of an hypothesis of law in relation to the principle of the limitation of independent variety, they must be supposing that the law is a proposition of necessary connexion. They tell us that according to the inversion formula the probability of a suggested law in relation to an observed uniformity is equal to the initial probability of the law divided by the initial probability of the uniformity. If, however, the law were only a larger conjunction of the same sort as that found in experience, there would be no reason at all to suppose that

$$\frac{P(\delta, \pi_1)}{P(\delta, {}^n\phi_1)}$$

tended towards 1 as n increased. For according to this interpretation of the nature of a law the numerator of the fraction could be written in the form $P(\delta, {}^\infty\phi_1)$ and any argument which showed that the denominator decreased towards 0 with increasing n would show also that the numerator was infinitesimal from the beginning. Lord Keynes's language leaves no doubt, however, that he regards laws as principles of necessary connexion between characters. Similarly, he and other philosophers who try to bring the inductive establishment of probability rules within the theory of chances must regard the probabilities they try to estimate as definable in some such way as that I have suggested. For, on the one hand, they show by their reliance on induction that the probabilities with which they are concerned are not to be explained subjectively by reference to the principle of indifference, and, on the other hand, they distinguish those probabilities from frequencies.

Now it is a mistake to suppose that there can be chances for or against the holding of such propositions as we try to establish by induction. It is only reasonable to speak of chances where it is also reasonable to speak of equipossible alternatives. But there can be no alternatives to the holding of a necessary connexion or to the holding of a probability relation. If α-ness necessitates β-ness, this truth cannot be one among a number of possibilities. For truths of principle, unlike matters of fact, are not set in a context of alternatives. It is true that we can always conceive the contradictory of an hypothesis of natural law, but we have seen that conceivability is no sure proof of possibility. The fact that I can in some sense understand the sentence 'There is an even number greater than two which is not the sum of two primes' does not entitle me to say that Goldbach's conjecture is false, nor yet that the conjecture, if true, is only one among a number of alternative possibilities. Similarly, when I put forward an hypothesis of natural law in a sentence of the form 'α-ness may necessitate β-ness', I do not use the word 'may' for the statement of a new kind of principle, more fundamental even than the principles we have already considered. I assert only that I have in mind no information which formally excludes the proposition that α-ness necessitates β-ness. If I presently discover an α thing which is not β, I withdraw my statement, because I then have information which entitles me to say that α-ness does not necessitate β-ness. There is, of course, a similarity between this use of 'may' and its use in the statement of principles of possibility. If, therefore, we find such phraseology convenient, we can speak reasonably of second-order possibility. But we should recognize that we are not justified in going on to talk of second-order chances.

The unsatisfactoriness of all attempts to bring induction within the theory of chances is illustrated very clearly by the curious assumptions we have to introduce in order to make the arguments of the last two sections seem plausible. When, for example, we try to work out what is involved in talking of the chances of there being a certain probability relation between two characters, we must first think of the characters as constituting an ordered pair and then suppose that there is some initial probability of this dyad's exemplifying a certain probability relationship *simply because it is a dyad of characters*. Similarly, the occurrence of a certain frequency of β things in a set of α things containing n members must be treated, for the purposes of one argument at least, as the exemplification of a certain relationship by the dyad of α-ness and β-ness, in order that we may presently say there is some initial probability for the exemplification of that relationship by *any* dyad of characters. This second assumption is difficult enough, but the first, which is essential, as we have seen, for any attempt to justify induction within the theory of chances, is fantastic. The fact that many mathematicians and philosophers have nevertheless made such attempts is to be explained by two circumstances. In the first place, the nature of the assumptions involved has often been concealed by inadequate symbolism; and, secondly, the project of dealing with induction in this way has been encouraged by the indifference theory, which makes ignorance a sufficient ground for assertions of initial probability.

The conclusion that the probability attaching to results of induction cannot be the same as probability in matters of chance is confirmed by reflection on our ordinary judgements. No one believes seriously that the probability of a scientific generalization or theory could be represented properly by a fraction. But if the probability of such a proposition is the proportion of chances in favour of its being true, there must be some fraction which represents that probability correctly. For it follows from the definition of probability in matters of chance that it is always measurable by a fraction,[1] even although the fraction may be unknown to us. Lord Keynes goes so far as to admit that some second-order probabilities are not measurable even in principle, but he does not see that this admission involves a distinction between two senses of 'probability'. The difference between being measurable and being not measurable even in principle is so great that it cannot be treated as a minor point.

The need for a distinction between two senses of 'probability' has been admitted more or less explicitly in recent years by a number of writers, but it has not been explained when and why the results of induction may be called probable. That is the problem to which we must turn in the last part of this book.

§ 41. SAMPLING AND THE USE OF STATISTICS

Although the problem of ampliative induction cannot be solved within the calculus of chances, the theory of sampling which is usually studied in connexion with the calculus has great importance for certain branches of inductive science, and it will be convenient to consider the subject very briefly here.

All ampliative induction may be described as the making of inferences from samples, but not all inference from samples is inductive in the sense in which I have used that word, and sometimes the propositions for which a sample provides evidence may be said to have probability in the sense of the theory of chances. This occurs only when the larger class about which we hope to obtain information from our sample is a finite population, e.g. the class of all persons now living in the United Kingdom. It may then be possible in principle to apply the inversion formula, but even so we can rarely obtain any precise estimate of the probability of a proposition about the composition of the population in those cases

---

[1] Or rather, that it would always be so measurable, if our terms were perfectly definite.

which are of most interest. The difficulty can be illustrated by a simple analogy.

Let us suppose first that we have a box in which there are four bags, the first containing three white balls, the second two white balls and one black, the third one white ball and two black, and the fourth three black balls. If a ball is drawn at random from one of the bags and found to be black, what in relation to this evidence is the probability of its being from the last bag? Here we have a simple problem to be solved by the use of the inversion formula. Writing α for 'drawn from one of the bags in the box', β for 'black', γ_0 for 'drawn from the bag containing no black balls', γ_1 for 'drawn from the bag containing one black ball' and so forth, we have:

$$P(\alpha\beta, \gamma_3) = \frac{P(\alpha, \gamma_3)P(\alpha\gamma_3, \beta)}{\sum\limits_{j=0}^{3} P(\alpha, \gamma_j)P(\alpha\gamma_j, \beta)}.$$

And, since the initial probabilities may be assumed equal,[1] this can be reduced to:

$$P(\alpha\beta, \gamma_3) = \frac{1}{0 + \frac{1}{3} + \frac{2}{3} + 1} = \frac{1}{2}.$$

Let us now suppose that instead of four bags we have only one and that we know it contains three balls, each of them either white or black. If a ball is drawn at random and found to be black, what in relation to this evidence is the probability of its being from a bag containing three black balls? The problem seems very similar to that with which we started. We can say that there are only four possible compositions for the population of the single bag and that each of these corresponds to the composition of the population in one of the four bags of our first problem. There is, however, an important difference. We may write α for 'drawn from a bag containing three balls each of them either white or black', β for 'black', γ_0 for 'drawn from a bag containing no black balls', γ_1 for 'drawn from a bag containing one black ball' and so forth, but we are not entitled to assume without further question that the initial probabilities, $P(\alpha, \gamma_0)$, $P(\alpha, \gamma_1)$, &c., are equal, and we have no means of estimating their values except induction from observation of many similar bags. When an investigator wishes to determine the probability of a certain composition for a population

---

[1] The word 'random' in the enunciation of our problem allows this.

from which he has drawn a sample, his situation is commonly like that of a person who tries to solve our second problem. He knows at least roughly the size of the population with which he has to deal, and he knows that there are only certain possible compositions for it with respect to the characters in which he is interested. He can calculate for each of these possible compositions what would be the probability of his getting the sample he has if that composition were realized in the population. But he has no *a priori* knowledge of the initial probabilities of the different possible compositions, and, although he may be able to make an estimate of these initial probabilities from empirical evidence, this will rarely be precise enough to justify an elaborate argument in the calculus of chances.

It may be, for example, that the investigator wishes to discover what proportion of the population of a South Sea island belong to a certain blood group. If he knows there are about two thousand persons living on the island and finds that 13 in a sample of 100 belong to the blood group in which he is interested, how is he to use this evidence? He may have reason to believe as a result of induction from previous observations in the Pacific that in general the probability of a South Sea islander's belonging to the group is $\frac{1}{8}$. With this assumption he can try to make an estimate of the initial probabilities for the various possible compositions of the population of this island; but his problem may be complicated already by the consideration that an individual's membership of the blood group is not independent of the membership of neighbouring individuals, since the character is inherited. The next step in an application of the inversion formula would be to calculate the probability of his getting a sample such as he has obtained on each of the possible hypotheses about the composition of the total population. Here again the problem may be complicated by consideration of the relationships between the individuals constituting the sample. But if all the special difficulties of this special type of investigation can be overcome, a strict application of the inversion formula will yield about two thousand different probabilities for as many different hypotheses about the composition of the population. Some of them will be extremely small and none will be large enough to be useful by itself. The best conclusion he can hope to draw is that the number of persons in the population who belong to the indicated blood group very probably lies within certain limits. In practice no experienced investigator would waste much time on calculations of this kind, because the data do not justify the effort. He would content himself with trying to get a sample that was both large and fair, and then assume that the proportion of the total population belonging to the group which interested him was in the neighbourhood of the ratio found in the sample, unless such a proportion seemed very unlikely in the light of any previous induction, in which case he would examine the evidence more thoroughly and try to determine whether the discrepancy arose from a peculiarity of the population as a whole or from a peculiarity of his sample.

The size of the sample from which we argue is important because when this is great the various expressions of the form $P(\alpha\gamma_j, \beta)$ will differ greatly in value and the differences between the initial probabilities be correspondingly less important. But it is also desirable that the sample should be fair. In saying this we do not mean that the sample should have the same proportion of members in the indicated group as the total population, for that could be determined only by one who already knew the composition of the total population. We mean rather that it should not contain an undue proportion of individuals with characters that are either favourably or unfavourably relevant to the character in which we are interested. Thus anyone who was trying to determine by the method of sampling what proportion of the population of the United Kingdom are foreign born would not behave wisely if he took as his sample the hundred persons whose names appear last in the *London Telephone Directory*, because it is known that persons whose names being with Z form a very small part of the total population and that possession of this character is favourably relevant to foreign birth. Even when we are ignorant of the mutual relevance of characters in the population with which we have to deal, we may still do something to make our sample fair by arranging for the various classes of the population to be represented in it so far as possible according to their known strength. If, for instance, we wish to forecast the result of a general election by means of a straw vote, we should question men and women, young and old, northerners and southerners, rich and poor, workers in different occupations, members of different religious sects, &c., and try to make our sample what is sometimes called a representative cross-section of the voting population.

The two requirements for the reliability of a sample, namely, size and fairness, are both justified, as we have seen, by the calculus of chances in those cases where the sample is taken from a finite population, but even here it is not possible to lay down any precise rules by which to determine when a sample is large enough or fair enough. The investigator's decision to be content with a sample of a certain size is a practical choice. He uses the method of sampling precisely because he cannot hope to examine each member of the population, and he must set against the advantage to be expected from taking a larger sample the expenditure of time and effort which that would involve. Much depends, therefore, on the importance of the estimate he has to make. Before accepting a sample as fair the investigator must naturally use all the knowledge he already possesses about the composition of the population and the mutual relevance of various characters, but here again the general theory of chances will not provide detailed guidance. In practice each investigator must rely on his knowledge of the special subject-matter with which he is concerned, and an investigator who is highly skilled in the sampling technique appropriate to botany may not be able to cope satisfactorily with the problems of sampling in economic studies, although he should at least be more cautious than a person who has never realized the need for any technique of this kind.

When we turn from the sampling of finite populations to the use of samples for the purpose of induction, we can no longer say that our argument is justified in principle by the inversion formula, because the existence of a law or a probability rule cannot, like the existence of a certain composition in a finite population, be described as matter of chance. In the last part of this book I shall try to show how certain notions derived from the calculus of chances may be used legitimately in an argument to justify induction, but it will be sufficient to say here that size and fairness are important also in the samples we use for the purpose of induction. Some logicians who do not use the language of sampling in this connexion speak of the number and variety of the instances required to provide evidence for an induction, but the thought is the same. It has sometimes been supposed that variety of instances is important only in a theory of induction by elimination, but this is a mistake; for variety will be demanded by anyone who wishes to get the best available evidence. The fact that large and fair samples are required both for the estimation of the composition of finite populations by use of the inversion formula and for the establishment of laws or probability rules by induction is no doubt one reason why logicians have failed to distinguish between the two types of argument. Provided, however, that we are aware of the difference between them, there is nothing but advantage to be expected from an attempt to deal in general terms with their common requirements. Such an attempt has been made in recent times by statisticians.

Originally the word 'statistics' signified the collection and classification of data useful in statecraft, but in modern times its usage is both wider and more specialized. Statistical method, as it is now understood, may be usefully employed in any field of inquiry where the data have the same kind of complexity as the data of the social sciences, and, since the ways of collecting data in different fields must obviously be different, the general theory of statistics is concerned rather with the analysis and presentation of data in a form useful for inference. The obituary columns of *The Times* announce day by day the deaths of various people, and the notices which appear there are mere records of particular facts. When, however, a correspondent reports that of the centenarians who died within a certain period 70 per cent. were women, his statement is a piece of statistical analysis. Any numerical abstracts from a collection of particular facts may be called statistics, but in the use of the percentage notation we have a simple example of a special technique for bringing out those collective properties of a set of data which may be of special significance. When a ratio is expressed in this way, we can compare it easily with other ratios and notice resemblances or differences which might otherwise have escaped attention. Another familiar device of the same kind is the use of averages. If a great many children receive a special issue of milk, it is not to be expected that they will all increase in weight by exactly the same amount, and a complete record of the various changes observed in all the individuals during a stated period may convey no clear impression. When, however, the mean increase has been calculated, the evidence for an assessment of the policy can be presented in a lucid fashion. Again, in some contexts it may be of importance to show clearly the dispersion of a great many measurements of some variable magnitude, and there have been invented for this purpose numerical measures such as the standard deviation and graphical devices such as the histogram or step-curve. The common purpose of all these developments of statistical method is the presentation of masses of data in a form in which they can be readily and safely used for inference. There are, however, certain statistical devices which have been introduced specially in order to facilitate the making of inferences from samples, and it will be useful to consider one of the simplest of these.

Let us suppose that we have a sample of α things (e.g. human beings) including some that are β (e.g. vaccinated), some that are not β, some that are γ (e.g. free from small-pox) and some that are not γ. If we wish to show clearly how the two characters β-ness and γ-ness are associated in the sample, we can begin by presenting the results of our observations in tabular form. Here w is to be understood as representing the number of things in our sample which are both β and γ, x as representing the number of things which are β but not γ, and so on.

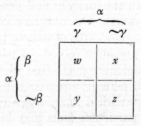

Now we say that β-ness and γ-ness are independent in our sample of α things, that is to say, without any factual association, if the proportion of $\alpha\beta$ things which are γ is the same as the proportion of α things which are γ, or in symbols, with s for the total number of α things examined, if

$$F_s(\alpha\beta, \gamma) = F_s(\alpha, \gamma).$$

As might be expected, this expression for lack of association is similar in structure to the formula for the irrelevance of characters in the calculus of chances. But it is important to remember that we are dealing here with factual relations of finite classes, not with probability rules. Interpreting the condition in terms of w, x, y, and z, we get:

$$\frac{w}{w+x} = \frac{w+y}{w+x+y+z},$$

which can be reduced in turn to the simple equation:

$$wz = xy.$$

The condition for lack of association can be stated in several other ways, e.g. by the formulae

$$F_s(\alpha\gamma, \beta) = F_s(\alpha, \beta)$$

and

$$F_s(\alpha\beta, \sim\gamma) = F_s(\alpha, \sim\gamma).$$

But interpretation of the various expressions in terms of w, x, y, and z always yields the same simple equation. It can also be shown in similar fashion that when β-ness and γ-ness are positively associated

$$wz > xy,$$

and that when they are negatively associated

$$wz < xy.$$

These considerations have suggested the introduction of a coefficient of association defined as follows:

$$Q = \frac{wz - xy}{wz + xy}.$$

If there is no association between β-ness and γ-ness in the sample, it is clear that Q must be equal to 0. If there is a complete positive association, i.e. if all β things are γ or all γ things are β or both these conditions are fulfilled, Q takes the value $+1$, because in this case either x or y or both must be equal to 0. If there is a complete negative association, i.e. if no β things are γ or no not-β things are not γ or both these conditions are fulfilled, Q takes the value -1, because in this case either w or z or both must be equal to 0. In all other cases Q has some value between $+1$ and 0 or between 0 and -1 according to the distribution of the individuals of the sample between the four sub-classes of the table.

Other devices of the same kind have been invented for more complicated situations. There is, for instance, a coefficient of correlation by the use of which we can express the degree of concomitance found in the variations of two variable magnitudes among a number of individuals, e.g. height and weight in a sample of schoolboys. Whatever the form of the device, the general purpose is the same, namely, to summarize the evidence furnished by a sample in order that it may be readily available for use in inference. It has sometimes been supposed, however, that statistical technique can in some way justify or validate the inferences we make from a sample. In order to see the error of this belief we need only reflect on the definition of the coefficient of association. If all β things in a sample of α things are γ, the coefficient of association between β-ness and γ-ness in the sample is $+1$, but such a state of affairs is quite compatible with any value for $P(\alpha\beta, \gamma)$ other than 0. In this simple case the use of the coefficient of association is superfluous, because the restricted universal statement to which it corresponds is already easy to grasp. In other cases a coefficient of association may be useful, but only because it summarizes the relations between the numbers in the four cells of our table. In short, the result of the statistician's work on a sample is not an inference to something beyond the sample, but a lucid presentation of the known facts about the sample.

PART IV

THE PROBABILITY OF INDUCTIVE SCIENCE

§ 42. RESTATEMENT OF THE PROBLEM

SINCE the time of Bacon it has been thought one of the principal tasks of philosophy to justify induction. But philosophers have not made sufficiently clear to themselves what sort of justification is required, and most of the attempts to solve the problem have been misconceived. At one time it was held necessary to establish some truth of high generality about causation which would serve as a premiss for an argument by elimination. The underlying assumption of this approach was that induction could be justified only if it was presented as a variety of deduction. We have seen, however, that induction is not always concerned with causes and that it is not an argument by elimination. Although the old way of thinking still has some defenders even among those who do not make the mistake of supposing that all induction is concerned with causes, it is now generally realized that we cannot hope to find any method of arguing with certainty from facts to laws. No self-conscious, reflective scientist wishes to claim that the induction he practises is infallible, and no philosopher who understands his job wishes to suggest that he can provide the scientists with a guarantee that if they follow a method prescribed by him they will always reach true conclusions. It has therefore become customary to say that the conclusions of induction are only probable, and various attempts have been made in recent times to justify induction by showing when and why its conclusions attain high probability in the sense of the theory of chances. Some of these attempts are adaptations of the argument by elimination, while others are supposed to be free from all association with the old doctrine, but we have seen that they are all alike open to the objection that the notion of probability appropriate to the theory of chances has no application to the results of induction.

In this situation we may be tempted to agree with Hume that our demand for justification has brought us to a position of scepticism from which there can be no escape except by a return to the natural, unreflective behaviour of ordinary life.

'The intense view of these manifold contradictions and imperfections in human reason,' he writes, 'has so wrought upon me, and heated my brain, that I am ready to reject all belief and reasoning, and can look upon no opinion even as more probable or likely than another. . . . I am confounded with all these questions, and begin to fancy myself in the most deplorable condition imaginable, inviron'd with the deepest darkness and utterly depriv'd of the use of every member and faculty. Most fortunately it happens, that since reason is incapable of dispelling these clouds, nature itself suffices to that purpose, and cures me of this philosophical melancholy and delirium, either by relaxing this bent of mind, or by some avocation and lively impression of my senses, which obliterate all these chimeras. I dine, I play a game of back-gammon, I converse, and am merry with my friends; and when after three or four hours' amusement, I wou'd return to these speculations, they appear so cold, and strain'd and ridiculous, that I cannot find it in my heart to enter into them any farther.'[1]

Everyone who has thought much about the problem must at some time have felt the same despair and tried the same cure; but the cheerfulness which follows a good dinner is no substitute for philosophical understanding, and the demand for justification will not remain suppressed for long. How then are we to proceed?

It is a good maxim of philosophizing that when we find ourselves involved in perplexities without hope of escape we should turn back and reconsider the form of the question with which we started. Now the problem of induction is to find a justification for the procedure which scientists follow, but what do we mean here by 'justification'? It is clearly a mistake to suppose that we can justify the procedure by showing that its conclusions are certainly true, for it is now a commonplace that its conclusions are only probable. And yet the attempt to justify induction by showing that its conclusions are probable also comes to grief, when we take 'probable' in the sense of the theory of chances. May it not be a misunderstanding of the situation to suppose that we should try to justify induction by proving anything at all about its conclusions? We do, indeed, wish to say that the conclusions of induction are probable, and any theory which will not allow us to use such language is plainly unsatisfactory. But we must admit that our usage of the word 'probable' in this connexion is not identical with that in the theory of chances, and here, I think, we have a clue to the solution of the problem. The custom of speaking of the results of induction as probable is comparatively recent, and it was presumably suggested by some analogy with other cases in which we use the word 'probable', since it would be absurd to maintain

---

[1] *Treatise of Human Nature*, Book I, Part IV, Section vii.

that passage from one sense to the other is a mere pun. Now we have seen that in the theory of chances a proposition is said to be probable on given evidence when for a person knowing that evidence and no more it is approvable as a basis for action because of a rule about the chances of a so-and-so's being such-and-such. In speaking of a result of induction as probable on its evidence we are undoubtedly saying that for a person knowing that evidence and no more it is approvable as a basis for action; but our ground for saying this cannot be any rule about chances, and there is nothing else on which we can base our approval except the simple consideration that the result has been reached from the given evidence by the method of induction. In short, the probability of the conclusions of induction depends on the justification of induction, and not vice versa. But this means that in order to justify induction we must show it to be rational without reference to the truth or even to the probability of its conclusions.

The thesis that induction is intrinsically rational has been maintained by a number of modern philosophers, but it has usually been presented as part of a positivist programme for dissolving philosophical problems, rather than as a solution of the problem of justifying induction. According to the philosophers whom I have in mind we raise a pseudo-problem for ourselves when we ask for a justification. The source of our trouble is a misguided wish to bring all arguments under the rules of deductive logic or the formulae of the theory of chances. The puzzle disappears, they tell us, when we realize that the word 'rational' has a number of different senses and that in one of these induction is rational by definition. I agree that the demand for a justification of induction has very often been put forward by philosophers who thought it should be possible to exhibit induction as an argument in deductive logic or in the theory of chances, and that for a proper understanding of the situation it is necessary to dispel this illusion, but I cannot accept the short way with inquirers which the positivists suggest. They apparently hold that the word 'rational' is equivalent to a disjunction 'deductive or inductive or . . .', where the various alternatives have nothing in common except that they are included in the disjunction. If this account of the matter were true, anyone who recognized that a particular argument conformed to the standards of induction and said that it was therefore rational would be making a trivial assertion comparable with the statement 'Since this object is a locomotive, it is either a kangaroo or a locomotive'. The assurance that induction is rational in this peculiar sense can give no comfort to anyone who is puzzled by Hume's problem; and it would seem curious that any philosophers have supposed it could, if there were not similar instances of self-deception to be found in other parts of the positivist faith, e.g. in the belief that the doctrine of physicalism removes all perplexities about the relations of minds and bodies. Philosophical devils cannot all be exorcized by the old formula 'Get thee behind me, Satan', for some of them may take us at our word.

To show that induction is rational, without referring to the truth or the probability of its conclusions, we must first conceive it as a policy to be adopted or rejected and then make clear that no one who understands his situation, that is to say, who realizes his needs and his resources, can fail to choose this policy. The source of Hume's despair was his discovery that reflection destroys our natural confidence in induction, and his only remedy was social intercourse, which distracted his attention from the question of justification and so enabled him to believe and act again. But his prescription cannot work a lasting cure, for reason has her rights as well as nature and will persist in raising awkward questions, as Hume himself confessed by his writing of the *Treatise*. If, then, we are to reach a state of intellectual equanimity, we must find a new ground of confidence acceptable to reason. This is not to say that we must regain by reflection the natural confidence which comes after a good dinner, for that is impossible. Rather we must discover something in induction which makes the activity worth while for a fully self-conscious man who no longer expects it to yield either the certainty of deduction or the probability of the theory of chances. For this purpose we may have to distinguish between primary and secondary induction, but in either case the first step is obviously to reach an understanding of the policy whose value we are to judge.

§ 43. THE POLICY OF PRIMARY INDUCTION

Primary induction may be concerned either with natural laws or with probability rules. Although I shall try to show that the procedure is fundamentally the same in the two cases, it will be convenient to begin by considering them separately.

The induction of laws is commonly presented as an argument from a premiss that all the α things observed have been β to a conclusion that all α things must be β. But this description is not illuminating, and may be seriously misleading. In order to understand what is involved in the attempt to establish a natural law we must return to the conception of laws as principles. Now principles have been described as truths about the possibility or the impossibility, the necessity or the non-necessity, of conjunctions of characters. But it is permissible, and useful for our purposes, to classify them under two heads only. If it is necessary for an α thing to be β, it is impossible for an α thing to be not-β; and similarly, if it is not necessary for an α thing to be β, it is possible for an α thing to be not-β. Within this simplified scheme the suggestion that natural laws are principles must be understood to mean that they are all principles of impossibility. The conjecturing of a law is, therefore, an attempt to say where one of the boundaries of possibility lies. Principles of possibility can be established with certainty by inference from observed facts; for if we discover anything which is both α and β, we are entitled to say without more ado that it is possible for an α thing to be β. When, however, we conjecture in natural science that it is impossible for an α thing to be β, the situation is very different. Our hypothesis may be decisively refuted at any time by the discovery of something which is both α and β; but it cannot be conclusively verified by any accumulation of facts. The most we can say is that we have looked for things which are both α and β but have not found them. To adapt a famous remark made by Aristotle in a different context,[1] whereas that which has happened is manifestly possible, we have no assurance either of the possibility or of the impossibility of that which has not happened.

According to this way of describing matters, the policy which we follow in the induction of laws consists of two articles: (*a*) to search for new conjunctions of characters, and (*b*) to assume the impossibility of conjunctions which are not discovered by continued search. When, like the animals, we practise induction unreflectively, we take for granted that the realm of possibility is no wider than our experience has shown it to be, and we make no effort to increase its known extent by the discovery of new conjunctions. If, however, we decide to practise induction in our reflective moments, we cannot, as fully self-conscious beings, have any interest in allowing ourselves to be misled by our own laziness. Our assumption of boundary principles is then an act of policy, rather than belief in any ordinary sense, and it is accompanied *at all*

[1] *Poetics*, 1451b16.

stages by a search for evidence which would compel us to revise our hypotheses. Thus at the beginning we do not say that α things cannot be β, unless we have inspected some α things; and even when a long experience of α things has revealed none which are β, we still look for an example which would refute the suggestion. This search for new conjunctions, which is an indispensable part of our policy, must be guided by a proper understanding of the hypotheses to be tested. A man who has seen several cats but not observed any of them eating cheese is not entitled on this ground alone to say that cats do not eat cheese. If the generalization is to be taken seriously, it must be understood to mean that hungry cats in the presence of cheese refuse to eat it; and this proposition is not adequately tested by the inspection of well-fed cats or cats not in the presence of cheese. The point is obvious enough to anyone who reflects, but the long survival of superstitions and prejudices shows that men are often unable or unwilling to plan satisfactory tests of the universal propositions they assert.

This account of the induction of laws applies generally, but when we have to do with laws of functional relationship between variable magnitudes, e.g. temperature and volume in a gas at constant pressure, our procedure involves a step which deserves special notice. Our data in such a case are certain pairs of numbers obtained by experiment. Associated with x_1 we have y_1, associated with x_2 we have y_2, and so forth. It may be that primary induction has already been applied to these data for the establishment of a number of universal propositions, e.g. about all specimens of gas at certain temperatures, but we need not discuss that complication. Since it is clearly impossible to perform an infinity of experiments, our data must be finite in number. For convenience they may be plotted on a piece of graph paper. If it is then found that all the dots representing the various data lie on a straight line, as in the first of the accompanying figures, we assume without more ado that x and y are related by an equation of the form:

$$y = ax+b,$$

where a and b are parameters or constants specifying a determinate function within the class of linear functions. It would be equally true, however, to say that all the dots lie on a wavy line such as that drawn in the second figure. There is, indeed, no limit to the number of different lines which may be drawn through all the dots, and, although the addition of dots representing further data may enable us to eliminate some of them, there will always remain infinitely many lines representing alternatives between which we must choose when we advance an hypothesis of functional relationship. We cannot say that the hypothesis represented by the

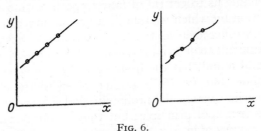

FIG. 6.

straight line restricts the field of possibility with which we are concerned more drastically than any other hypothesis, for each of them allows only one value of y for each value of x. Why, then, do we choose the hypothesis represented by the straight line?

The answer seems to be that in any such situation we choose the simplest hypothesis which accords with the known facts, but this requires further elucidation. Functions can be arranged in classes according to the number of parameters they involve. Thus the functional relationship of two variables which is represented graphically by a straight line involves two parameters, while that represented by a circle involves three. We can put the same truth in another way by saying that a certain number of points must be given to specify a curve of a certain kind. Two points are required to determine a straight line, three points to determine a circle, and so forth. Here, then, we have a quite objective criterion for deciding which of the hypotheses of functional relationship allowed by our data is the simplest, and it is easy to see that the hypothesis which is simplest in this sense is also that which we can hope to eliminate most quickly if it is false. If we have only one dot on our graph paper, we have no ground for preferring any hypothesis to any other, because our evidence is not enough to enable us to assign parameters in any function whatsoever. We can, of course, conceive any number of curves passing through the point, but it would be fantastic to assume that any particular one represented the required functional relationship. If, however, we have two dots on our paper, we can at least suppose that the functional relationship may be that represented by the straight line which they determine. This hypothesis may be refuted as soon as a third dot is added; but if it survives, it may be said to be confirmed by the new evidence. A similar argument can be applied in more complicated situations. In short, the policy of assuming always the simplest hypothesis which accords with the known facts is that which will enable us to get rid of false hypotheses most quickly.[1]

The induction by which we establish probability rules seems at first sight very different from that by which we establish laws, and much more difficult to describe. When we have observed a number of α things and found that the frequency of β things among them is f, we assume that $P(\alpha, \beta) = f$. According to the explanation given in an earlier section the probability rules we assume may be conceived as truths of principle; but they certainly cannot be regarded as principles of impossibility, and it is not obvious that they limit the fields of possibility left open by our concepts, since any frequency of β things among the α things observed would be consistent with any value of $P(\alpha, \beta)$ between 0 and 1. For an understanding of the situation we must consider once more the nature of probability rules.

When we speak of the probability of an α thing's being β, we are thinking of the range of alternatives or field of possibility left open by the character α-ness and assuming that some part of this belongs also to the range of β-ness. If we knew all the principles of impossibility and knew also that there were no more, we could determine *a priori* what proportion of the range of α-ness was included in the range of β-ness, but we cannot attain this knowledge and must therefore rely on ampliative induction for any estimates of probability we may make in natural science. When, however, we use induction for this purpose, we are, in effect, trying to say what proportion of the range of α-ness is included in the range of β-ness without determining the exact line of their intersection; and the only evidence we have to help us is the fact that we have examined n α things and found fn of them to be β. How do we proceed? According to the customary account of the matter we assume that $P(\alpha, \beta) = f$. This reply is correct, but it is important to understand why it is correct.

The significant point is that the value we assume for the required probability $P(\alpha, \beta)$ is that which entails the maximum value for the derivative probability $P(^{\alpha}\sigma_n, {}^{\beta}\rho_f)$, i.e. for the probability that

---

[1] Cf. H. Weyl's *Philosophie der Mathematik und Naturwissenschaft*, p. 116, and K. Popper's *Logik der Forschung*, pp. 79 ff.

an α-set of n members will have a β-ratio of f. For if $P(\alpha, \beta) = x$, it follows according to the calculus of chances that

$$P(^{\alpha}\sigma_n, {}^{\beta}\rho_f) = {}^nC_{fn}(\mathrm{I}-x)^{n-fn}x^{fn}.$$

But ${}^nC_{fn}$ is independent of x, and the value of the derivative probability will therefore be at its maximum when

$$d/dx\,(\mathrm{I}-x)^{n-fn}x^{fn} = \mathrm{o},$$

i.e. when $x = f$. Now the derivative probability is the ratio which the field of possibility left open by the character of being an α-set of n members with a β-ratio of f bears to the total field left open by the character of being an α-set of n members, or in symbols

$$P(^{\alpha}\sigma_n, {}^{\beta}\rho_f) = \frac{R(^{\alpha}\sigma_n{}^{\beta}\rho_f)}{R(^{\alpha}\sigma_n)}.$$

In assuming that the required probability $P(\alpha, \beta) = f$ we are therefore adopting that hypothesis which brings the boundaries of possibility (i.e. the limits imposed by natural laws, including those we do not know) closest to the ascertained facts. We cannot formulate any hypothesis which allows only for the actual frequency of β things we have found among the α things examined; but if we adopted any other value for $P(\alpha, \beta)$, we should be allowing a larger field of possibility for the occurrence of frequencies different from that we have found. We can show this most clearly by rewriting our equation in the form:

$$P_x(^{\alpha}\sigma_n, {}^{\beta}\rho_f) = \frac{R(^{\alpha}\sigma_n{}^{\beta}\rho_f)}{R_x(^{\alpha}\sigma_n)}.$$

Here $P_x(^{\alpha}\sigma_n, {}^{\beta}\rho_f)$ indicates the value of the derivative probability on the assumption that the required probability is x, and $R_x(^{\alpha}\sigma_n)$ the range or field of possibility left open on the same hypothesis by the character of being an α-set of n members. But $R(^{\alpha}\sigma_n{}^{\beta}\rho_f)$ requires no subscript, because the size of the field left open by the character of being an α-set of n members with a β-ratio of f is independent of the value of $P(\alpha, \beta)$, and this implies that $R_x(^{\alpha}\sigma_n)$ is at its minimum when the derivative probability is at its maximum.[1]

---

[1] This way of choosing a value for $P(\alpha, \beta)$ is like that described by R. A. Fisher as the Method of Maximum Likelihood. The application of the method to more complicated cases is explained in his *Statistical Methods for Research Workers*. In his usage the word 'likelihood' stands for the derivative probability, or rather for the more easily calculated quantity

$$(n-fn)\log(\mathrm{I}-x)+fn \log x,$$

which is the logarithm of $(\mathrm{I}-x)^{n-fn}x^{fn}$, and he wishes to suggest by the name that

It is not easy to put this account of the establishment of probability rules into ordinary English, but an illustration may make the special notation more familiar and so prepare the way for a more extensive use of it later. Let us suppose that we try to determine *from statistics alone* the probability that a throw of a given die (α) will result in a six (β). Perhaps we have some reason to think that the die may be loaded, but no evidence, except the results of a number of trials, to show what the bias is. If there have been so far 1,000 throws of the die and 237 of these have resulted in sixes, the inductive policy requires us to assume that the probability of a throw's resulting in six is 0·237. Now the interesting feature of this hypothesis about the value of $P(\alpha, \beta)$ is that it makes the derivative probability $P(^{\alpha}\sigma_{1000}, {}^{\beta}\rho_{0·237})$ larger than it would be on any other hypothesis. But this derivative probability, like all others considered in the calculus of chances, is a ratio between two ranges. When we express it in the form

$$\frac{R(^{\alpha}\sigma_{1000} {}^{\beta}\rho_{0·237})}{R(^{\alpha}\sigma_{1000})}$$

we see that its dependence on the value of $P(\alpha, \beta)$ is due to its denominator. Being a set of 1,000 throws is a character whose range or field of possibility depends on the range of the character of being a throw of the given die, and therefore on the value of $P(\alpha, \beta)$. On the other hand, being a set of 1,000 throws of which just 237 result in sixes is a character whose range is not determined in any way by the required probability. From this it follows that if we assume $P(\alpha, \beta) = 0·237$, as the inductive policy requires in the circumstances we are now considering, we adopt in effect that hypothesis which allows as little as may be in $R(^{\alpha}\sigma_{1000})$ beyond $R(^{\alpha}\sigma_{1000}{}^{\beta}\rho_{0·237})$. This latter, of course, must be allowed in any case, since we have already found a set of 1,000 throws of which just 237 result in sixes. Expressing the minimum value for the denominator of the derivative probability by the symbol $R_{0·237}(^{\alpha}\sigma_{1000})$, we can formulate its relation to any other value in the equation:

$$\frac{R_{0·237}(^{\alpha}\sigma_{1000})}{R_x(^{\alpha}\sigma_{1000})} = \frac{P_x(^{\alpha}\sigma_{1000}, {}^{\beta}\rho_{0·237})}{P_{0·237}(^{\alpha}\sigma_{1000}, {}^{\beta}\rho_{0·237})},$$

where the subscripts 0·237 and x placed after R and P refer always to hypotheses about the value of $P(\alpha, \beta)$.

this quantity can be used as an instrument for the selection of that hypothesis about the value of the required probability which is most likely in the special sense appropriate to the conclusions of induction.

It is now clear that our procedure is fundamentally the same in the two applications of primary induction. Whether we are concerned with laws or with probability rules, we assume that the boundaries of possibility lie close to the actual conjunctions we have observed, as close, indeed, as we can conceive them. When we do this deliberately, we cannot believe our hypotheses either in the sense of taking them for granted with natural confidence or in the sense of holding them for probable according to the theory of chances, for neither of these attitudes would be justifiable. We can assume them only in the sense of deciding to proceed as though they were true, should there occur any occasion for activity, whether physical or purely intellectual, to which they would be relevant. From one point of view this policy is conservative, since we admit no possibilities except those that experience compels us to admit; but it is by no means a timid plan for avoiding error by saying as little as possible. On the contrary, in placing the boundaries of possibility as near as we can to the observed facts we invite refutation as soon as may be; and if we are honest with ourselves in our practice of the policy, we even search continually for counter-evidence, i.e. for facts which would refute our hypotheses of law and so compel us to admit larger fields of possibility than we have hitherto allowed. In this respect primary induction, as I have explained it, is very different from the account of it given by Lord Keynes and other writers who try to justify it within the theory of chances. According to their doctrine we should always prefer the safer of two hypotheses, i.e. that which is least open to refutation by experience. If, for example, our experience up to date allows us to choose between the suggestion that all α things are β and the suggestion that all $\alpha\gamma$ things are β, we should prefer the second, because any fact which disproved the second would certainly disprove the first also but there might be some fact which disproved the first without disproving the second. It is a sufficient argument against this view to point out that, if our chief concern in making hypotheses were to avoid the risk of refutation, we should be well advised to make no hypotheses at all, since we should then run no such danger. For a correct understanding of the spirit of scientific research we must abandon all thought of safety first and conceive induction as a policy of the utmost intellectual audacity controlled by scrupulous respect for facts. If we have to choose between the suggestion that all α things are β and the suggestion that all $\alpha\gamma$ things are β, we should adopt the former, but go out of our way to look for α things which are not γ in order that we may make our tests as rigorous as possible. This is the sense of the demand for variety in the instances which provide evidence for an induction.[1]

§ 44. THE JUSTIFICATION OF PRIMARY INDUCTION

In order to justify primary induction it is now necessary to explain why we should adopt the policy I have described. The explanation I have to suggest is very simple. We often wish to find the answer to some question which refers beyond the limits of our actual experience, and primary induction is the only method of trying to do this. The first point requires no discussion. If there is any intelligent being who has no curiosity about matters beyond the limits of his own observation, either because he is omniscient or because he has no desires for the satisfaction of which he must act on mere opinion, he can afford to ignore any suggestion of a method for extrapolating beyond experience. For the rest of us the only question is whether the claim made on behalf of the inductive method is correct, and I shall therefore concentrate on this.

Whenever we try to extrapolate beyond experience, we must rely on some supposed law or probability rule; for even the attempt to make predictions without the help of science involves a kind of pseudo-science.[2] If anyone decides to guide his life by prophecies, he must use some criterion to select those statements about the future which he will adopt as prophecies, and in so doing he shows his reliance on some supposed law or probability rule, even if it be only the assumption that whatever comes into his head first is most likely to be true. Now we have no *a priori* knowledge, whether intuitive or demonstrative, of laws or probability rules that will help us in making inferences from the observed to the unobserved; and it is a mistake to suppose that such propositions can have probability in the sense of the theory of chances. We cannot as reflective beings take anything for granted. If, therefore, we assume any law or probability rule for the purpose of making predictions or other inferences to the unobserved, we must

---

[1] The main thesis of this paragraph has been very ably stated by K. Popper in his *Logik der Forschung*. His view of laws and probability rules is very different, however, from that stated in this book and he would almost certainly disapprove what I have said about principles of impossibility.

[2] For convenience I speak sometimes of predictions only, although inferences to the past or to the unobserved present raise exactly the same problems.

do so as an act of policy. This is as much as to say that when we try to make predictions we must first make tentative hypotheses about the boundaries of possibility. But it is not enough to choose just any hypothesis of this kind. On the one hand, it is obviously essential that those we entertain should be compatible with all the facts we have observed, for we cannot intelligently use an hypothesis that has already been refuted by experience. Indeed, it is to our interest to get rid of false hypotheses as soon as we can, and we should therefore search diligently for counter-evidence. So far from regretting the need to abandon a suggestion of law that has been disproved by facts, we should rejoice that we have gained some definite information about the field of possibility left open by one of our concepts and so learnt not to rely on a false assumption about its limitation. On the other hand, it would be foolish to suppose the range of any concept larger than we know it to be, for in so doing we should deprive ourselves of the opportunity of making some predictions which might be true. The stronger our assumptions are, the more we may hope to achieve by their help; but in this connexion the strongest assumptions are those which most restrict the ranges of our concepts. Moreover, once we depart from the policy of making the strongest assumptions consistent with the known facts, we have no conceivable reason for placing the boundaries of possibility anywhere rather than anywhere else. The conclusion to be drawn from these considerations is that, if we wish to extrapolate beyond experience, we must adopt the inductive policy as it has been described in the previous section.

Primary induction is a rational policy, not because it is certain to lead to success, but because it is the only way of trying to do what we want to do, namely, make true predictions. Our fundamental reason for practising primary induction holds good, therefore, so long as we wish to extrapolate, however much we may be disappointed in our use of it. And when we are engaged in the search for natural laws, which are the more useful of the two kinds of propositions said to be established by this sort of induction, we have an additional reason for persevering, namely, the consideration that our procedure is self-corrective. As new facts are observed, so false hypotheses about the boundaries of possibility are disproved; but if there are any boundaries, that is to say, if there are any laws or principles of impossibility, we should reach them in the end by continuing the policy systematically. When we reach a boundary, we shall have no means of knowing that our work is done, and we must therefore continue to treat the law we have found as a mere hypothesis that may be refuted by further experience; but the predictions we make by means of the law will be correct, and our end will in fact be achieved.[1]

When we assume laws or probability rules inductively, we say that they are probable in relation to our empirical evidence because we have formulated them in accordance with a rational policy after consideration of that evidence. Since, however, there is some danger of misunderstanding in the use of a word which has acquired a special sense in the theory of chances, it may on occasions be wiser to speak of the *acceptability* of the results of induction. I shall follow this practice in future, when the context seems to require it. Similarly we may, if we like, say that the conclusions of primary induction are reliable, or even that they are established, provided that we recognize that we are using these expressions in a special way. As fully self-conscious beings we can accept the results of induction only in the sense of deciding to proceed as if we knew them to be true. To behave unreflectingly as if we knew them to be true would be to lapse into natural confidence and take them for granted. When, however, we decide to use an hypothesis as a *premiss* for further argument, we are in a sense treating it as established, even although we recognize that it is subject to review. For we no longer say merely 'The hypothesis entails A', but rather 'A . . . provisionally'. It is admittedly difficult to find phrases which express the attitude of reflective induction correctly, but this should not surprise us. The simple words of our language are very ancient, whereas the fully self-conscious inductive attitude is comparatively new, and almost any term we choose will therefore have misleading associations. In the course of time this difficulty may decrease as the nature of the scientific enterprise becomes more widely known, but it is too much to hope that every danger of misunderstanding will disappear. For the perplexities of the subject arise for each of us afresh from confusion between natural confidence and the critical or reflective adoption of hypotheses; as we all start with the first, so we must all return to it for a large part of our lives. Hume was wrong in supposing that reflection leads us to despair from which we can be rescued only by some distraction of attention; but he was right in his belief that we need to dine and make merry with our friends, and also in

---

[1] For a somewhat similar argument see Reichenbach's *Wahrscheinlichkeitslehre* and his *Experience and Prediction*.

holding that during these activities we cannot maintain the reflective attitude.

§ 45. DEGREES OF ACCEPTABILITY IN PRIMARY INDUCTION

So far we have shown only that the results of primary induction are probable or approvable because this kind of induction is a rational policy. But we do not treat all inductive conclusions as equally acceptable. If, for example, I have observed only three α things and found them all to be β, I may adopt the hypothesis that all α things are β, but I do so very tentatively, whereas if I have observed a thousand α things and found them all to be β, I am much more confident about the hypothesis. How are we to account for this? Since induction is not more rational at one time than it is at another, it seems at first sight that the acceptability of inductive conclusions cannot admit of degrees. The solution of the problem is to be found by consideration of the different degrees of irrationality involved in departure from the inductive policy in different circumstances. Although it is always rational to practise the policy of induction, and not more rational on one occasion than on another, departures from the policy may be more or less irrational; and it seems that whenever we speak of the degree of acceptability attained by an inductively approved hypothesis on such-and-such evidence, our expression can be understood as a reference to the degree of irrationality involved in departing from the inductive policy with such evidence available.

One departure from the inductive policy may be said to be more irrational than another because the first is more *extravagant* than the second, that is to say, makes a larger gratuitous addition to the field of possibility with which we are concerned. This consideration is relevant whether the hypothesis indicated by the inductive policy is one of law or one of probability in the narrow sense; but in the special case where the hypothesis indicated by the inductive policy is one of law, a departure from that policy may be described as more or less *negligent* according to the value of the prize which is abandoned by such departure. These two notions of extravagance and negligence require to be examined separately; and it is convenient to consider extravagance first, since this fault is to be found in any departure from the inductive policy. For simplicity of exposition we may here treat laws as limiting cases of probability rules, writing $P(\alpha, \beta) = 0$ for 'No α things are β' and $P(\alpha, \beta) = 1$ for 'All α things are β'. In order to

avoid confusion we must, of course, remember that an hypothesis
of law can be conclusively refuted, whereas an hypothesis ascribing
a value other than o or 1 to $P(\alpha, \beta)$ is compatible with any frequency of β things among the α things observed by us. But even
this difference has its appropriate expression in the symbolism of
probability rules. For if $P(\alpha, \beta) = o$ or 1, the derivative probability $P(^{\alpha}\sigma_n, {}^{\beta}\rho_f) = o$, unless $f = o$ or 1, as the case may be,
whereas for other values of $P(\alpha, \beta)$ the derivative probability is
always greater than o, whatever f may be.

When in accordance with the inductive policy we assume that
$P(\alpha, \beta)$ is equal to f, the relative frequency of β things among the
n α things observed so far, we choose that hypothesis which constricts $R(^{\alpha}\sigma_n)$ to a minimum. This way of describing matters was
explained in an earlier section by means of an example from dicing
in which we supposed that $f = 0.237$, but it is quite general in its
application. If $f = o$ or 1, the inductive policy requires us to
assume that $P(\alpha, \beta) = o$ or 1, as the case may be, and we can then
say in the special symbolism we have introduced that

$$P_0(^{\alpha}\sigma_n, {}^{\beta}\rho_0) = \frac{R(^{\alpha}\sigma_n{}^{\beta}\rho_0)}{R_0(^{\alpha}\sigma_n)} = 1,$$

or $$P_1(^{\alpha}\sigma_n, {}^{\beta}\rho_1) = \frac{R(^{\alpha}\sigma_n{}^{\beta}\rho_1)}{R_1(^{\alpha}\sigma_n)} = 1.$$

Here the field of possibility left open by the character of being an
α-set of n members is equated with the field which just contains
the observed facts. But these are special cases. If f is greater than
o and less than 1, $R_f(^{\alpha}\sigma_n)$ is inevitably greater than $R(^{\alpha}\sigma_n{}^{\beta}\rho_f)$. In
order to describe primary induction quite generally we must there-
fore say that it is the policy of supposing no possibilities outside
$R_f(^{\alpha}\sigma_n)$, which is the smallest field the evidence allows us to suppose for the character of being an α-set of n members. For, whatever x may be,

$$\frac{R_f(^{\alpha}\sigma_n)}{R_x(^{\alpha}\sigma_n)} = \frac{P_x(^{\alpha}\sigma_n, {}^{\beta}\rho_f)}{P_f(^{\alpha}\sigma_n, {}^{\beta}\rho_f)}$$

according to the explanations given above; and if x is not equal to
f, this ratio must be less than 1.

Now whenever we depart from the inductive policy by assuming
for $P(\alpha, \beta)$ any value x such that

$$R_x(^{\alpha}\sigma_n) > R_f(^{\alpha}\sigma_n),$$

we make a gratuitous addition to the field of possibility left open by the character of being an α-set of n members. This situation can be represented in a geometrical diagram by shading that part of the area representing $R_x(^\alpha\sigma_n)$ which is not contained in the area representing $R_f(^\alpha\sigma_n)$. The degree of irrationality involved in such a departure from the inductive policy may quite naturally be said

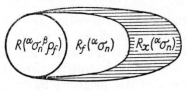

FIG. 7.

to depend on the ratio which the gratuitous addition bears to the whole of $R_x(^\alpha\sigma_n)$. Let us call this the extravagance of the hypothesis and symbolize it by $E_{n,f}(x)$, in which the subscripts refer to facts of observation, namely, that an α-set of n members has been examined and found to have a β-frequency of f. Then

$$E_{n,f}(x) = \frac{R_x(^\alpha\sigma_n) - R_f(^\alpha\sigma_n)}{R_x(^\alpha\sigma_n)}$$

$$= 1 - \frac{R_f(^\alpha\sigma_n)}{R_x(^\alpha\sigma_n)}$$

$$= 1 - \frac{P_x(^\alpha\sigma_n,\ ^\beta\rho_f)}{P_f(^\alpha\sigma_n,\ ^\beta\rho_f)}$$

$$= 1 - \frac{^nC_{fn}(1-x)^{n-fn}x^{fn}}{^nC_{fn}(1-f)^{n-fn}f^{fn}}$$

$$= 1 - \left[\left(\frac{1-x}{1-f}\right)^{1-f}\left(\frac{x}{f}\right)^{f}\right]^{n}.$$

Two interesting consequences follow immediately from this definition. First, the extravagance of an hypothesis is o, if $x = f$. Secondly, the extravagance is 1, if $x = o$ or 1, when f has any other value. In other words, an hypothesis indicated by the inductive policy involves no extravagance, and an hypothesis of law which has already been refuted by experience involves the maximum extravagance. These are limiting cases, however, and it will be noticed that in them the measure of extravagance is independent of n. In all other cases the extravagance is greater than o but less than 1 and increases with increasing n, but not so fast as n. For in these other cases

$$0 < \left(\frac{1-x}{1-f}\right)^{1-f}\left(\frac{x}{f}\right)^{f} < 1,$$

and

$$\left[\left(\frac{1-x}{1-f}\right)^{1-f}\left(\frac{x}{f}\right)^{f}\right]^{n},$$

must therefore tend to o as n increases without limit. The truth that no accumulation of evidence in favour of an inductively approved hypothesis can ever lead to the complete elimination of all arbitrary hypotheses is represented here by the statement that, except for hypotheses of law, arbitrary hypotheses never involve an extravagance of 1, however great n may be. If $f = 1$, i.e. if all the α things examined have turned out to be β, the extravagance of assuming that $P(\alpha, \beta) = x$ instead of assuming the hypothesis of law which is favoured by the inductive policy can be expressed very simply in our scheme. For we then have

$$E_{n,1}(x) = 1 - x^{n}.$$

Similarly if $f = 0$, i.e. if none of the α things examined have turned out to be β, we have

$$E_{n,0}(x) = 1 - (1-x)^{n}.$$

All these results correspond closely to the judgements which educated common sense makes about the irrationality of departing from the inductive policy, and we may therefore say that extravagance as defined here is a proper gauge of such irrationality. Now I have suggested that when we speak of the degree of acceptability attained by an inductive conclusion we are referring to the greater or less irrationality which would be involved in departing from the inductive policy in that case; if my view is correct, we have discovered a justification for saying that an inductive conclusion about the value of $P(\alpha, \beta)$ becomes more acceptable as we increase the number of α things examined. For we have found that the extravagance of a non-inductive hypothesis is greater when the number of α things examined is greater. Our argument is, in effect, an elaboration of one we commonly use when we wish to give special commendation to an inductive hypothesis that is supported by much evidence: 'How unlikely it would be that we should find what we do in a sample so large as this, if the hypothesis were not true.' Although there is a fallacy in the attempts

which have been made to exhibit this method of estimating acceptability as an argument in the calculus of chances, depending on the
use of the inversion formula, the method itself is essentially sound.

We must not suppose, however, that the notion of extravagance
will supply us with a method of measuring the acceptability of
inductive conclusions in any strict sense of the word 'measure'.
When we say that such a conclusion has been made more acceptable by the addition of new evidence, we are referring to the greater
extravagance of arbitrary hypotheses, but not to the greater
extravagance of any particular one among the infinitely many
conceivable hypotheses, and our statement of the degree of acceptability attained must therefore have a certain vagueness. For
although each arbitrary hypothesis becomes more extravagant as
the evidence accumulates, they do not all increase in extravagance
at the same rate. When f is taken as constant, the value of
$E_{n,f}(x)$ depends not only on n but also on x. In this connexion it
is interesting to notice a distinction between our attitude to suggestions of law and our attitude to suggestions of probability rules
in the narrow sense.

If we have examined n α things and found m of them to be β
(where m is greater than o but less than n), the inductive policy
requires us to assume m/n as the value of $P(\alpha, \beta)$; but, however
great n may be, we recognize that there would be no very great
extravagance in assuming either $(m+1)/(n+1)$ or $m/(n+1)$ instead as the value. For if n is very large, the difference between
either of these arbitrary values and the inductively approved
value is correspondingly small. Moreover, we know for certain that
when we have the opportunity of observing another α thing the
inductive policy will require us to assume one or other of these
values in place of that which it now favours; and we can argue in
a similar fashion that any small departure from the inductively
approved hypothesis may presently be condoned by the inductive
policy itself. We therefore do not regard it as very probable that
$P(\alpha, \beta) = m/n$ exactly, but consider this hypothesis rather as the
best approximation we can make in the light of the evidence
available and claim high probability only for the less precise
assertion that the value of $P(\alpha, \beta)$ is in the neighbourhood of m/n.
This claim can itself be justified within the account of inductive
probability or acceptability given here; for when n is large, the
value of $E_{n,f}(x)$ increases rapidly with any large increase of the
difference between x and f.

If, on the other hand, all or none of the α things we have examined have turned out to be β and the inductive policy therefore
requires us to assume a law, we are not content to treat our hypothesis in this fashion. When the number of α things examined is
large, we do not merely say that it is probable that the true value
of $P(\alpha, \beta)$ is near to 1 or 0, as the case may be, but claim that the
hypothesis of law, considered by itself, is highly acceptable. If
presently the hypothesis is refuted by the discovery of a contradictory instance, we must naturally adopt in our future estimates
of $P(\alpha, \beta)$ the attitude we usually adopt towards any suggestion
of a probability rule in the narrow sense. But even when our
expectations have been disappointed in this way, we do not readily
abandon all hope of formulating a law. We are much more interested in the amending of our original suggestion by some qualification of the first term (α) than in the making of new estimates of
$P(\alpha, \beta)$. We therefore examine the contradictory instance carefully in order to learn how it differs from the other α things
examined; and if we find that it is not γ, whereas all the other α
things examined have been γ, we assume that all or no $\alpha\gamma$ things
are β, as the case may be. In order to explain and justify this
difference of attitude we must consider the second type of irrationality which may be involved in a departure from the inductive
policy, namely, negligence.

The most obvious peculiarity of hypotheses of law is that they
can be decisively refuted by experience. If all or none of the α
things examined have been found to be β, the relative frequency
of β things among the α things *may* remain unaltered by future
observations (whereas in other cases it cannot, because of the way
in which the numerator and denominator of the fraction change),
but if the relative frequency is once altered by observation, the
hypothesis of law which we have entertained hitherto must be
abandoned for ever. Now this peculiarity of hypotheses of law is
not, as some theories of induction would appear to suggest, a
reason for prizing them less than hypotheses of probability in the
narrow sense, which can never be refuted, but is rather a sign of
their great value. For it is only by assuming some hypotheses of
this kind that we can hope to make any precise and unqualified
inferences about the unobserved. We have therefore a special
reason for not departing from the inductive policy when it offers
us such hypotheses. As the prize, both intellectual and material,
which may be gained is greater than in those cases where we can

formulate only a probability rule in the narrow sense, so too the irrationality of abandoning our opportunity is greater because of the negligence it involves. But, according to the account of acceptability given here, this is as much as to say that an hypothesis of law can become more acceptable than any other inductive hypothesis could on a similar amount of evidence; and so our common judgements are explained.

The same considerations are relevant in the estimation of the acceptability of different suggestions of law. It has been assumed for a very long time that iron melts in great heat, and the evidence in favour of this vague generalization is very extensive. The more precise hypothesis that iron melts at 1,527° C. has been adopted only in comparatively recent times, and the direct evidence in its favour is clearly less extensive. Since the second suggestion entails the first, it cannot on any theory be better established than the first, but according to some accounts of induction it should be considered as much less acceptable because it could be refuted by evidence which would leave the first untouched and has in fact been confirmed by experiment less often. This judgement does not agree with educated common sense. For a full explanation of the reasons why we esteem the precisely formulated hypothesis of law as highly as we do, it would be necessary to consider the development of physical theory about melting-points; but, without claiming to give an exhaustive analysis of this complicated situation, we may say that the more precise hypothesis delimits the range of the concept of iron more narrowly and so enables us to make more precise predictions. To persist in using the vaguely formulated suggestion on occasions when we could use the more precise hypothesis would be a departure from the inductive policy by negligence.

With the two notions of extravagance and negligence we can explain why some departures from the inductive policy are more irrational than others and justify the common view that some conclusions of induction are more acceptable than others. But we cannot in this way introduce any measure of acceptability analogous to the measure of probability in matters of chance, because the whole structure of our judgements of acceptability is different from that of our estimates of probability in matters of chance. There is nothing, for example, in our grading of inductive conclusions to correspond with the distinction between probabilities less than $\frac{1}{2}$ and probabilities greater than $\frac{1}{2}$. Whenever we practise the inductive policy our conclusion has some merit, however small, and this consideration may tempt us to say that its acceptability is slightly greater than $\frac{1}{2}$. But such language would imply that there could in principle be a degree of inductive acceptability less than that attaching to the feeblest conclusion of induction, which is absurd. Whereas the negation of a statement which is probable in the sense of the theory of chances may be said to have a probability less than $\frac{1}{2}$, the negation of an inductive conclusion is not itself an inductive conclusion, and so cannot have any degree of acceptability. Furthermore, we cannot speak meaningfully of ratios between degrees of acceptability. It is generally agreed that an increase in the number of instances confirming an hypothesis of law may make the hypothesis more acceptable, but it is useless to ask what number of new instances would make it twice as acceptable, because the conditions for the use of such language are not fulfilled. The acceptability of a suggestion favoured by the inductive policy has no parts which are themselves accepta-bilities, and so there can be no measurement of acceptability in any precise sense of the word 'measurement'.

We should not be surprised, however, at this limitation. If the acceptability of inductive conclusions is to be conceived in the way I have suggested, we have no reason to expect more. And in practice we need no more. For there are no occasions on which the measurement of acceptability by fractions would help us, even if it were attainable. In matters of chance precise numerical estimates of probability are useful for two reasons. In the first place, they enable us to judge the rationality of our ventures by the method of mathematical expectations, i.e. by comparing the stake with the product of the possible gain and the probability of success. Secondly, they allow us to plan securely on a large scale by the use of Bernoulli's theorem. But in the practice of induction there is nothing analogous to either of these situations. Induction is a rational policy because it is the only way of trying to do what we want to do, and there is no need to consider different degrees of acceptability unless we have to choose between two hypotheses of law or probability which are both confirmed to some degree by experience. Let us suppose, for example, that our experience up to date has led us to assume a law that all α things are γ and another that no β things are γ. If presently we find something which is both α and β, we can be sure that one at least of our hypotheses is false, but we cannot tell for certain which of them to reject until we learn whether or not our $\alpha\beta$ thing is γ. Should it be necessary meanwhile to take some practical decision which depends on the answer to this question, we must consider which of the incompatible hypotheses is more acceptable in the light of previous experience and rely on that. But for this purpose no measurement of acceptability is required. It is sufficient that we should be able to place the two hypotheses in order of merit.

This schematic example shows in a simple way how the notion of degrees of acceptability may be used in practice, but it is rather artificial. Our interest in laws is so great that, when we find a situation such as I have described, we go out of our way to look for things which are both α and β. If, therefore, any such thing is found, it will almost certainly be at a time when we are content to wait for a decisive refutation of one of our previous hypotheses, because our immediate interest in the outcome is wholly theoretical. For a convincing illustration of the way in which some practical interest may compel us to choose between inductive hypotheses on grounds of acceptability we should consider rather hypotheses about probability in a narrow sense. Let us suppose that a society of vegetarians claims to have established from the health records of its members that sufferers from a certain disease (α) who are also vegetarians (β) are more likely to recover (γ) than the common run of sufferers. If we try to form an opinion about the survival of some new sufferer who is a vegetarian, we have to decide whether or not to attach any weight to the consideration that he is a vegetarian. That is to say, we have to decide whether to use the hypothesis that

$$P(\alpha, \gamma) = p,$$

which is suggested by the national statistics, or the hypothesis that

$$P(\alpha\beta, \gamma) = q,$$

which is put forward by the vegetarian society. There is, of course, no inconsistency between the two hypotheses, for they may both be true. If we knew that they were both true, we should have no hesitation in applying that of the vegetarian society to our new case, since it takes account of more of the available evidence. But, as things are, we must make a choice between them, and the crucial question we have to settle is whether the hypothesis of the vegetarian society is sufficiently well established. Naturally this hypothesis cannot be more acceptable than the other; for, however large and well kept the society's records may be, they cannot be so extensive as those of the national authorities for the population as a whole. To justify us in attaching importance to the patient's vegetarianism it would be sufficient, however, that the society's suggestion should be about as acceptable as the more general hypothesis; and this condition might conceivably be fulfilled. For the acceptability of an hypothesis is not increased in constant fashion by the addition of new items to the record on which it is based, and the more special of the two hypotheses we have to consider might perhaps get some outside support from its consilience with other hypotheses under a plausible theory. In any case we need not think of degrees of acceptability as fractions like the degrees of probability in matters of chance.

§ 46. THE POLICY OF SECONDARY INDUCTION

Secondary induction is concerned with theories as opposed to laws or probability rules. In an earlier discussion we have seen that theories are expected to explain natural laws, and that genuine explanation always involves a simplification of what we have to accept. In order to understand the policy of secondary induction we must consider once more what we mean by our use of the word 'simplification' in this connexion. For there seem to be two notions involved, both distinct from that idea of simplicity which we have already noticed in our discussion of laws of functional relationship.

In the first place an hypothesis of secondary induction which is to explain a number of empirical generalizations established by primary induction must entail all those generalizations and have in addition some other testable consequence or consequences. It is not enough for the hypothesis to entail the generalizations which it is intended to explain, for the mere conjunction of them would satisfy this condition and we should not describe that as an explanation. Nor is it sufficient that the hypothesis should entail some new consequence which is untestable; for we can always formulate a fantastic proposition which satisfies this weak condition by merely adding to a conjunctive statement of the generalizations we wish to explain a clause such as 'All undetectable devils love hopscotch', and no one would dream of saying that a proposition so formulated was an explanation of the generalizations it covered. The history of thought shows that men have no difficulty in inventing any number of hypotheses which entail generalizations they wish to explain, and the fact that some of these which are not explanations have been accepted as such by intelligent men only proves the strength of the human craving for explanations and the deceptive power of words. For an example we may take the doctrine of vital force, once popular in biology. When philosophers of the positivist school declare that metaphysical theories are only pseudo-explanations, their objection is based on the same consideration; but they are unwise in their attempt to draw a firm line of demarcation for all time between science and metaphysics. It is not always easy to settle the question whether an hypothesis entails consequences which are both new and testable; and those who think they can give a simple rule should remember that the atomic theory of matter and all speculations about the chemical constitution of the stars were condemned as metaphysical by positivists of an earlier generation.

Let us suppose, then, that an hypothesis has been put forward in secondary induction to explain a number of generalizations established by primary induction, and that some further generalization which can be tested by observation has been derived from it. If this further generalization is confirmed by experience, are we to say that the hypothesis explains all the generalizations, both old and new? Had the new generalization been established by primary induction before the suggestion of the hypothesis, we should certainly not say that the hypothesis explained all the various generalizations merely because it entailed them all; for again the bare conjunction of the generalizations would satisfy this weak condition. But it is at least conceivable that the new generalization might have been established earlier, and the answer to the question whether the hypothesis is or is not an explanation cannot depend on an historical accident. It seems, therefore, that our hypothesis cannot be an explanation unless it entails yet another consequence which is testable by observation; and so we may continue *ad infinitum*, demanding a new testable consequence whenever a generalization derived from the hypothesis has been confirmed. In short, an hypothesis which is to be worthy of consideration in secondary induction must entail infinitely many empirical generalizations. If any of these is disproved, the hypothesis is disproved, but so long as it survives such indirect tests it may be said to explain all its consequences. Here we have one reason for speaking of the simplicity achieved in explanation. An explanatory hypothesis not only co-ordinates a number of generalizations established by primary induction, but gives promise of infinitely many others; and so long as it survives it constricts the realm of possibility more than any number of empirical generalizations entailed by it.

This conclusion seems surprising at first sight. In order to remove the appearance of paradox we must go on to consider the second kind of simplification involved in the making of theories. When we try to find an explanation of a number of empirical generalizations, we look for the hypothesis which is simplest in the sense that it employs the smallest number of independent *concepts*. It is this reduction of the number of independent concepts which makes possible a reduction of the number of independent propositions we need to accept and so gives hope of a drastic constriction of the realm of possibility. Clerk-Maxwell's general theory of electro-magnetic waves has co-ordinated empirical generalizations about heat, light, and electricity which were formerly thought to belong to separate fields of physics, and has suggested many new generalizations now confirmed by experience. But the novelty of the theory, which has made all this possible, is the provision of a single scheme within which a number of physical concepts, hitherto considered independent, can all be defined. For such reductive definition of concepts a transcendent object terminology is needed. There can therefore be no secondary induction without such terminology. But once this is recognized it can be understood how the hypotheses of secondary induction may entail infinitely testable consequences.

The assertion that a transcendent hypothesis entails an infinity of generalizations about perceptual objects is analogous to the assertion that a statement of the perceptual object terminology entails an infinity of statements in the sensum terminology. For just as we cannot replace a statement about perceptual objects by any string of statements about sensa, so too we cannot replace a statement about transcendent objects such as electrons by any string of statements about perceptual objects. It is characteristic of the relationships holding between the three terminologies that each higher terminology provides means of saying what cannot be said in the next lower terminology. And the fact that the transcendent object terminology is superior in this sense to the perceptual object terminology should not surprise us, since we have ourselves invented it in order that we may overcome the limitations of the perceptual object terminology. That we are neverthe-

less puzzled is to be explained by the gradual development of the
theories formulated in the new terminology.

When physicists first entertained the atomic theory of matter,
they did not attempt to say exactly how large the atoms were of
which they spoke. They may even have thought it impossible to
make any estimate of size other than the vague statement that
atoms are very small in comparison with all perceptual objects.
They were already committed, however, to the assertion that
atoms have some size, and in the course of time their successors
realized that testable consequences could be derived from more
precise suggestions. Experiments were then devised for the purpose of deciding between the alternatives which had hitherto been
left open, and so the work went on. At the beginning an hypothesis is valued chiefly for its co-ordination of already established
generalizations, and may be little more precise than is necessary
for this purpose; but if it is to retain a place in the structure of
science it must be capable of development. We may, if we choose,
say that the precise suggestion put forward by a later scientist is a
different hypothesis from the vague suggestion put forward by his
predecessor; but we may then have to declare that the earlier
scientist explained nothing, because the testable consequences to
be derived from his hypothesis were limited in number, and to say
this is to abandon ordinary usage. There are revolutions from
time to time in science, but there are also long periods of steady
progress during which theories are developed by successive specifi-
cations. Newtonian physics, for example, was developed in this
way for more than a century after Newton's death.

So far I have been engaged in describing the results of secondary
induction, but the purpose of the description is to show the nature
of the policy which leads to such results. It should now be clear
what is the correct account of the matter. There is no rule of
thumb for the making of valuable suggestions at this stage in
scientific inquiry, because the theoretical scientist must be inventive in somewhat the same way as a novelist or a playwright.
For the making of a Clerk-Maxwell a primer of scientific method
is of little more use than a correspondence course in authorship
would be for the making of a Shakespeare. Looking back over the
history of science, we can, it is true, discuss the psychological
origins of some theories. We can say, for example, that analogies
have often suggested fruitful hypotheses, as when a terminology
for talking of electricity was created by adaptation of that used

for describing the behaviour of liquids. But analogies suggest hypotheses only to those who can see analogies, and there is no method by which we can make sure that we shall *see* in this sense of the word. No doubt persons who are familiar with what has been done already may acquire a flair for the construction of useful hypotheses, just as those versed in mathematics may acquire a facility in the construction of proofs; but is not possible in either case to formulate rules of invention. Apart from past achievements nothing can be taught systematically. In short, secondary induction is not, like primary induction, a policy for finding good things, but rather a policy of welcoming good things when they are found.

It is this difference which accounts for a confusion to be noticed in many discussions of induction. Some writers of the Baconian tradition ignore secondary induction and try to represent all scientific effort as the application of simple rules which give even fools a good hope of success. Others ignore primary induction and deny in effect that there can be any rules of discovery. Both parties are mistaken; but the mistake of the second group is more pardonable, because the work of primary induction is taken for granted in the more advanced stages of science.

§ 47. THE ACCEPTABILITY OF THEORIES

I have spoken of secondary induction as a policy. This way of approaching the problem is reasonable, because in spite of the difference between the two types of induction we speak in the same way of the probability or acceptability of their conclusions. We cannot, in the strict sense, demonstrate the truth of any theories in empirical science, nor can we say that they have probability in the sense of the theory of chances. If, then, we regard them as approvable or acceptable, this must be because they have been produced in accordance with a policy which is the only way of trying to do something we want to do. But what is it that we want to do when we welcome theories which provide simplification in the two senses mentioned above?

If the only human interest which led to the development of science were the desire to predict particular matters of fact, it would be very difficult, perhaps even impossible, to explain the importance which secondary induction has in the more advanced stages of science. Laws and probability rules of the kind we establish by primary induction are sufficient for this purpose, and secondary induction cannot help in the work except by providing theories from which further suggestions of this kind can be derived. Admittedly a great many of the generalizations we now use in making predictions were first conceived by scientists as consequences to be deduced from theories, but they are not accepted without question merely because they follow from theories. On the contrary, the continued acceptance of the theories from which they follow depends on their confirmation by primary induction. It may be argued, therefore, that, if we were more observant, all those generalizations we use for the making of predictions could have been established by primary induction alone, i.e. without the help of any suggestions from the theories with which secondary induction is concerned. In practice we can never be so observant as to notice all regularities in experience which may provide evidence for primary induction, because observation must always be directed by a selective interest of some sort. The mere determination to amass empirical information in the Baconian style would carry us a very little way on the road of scientific progress, and even false theories may be better than none at all, since, at least, they suggest lines of research. But it is true that, with good fortune in the direction of our attention, any of the empirical generalizations we use in making predictions might conceivably have been established by primary induction alone.

There is undoubtedly a strong continuity of interest between primary and secondary induction. Hypotheses of secondary induction can be confirmed or rejected only indirectly, i.e. through consideration of empirical generalizations which they entail. And conversely, the increase of acceptability which empirical generalizations get from consilience often depends on their being all subsumed under some theory of secondary induction. But it would be foolish to maintain that the sole purpose of secondary induction is to make possible more predictions. For it cannot be maintained that theories are merely devices for producing suggestions of law or probability in advance of observation and so directing our attention to aspects of experience from which we may perhaps be able to derive acceptable conclusions by primary induction. And it is not enough to say that secondary induction makes our predictions safer. The fertility of theories is due, as we have seen, to the transcendent object terminology in which they are formulated; and this is not to be treated as a shorthand system for the compendious statement of propositions about observables. In order to justify secondary induction we must therefore find some new motive or interest which it serves.

The fact that we may derive satisfaction for a time from pseudo-explanations which do not entail new testable consequences shows that we desire explanations for their own sake; and any account of scientific effort which does not give a prominent place to this desire must be seriously incomplete. Secondary induction pre-supposes primary induction, and is in some respects a continuation of the work of primary induction, but it begins with the attempt to find explanations for their own sake. From very early times the desire to explain has been as important in the development of science as the wish to be able to predict, and in our own time it is the dominant interest of those we call pure scientists. When the matter is considered historically, it is clear that the other benefits to be derived from secondary induction are incidental to the satisfaction of curiosity.

The intellectual satisfaction to be obtained from theories has sometimes been compared with the satisfaction derived from works of art, and there is certainly some resemblance. When we contemplate a theory which unifies a large field of science by a reduction in the number of independent concepts, we are pleased by its coherence much as we are pleased by the coherence of a good poem or a piece of good music; and we admire the skill of a great scientist much as we admire the skill of a great artist. There is, indeed, no reason why we should hesitate to speak of science as a source of aesthetic enjoyment. But it is important to recognize a difference between scientific theories and works of art in the ordinary sense. The scientist is inventive in the making of theories, but his activity is never autonomous like that of the poet or the musician. The products of his construction are hypotheses, that is to say, propositions, which must be true or false; and only those are thought worthy of consideration which may be true, i.e. are consistent with known facts. His work is more like that of a portrait-painter or that of an architect who designs a building to make the best use of a given site for a given purpose. But neither analogy is perfect. The scientist wishes for no liberty in the construction of hypotheses. He has, of course, the ordinary freedom of a prose-writer in the presentation of his theory, for there may be individual style in scientific writing just as in other branches of literature; but if he finds that recorded experience leaves him with a choice between alternatives in the development of his theory, he immediately begins to plan new observations which will strengthen the conditions he has to satisfy. His aim is to make a theory which fits *all* the facts and *has no rival.* It is true that he can never be sure he has succeeded in this; but his refusal to be content with any theory which is only one way of co-ordinating known facts shows clearly that his interest in simplification is not merely aesthetic.

When we look for an explanation we want to discover not merely *a* theory which co-ordinates some, or even all, of the empirical generalizations hitherto established by primary induction, but, if possible, *the* theory under which all possible generalizations can be subsumed. As Kant maintained, our thought is guided by the ideal of a single, all-inclusive system of natural necessity. Why we should have a craving to discover this I cannot say, but the fact seems to be beyond doubt. The rationalist metaphysician, assuming that the existence of the craving proves the possibility of satisfying it completely, tries to construct a theory of nature which shall be intrinsically necessary. He believes in effect that false theories must reveal their falsity not merely by inconsistency with observed facts, but also by internal contradictions. The empirical scientist is less confident in the power of human reason, but no less eager to find an intellectually satisfactory system. He too wants a single, inclusive theory; but he recognizes that he cannot hope to formulate it *a priori*, and adopts instead the policy of secondary induction, i.e. the policy of welcoming partial systems which accord with all known facts. In this his conduct is surely reasonable. Anyone who is not interested in understanding need not worry himself about methods of explanation; but for the rest of us the only question is how we should try to get what we want. If, as now seems obvious, we cannot get what we want in any other way, we do well to accept those partial explanations which survive all empirical tests. When we reflect on our procedure, we must admit we have no guarantee that our desire will ever be satisfied in full; but so long as a theory survives it gives us some satisfaction, and those which simplify most give most satisfaction. This is a sufficient reason for practising secondary induction.

§ 48. CONCLUSION

The view of induction which has been presented in the last few sections is like the positivist account in excluding all pretence of justification by deductive reasoning or by the calculus of chances.

But it is unlike the positivist account in not making the rationality of the inductive policy a mere matter of definition. This difference is fundamental, for it involves a radical opposition of views about truths of principle. Whereas the thorough-going positivist tries to maintain that all necessity or impossibility is made by human convention, I have based my argument on the assumption that there may be truths of principle which we cannot know *a priori*. In an earlier section I have tried to answer the objections of Hume which are commonly thought fatal to this doctrine, but I realize that the reader may very well remain dissatisfied, and for this reason I shall try once more to make my position clear. I cannot produce new arguments, but it is important that the reader should be left in no doubt about the implications of the doctrine he is asked to accept. In particular there are three points which seem to require emphasis.

1. The doctrine that there are truths of principle which we cannot know *a priori* is presupposed by the activity of natural scientists. The way in which they speak of their conjectures of law shows that these cannot be analysed according to the constancy theory; and it is equally clear that their conjectures of probability in matters of chance cannot be explained in accordance with the frequency theory. Other suggestions which have been put forward to avoid the difficulties of talking about truths of principle are inadequate. Until recently, indeed, natural scientists always assumed the existence of such truths without question. If they heard of the philosophical perplexities of Hume, they dismissed these as fantastical and irrelevant to their own work. Within the last few years, however, some physicists have argued that the quantum theory enables, or even requires, them to dispense with the notion of natural necessity or impossibility. If this contention were true, it would show that my account of induction is false; but it is not universally accepted by those most competent to discuss the scientific developments on which it is supposed to be based, and I think it can be shown to be a mistaken interpretation of those developments.

The quantum theory is an hypothesis of secondary induction introduced to replace a theory that has been discredited by empirical evidence. Like other hypotheses of secondary induction, the old theory was an attempt to explain empirical generalizations by translating them into a transcendent object terminology, but so too is the quantum theory. Where, then, is the difference? According to the old theory many of the formulae by which empirical

generalizations were rendered in the transcendent object terminology were statements of necessitation. Some others, it is true, were
only statements of very high probabilities (e.g. some formulae of
thermodynamics), but even these were supposed to be grounded
on principles of necessity or impossibility. And so it might be
said that the whole scheme of explanation was an attempt to
represent empirical generalizations as truths of principle which
we cannot discover *a priori*. It seems, however, that some consequences of the assumptions of this theory concerning transcendent
objects such as electrons are found to be contradicted by observations, and the theory must therefore be abandoned. It is said,
moreover, that we cannot by any modification of our assumptions
concerning these objects construct a new theory in which empirical
generalizations are explained by reference to necessities in the
behaviour of these objects. This is the situation with which the
quantum theorists try to cope, and the important novelty of their
suggestion is that we should continue to speak of transcendent
objects such as electrons but assume only probability rules about
their behaviour. On this basis all empirical generalizations are to
be explained by the help of Bernoulli's theorem. For they, too,
will be probability rules, but rules concerned with probabilities
very near to 1.

There is, of course, a great deal more to be said about the theory,
although not by me. This very bare abstract is supposed to contain only what is relevant to our purpose, and so far as I can see,
there is nothing in it which need shock the most conservative
philosopher. We are already familiar with the notion that some of
the laws we claim to have established by primary induction may
be replaced in physical theory by probability rules involving probabilities very near to 1, and there is no good reason for refusing to
admit an extension of this kind of explanation. The thesis which
I wish to dispute is not part of the quantum theory itself, but a
philosophical gloss by some of the expositors, namely, that probability rules concerning transcendent objects such as electrons are
ultimate and presuppose no principles of necessity or impossibility
whatsoever. When the notion of probability has become as important as it now is in physical science, the need for a satisfactory
definition is urgent, and physicists do well to think about this
question. But what is the definition adopted by those who try to
treat probability rules as ultimate? Clearly they cannot hold any
form of the subjectivist theory, and they are debarred from defining

probability by reference to ranges or fields of possibility, because they have denied that there can be truths of principle in this domain. They must therefore be committed to the frequency definition, and this by itself is enough to condemn their view. For they are after all assuming laws, but laws of the wildest kind about the convergence of frequency sequences to limits.

If we reject the philosophical gloss of which I have spoken, we do not thereby assert that it is possible to reinstate a theory of the old kind about the behaviour of electrons, but we do restore the reason for practising induction. So long as we believe that there are or may be principles of necessity or impossibility, we have good reason for conjecturing probability rules, whereas without that belief we should have no reason. The fact that we cannot at present make any profitable conjectures about the form of the principles presupposed by probability rules about transcendent objects is no obstacle to the attempt to formulate such rules, for we are often in a similar situation when we practise primary induction. Nor should it make us give up the hope that by a further refinement of our transcendent object terminology we may some day get an explanatory hypothesis which satisfies us better. No doubt, we are farther from the ideal of secondary induction than we once thought, but the only insurmountable obstacle to scientific progress is defeatism.

2. There is nothing peculiar in the notion of necessity or impossibility used by natural scientists. Since the time of Hume many philosophers have supposed that the assumption of necessity in nature must be explained away as an error due to insufficient analysis of mental processes or linguistic practices. But this supposition is itself an error due to insufficient analysis of the situation. If anyone objects, 'But surely you do not wish to maintain that the necessitation of which you speak in connexion with natural laws is just the same as logical entailment?', my answer is 'Yes and no'. The notion of necessity is the same as that used in logic and phenomenology (i.e. the domain of what is usually called intuitive induction). For it is simply the notion of a boundary to the possible. But the concepts between which necessary connexions are said to hold in natural science are very different from those of the other two studies. Logic is concerned with formal concepts, and phenomenology with concepts which are not formal, but in each case we can have *a priori* knowledge because the concepts involved are completely determinate in a sense in which

those connected by hypotheses of natural law never are. The peculiarity of natural science is that the concepts with which it starts always allow room for further specification. To put the matter more fully and more precisely, if I say that a perceptual object belongs to a certain natural kind, I think of it as having a nature which is not, and cannot be, manifested in any single perception nor yet in any sequence of perceptions, however long. Our difficulty in describing ampliative induction arises from our failure to realize this strange feature of perceptual object terminology. We assume wrongly that a word like 'iron' must have meaning in precisely the same way as words like 'two' and 'red'; and this commits us to saying that if there are any truths of principle concerning iron, they must be knowable *a priori* by anyone who is able to use the word 'iron' significantly.

There are two different ways in which philosophers have tried to remove the peculiarity of the perceptual object terminology, or rather to avoid admitting it. Both attempts are unsatisfactory, but it is instructive to see how and why they fail. The first suggestion, and the more common, is that perceptual object terminology should be reduced to sensum terminology. This is the programme of the phenomenalists. If it were feasible, it would get rid of the oddity of words like 'iron' by allowing them to have only the *minimum* of meaning required for their use in the description of actually perceived objects. The word 'iron', for example, would be understood to mean no more than is manifested when something is recognized as a piece of iron. From this it would certainly follow that all natural laws were contingent truths, or bare matters of fact. But perceptual object terminology cannot be reduced in this simple way to sensum terminology. Whenever I use the word 'iron', I always mean something more than is manifested to me at the moment. And so phenomenalists find themselves driven to make statements about what would be sensed in certain conditions which are not realized, although such unfulfilled hypothetical statements are inadmissible according to the general theory of meaning with which they start. The second suggestion is that sentences which purport to state natural laws should be regarded as implicit definitions of the words of the perceptual object terminology by means of which they are formulated. This is the programme of the philosophers who are called conventionalists.[1]

[1] A version of the theory can be found in C. I. Lewis's *Mind and the World Order*.

If it were feasible, it would remove the puzzle by giving to words like 'iron' the *maximum* of meaning consistent with their use in describing the perceptual objects that have already been noticed. And it has a certain plausibility, for just as we may sometimes try to explain our use of the word 'iron' by saying what we should expect to sense in certain circumstances if a piece of iron were present, so too we may find it convenient to incorporate some results of primary induction in our definition of 'iron'. But perceptual object terminology cannot be radically altered in this way. If all the results of primary induction were incorporated in the definitions of its terms, these terms would become unusable for ordinary purposes. For it would then be impossible to say that any perceptual object was of a certain kind until it had been found to have all the attributes included in the concept of that kind, and if the task could be completed, there would be no room left for any predictions about its behaviour.

The upshot of these considerations is that we must take the perceptual object terminology as we find it, when we try to give an account of induction. The puzzles of induction spring from failure to understand the peculiarity of that terminology. I am far from believing that all these puzzles have been solved by the argument presented here, but I think it has been shown that the line of progress for philosophy is through the development of the theory of perception rather than through any attempt to find a new sense for 'necessity'.

3. It is evident from the nature of the case that no one can produce an unquestionable example of a truth of principle which he does not know *a priori*. For, although we may suggest that some hypotheses of natural science are such truths, the inductive method on which we rely when we accept these hypotheses does not allow us to claim knowledge of them. But it should not be supposed that this consideration is a strong objection to the theory put forward here. In order to show that ampliative induction, whether primary or secondary, is a rational policy it is not necessary to prove that there *are* truths of principle. It is sufficient to establish that there *may be*, i.e. that the suggestion is not absurd. When they are engaged in their ordinary concerns, inductive scientists usually assume the existence of such truths with natural faith. If this assumption could be *disproved*, there would, indeed, be no reason why they should continue their efforts. But I have argued that the common attempts to disprove it rest on a misconception; and

this is all that is required, at least until someone produces an objection which is more difficult to meet. For we want to make true conjectures about the boundaries of possibility, and induction is the only systematic way of trying to do what we want to do. A traveller in the desert who is dying of thirst will struggle towards the place where he thinks he sees an oasis. If presently he is satisfied that what he saw was only a mirage, he may as well lie down and die. But, for a man who understands his situation, even the thought that he may reach water by going in that direction is enough to justify further effort.

INDEX

PRINTED IN GREAT BRITAIN
AT THE UNIVERSITY PRESS, OXFORD
BY CHARLES BATEY, PRINTER TO THE UNIVERSITY